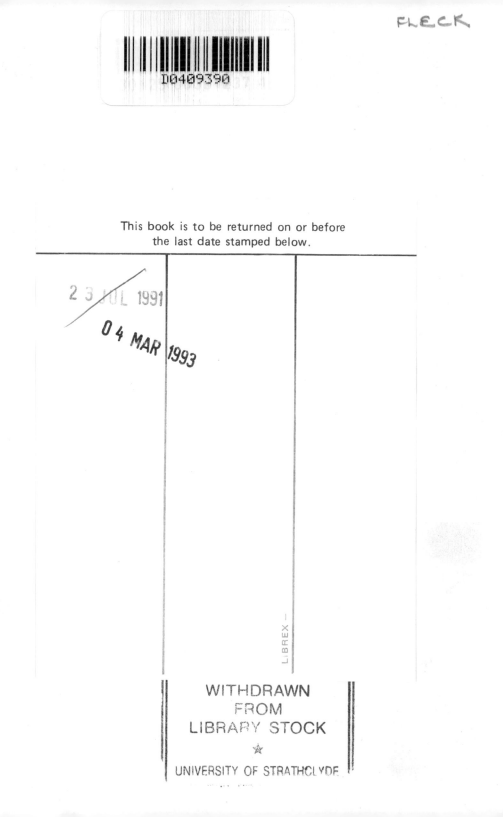

SYNCHROTRON LIGHT: APPLICATIONS AND RELATED INSTRUMENTATION II

SYNCHROTRON LIGHT: APPLICATIONS AND RELATED INSTRUMENTATION II

Proceedings of the Second Workshop
Campinas, SP, Brazil
September 4 – 8, 1989

Organized by
National Laboratory for Synchrotron Light (LNLS)/CNPq
Cx. Postal 6192 — Telex (19) 7517 LNLS
13081 Campinas SP, Brazil

Editor
Aldo Craievich
National Laboratory for Synchrotron Light (LNLS)/CNPq, Campinas,
and Institute of Physics/USP, São Paulo, Brazil

World Scientific
Singapore • New Jersey • London • Hong Kong

Published by

World Scientific Publishing Co. Pte. Ltd.

P O Box 128, Farrer Road, Singapore 9128

USA office: 687 Hartwell Street, Teaneck, NJ 07666

UK office: 73 Lynton Mead, Totteridge, London N20 8DH

SYNCHROTRON LIGHT: APPLICATIONS AND RELATED INSTRUMENTATION II

ISBN 981-02-0088-9

Printed in Singapore by Utopia Press.

PREFACE

Electron storage rings acting as synchrotron light sources are used in many countries for applications in physics, chemistry, materials science and other research fields. The unique features of synchrotron light, namely high intensity, wide photon energy spectrum, high degree of polarization, pulsed structure and collimation conditions, make it extremely useful for performing diffraction, scattering, absorption and emission experiments which would be impossible using conventional ultra-violet and X-ray sources. These experimental methods are widely used for applications concerning atomic, electronic and magnetic structures of inorganic and biological materials.

Several developed countries such as the USA, URSS, England, France, Italy, Sweden and Japan have one or more of these synchrotron light facilities operating or under construction. Some developing countries have constructed (China) or are building (Taiwan, India, Korea, Brazil) synchrotron light facilities. The construction of the Brazilian synchrotron source began in June, 1987. After two years of activities, the injector linac for the electron storage ring is in its final stage of construction.

The initial LNLS project contemplated a 2 GeV electron storage ring, an electron linac and a booster for injection at full energy. This project was revised in the first semester of 1989. The new LNLS project consists of a 100 MeV linac and a 1.15 GeV electron storage ring which will be directly injected by the electron linac. The II Workshop "Synchrotron Light: Applications and Related Instrumentation" was dedicated to oral presentations about applications of synchrotron light, most of which were not covered during the I Workshop, organized by LNLS in 1988, and the Proceedings of which were published by World Scientific. The II Workshop included discussions on the application possibilities for the newly designed LNLS 1.15 GeV storage ring, and on the modifications which would eventually be necessary for the work-station and instrumentation projects currently in progress at LNLS and at various external user laboratories.

These Proceedings contain the Invited Lectures presented at the Workshop by specialists working on synchrotron light applications and related instrumentation and by members of LNLS regarding technical details of the Brazilian project. The Proceedings also contain contributed, refereed papers which were presented in the Poster Session.

It is expected that these Proceedings, together with those already published corresponding to the I Workshop on the same subject, will be of interest to scientists who are users or potential users of synchrotron light. It is expected that they will motivate, in particular, Brazilian scientists for the future use of the synchrotron light source which is at present under construction at LNLS, and which will be available for users in 1993.

The Editor thanks Diane Petty, Rosana Sirbone, Érica Tarchiani and Marina Marino from LNLS, for their efficient assistance in the organization of the Workshop and in the editing of these Proceedings.

The Workshop received the generous sponsorship of the following agencies: Conselho Nacional de Desenvolvimento Científico e Tecnológico-CNPq, Fundação de Amparo à Pesquisa do Estado de São Paulo-FAPESP, Banco Nacional de Desenvolvimento-BNDES (Brazilian agencies), Centre Nacional de la Recherche Scientifique (France), British Council (England), DAAD (Germany), Istituto Nazionale di Fisica Nucleare (Italy) and IBM (USA).

The Editor

CONTENTS

Invited Papers

Contributed Papers

Invited Papers

The Laboratório Nacional de Luz Síncrotron: some personal reflections

C.E.T. Gonçalves da Silva

Laboratório Nacional de Luz Síncrotron / CNPq / MCT
Cx. P. 6192   Campinas SP Brasil
and
Instituto de Física "Gleb Wataghin"
Campinas SP Brasil

The problems of developing Science in a developing country have received, over the years, considerable attention on the part of scientists and science administrators in the developed countries. Special institutions have been created to foster the goals of Science in the Third World and, through the goodwill of many individuals and institutions, opportunities are available to give deserving young researchers access to first class laboratories in the developed countries.

But development, not only of Science, but understood in its broad economic, social and political terms, is, and will forever remain, the exclusive responsibility of the citizens of the Nation concerned. It is up to them to decide what sort of society they wish to create for themselves and their children; on the basis of which values, ethical, moral, social, political, they want to shape their lives and actions; which organizations they want to set up to govern their collective efforts and by which principles these organizations shall be ruled.

Brazil is the eighth industrial power in the world, one of the largest exporters, has a large territory (bigger than that of continental USA), rich natural resources, and a population which is approaching 150 million inhabitants. The economic indicators all point to the fact that Brazil will be a power to be reckoned with in the near future, in spite of short term problems, such as the external debt. The social indicators, alas, are far from bright. The distribution of wealth, the educational level, the infant mortality rate, to mention just three of them are appalling, ranking Brazil among the poorest countries in Africa or Asia. There are well documented historical reasons for this sad state of affairs, but here is not the place to discuss them. Looking towards the next generation, the first priority for the Nation is to improve these social indicators, for, without this, in the long run, the economic promises will not come true. Fortunately, there seems to be an almost universal understanding in Brazil of the urgency of the task facing the government and private entreprises to correct longstanding social injustices. Brazilians can, and should, look to the future with optimism, because, although the road ahead is hard, the reward is immense.

These considerations serve to place in proper perspective the efforts of Brazilian scientists to develop Science and Technology in their country and to integrate these activities into a productive economy. It is, literally, a matter of life or death. Projects such as the Laboratório Nacional de Luz Síncrotron aspire to much more than just providing Brazilian scientists with a powerful tool for materials research. Their aim is to create a fruitful interaction between the industrial infrastructure of the country, the turning wheels of the economy, and the scientific and technologic community, responsible for the training of human resources and the creation of new knowledge. This whole process is conditioned by forces which transcend the narrow scope of developing Science and Technology. Political and economic conflicting forces, on the one side, those which strive to defend national values and seek to give the country a proper measure of independence and autonomy, and, on the other, those which seek to perpetuate the dominant role of colonial values, clash constantly in a tug-of-war, the outcome of which will, ultimately, determine the success or failure of our entreprises. By demonstrating technical competence and seriousness of purpose, LNLS is clearly taking sides in this conflict.

The aim of LNLS is to become an internationally competitive research center. This is the best way to repay the national and international community for the support granted the project. Starting from scratch, a team has been set up which, in a little over two years, acquired enough technical competence to build a linear accelerator of modest proportions by international standards, but impressive enough if looked upon in the context. For the next few years, LNLS will concentrate on the design and construction of its first electron storage ring. The challenge to build an electron storage ring looks almost insignificant, compared with the challenges already met and overcome. Hence, we have no doubts that LNLS will accomplish what it set out to do.

The present Workshop is one of a series of events organized by the Scientific Division of LNLS with the aim of training future users, drawing attention to the enormous research potential of a synchrotron light source, and planning experiments and experimental stations for when the first photons are made available to users. These Proceedings bear witness to the variety and quality of the applications of synchrotron radiation. The steadily growing number of Brazilian researchers using synchrotron light sources abroad will provide LNLS with a strong users' community by the time the facility becomes operational. This will mark the beginning of a new era for Brazilian Science: small Science done with Big Machines.

SCIENTIFIC CASE FOR THE LNLS VUV-III PROJECT

A. F. Craievich

National Laboratory for Synchrotron Light/CNPq
Campinas, Brazil
and
Institute of Physics, USP, São Paulo
Brazil

ABSTRACT

The initial project of LNLS contemplated the construction of a 2 GeV electron storage ring to be dedicated to the production of synchrotron light. A recent revision of the project involves the construction of a 1.15 GeV electron storage ring as a first step. This paper discusses to what extent this modification may affect the planning for the construction of experimental work-stations and related instrumentation. The addition of wiggler insertions was decided upon so as to mantain most of the scientific planning elaborated for the initial LNLS project.

1. INTRODUCTION

The Brazilian National Laboratory for Synchrotron Light (LNLS) is an open institution which is building a dedicated synchrotron light facility for applications in science and technology. The initial project (Project I) [1,2] intended the construction of a 2 GeV electron storage ring and an injection system composed of a 100 MeV LINAC and a synchrotron booster for electron injection at full energy.

During the first two years of LNLS activities, which started in 1987, a significant delay in the construction chronogram occured, mainly due to a reduction of the expected annual budget. Therefore, the LNLS decided, by the end of 1988, to revise the Project I in order to be able to deliver photons to users within the initial 6 year time schedule.

The project for the construction, as a first step, of a low energy (about 1 GeV) storage ring was then extensively discussed. Its technical design was completed by the Project Division of LNLS and submitted to the appreciation of an international board during the first semester 1989. This lead to several successively up-graded technical projects and, finally, to the project of a 1.15 GeV electron storage ring (VUV-III ring). The technical characteristics of the storage ring lattice are presented in another paper in these Proceedings[3].

The first stage of the new synchrotron light source project which involves the construction a 100 MeV electron LINAC is well advanced. The LINAC will initially inject electrons directly to the 1.15 GeV ring. This low energy injection procedure is less costly than full energy injection techniques and has been proven to work up to now in two operating rings: Aladdin (Madison) and MAX (Lund).

It is expected the VUV-III storage ring will be commissioned and available for users by 1993. Subsequently, the initially planned 2 GeV storage ring will be built. It will be injected through the 1.15 GeV storage ring acting as a non-ideal injector booster. Later, the synchrotron booster, included in Project I, will be constructed for injecting at full energy both the 2 GeV and 1.15 GeV storage rings. The time schedule for construction of the 2 GeV storage ring and booster has not been defined yet.

The extension of the spectra of light generated by electron storage rings depends on the electron energy E and on the magnetic field B of the bending magnets. The parameter E_c (critical energy) characterizes the photon spectrum. It is defined as the energy value which divides the spectrum in two parts of equal integral irradiated power [4]. The photon critical energy is related to the electron energy and the magnetic field of the bending (or wiggler) magnets, by[4]:

$$E_c \text{ [KeV]} = 0.665 \text{ B [Tesla] } E^2 \text{ [GeV}^2] \qquad (1)$$

The photon flux decreases rapidly for energies $E > 3 E_c$. For many experiments, it is possible to obtain usable photon flux with photon energies up to $E_{max} \cong 5 E_c$.

The first experimental work-stations which have been planned to be installed around the LNLS 2 GeV ring are the following [5]:

a. Molecular spectroscopy[6].

b. Photoemission spectroscopy (solids).

c. Microlithography.

d. EXAFS.

e. SAXS.

f. "Perfect crystal" crystallography[7].

g. Surface crystallography.

These stations correspond to experimental techniques for which external users demonstrated concrete interest. Other stations for X-ray applications requiring relatively simple installations like protein crystallography (film recording) and powder diffractometry, were also planned to be available at the beginning of the storage ring operation or later on, depending on the funding levels.

The question is how the initial LNLS plans for scientific and technological applications of synchrotron light will be affected by the recent decision of first building the VUV-III storage ring.

2. GENERAL CONSIDERATIONS

The low electron energy associated with the VUV-III ring (1.15 GeV) as compared to that of Project I (2 GeV), will not seriously affect the planned experiments which utilize mainly ultraviolet or soft X-ray photons, namely atomic, molecular and photoemission spectroscopies as well as microlithography. The photon energy domain corresponding to the above mentioned techniques ranges from 30 to 2000 eV. This range is covered by the emission from the 2 GeV storage ring as well as by the 1.15 GeV ring. The flux and brilliance of the VUV-III ring will be lower than that expected for the 2 GeV ring of Project I, as can be seen in Fig. 1 and 2. Nevertheless, the flux and the brilliance expected for the VUV-III storage ring are high enough for a number of interesting applications in this energy range. The beam line and the monochromator for VUV applications are presently being constructed at LNLS[8].

The thermal load on beam-line optical elements (mirrors and monochromators) installed in a 1.15 GeV storage ring is lower than that in a 2 GeV ring. This represents an advantage for the construction of the instrumentation associated with the VUV-III ring.

The expected emittance for the VUV-III light source[3] is on the same order of magnitude as some of the recently built and sucessfully operating facilities. This guarantees the possibility of performing a great number of interesting experiments needing high brilliance using the spectral domain of ultraviolet and soft X-ray photons produced by the bending magnets.

Since the maximum of the photon flux spectrum of the VUV-III storage ring corresponds to the photon energy range of about 1 KeV which is usually required for microlithography, the newly planned source is especially well adapted for this application.

The VUV-III storage ring has six three meter straight sections, four of which are completely free for insertions [3]. The dedication of two of these straight sections to the insertion of classical undulators is being considered. When these insertions become operational, visible and ultraviolet light will be produced for atomic, molecular and solid state spectroscopy applications requiring very high brilliance and for special applications like free electron lasers.

The other experimental stations which are being planned use hard X-rays. For classical crystallographic applications like SAXS, powder diffractometry and protein crystallography, 8 KeV monochromatic photon beams are usually required. As can be seen in Figure 1, the flux from the bending magnets of the VUV-III storage ring is very low above 6 KeV, i.e. for $E > 5 E_c$ ($E_c = 1.23$ KeV for VUV-III). This makes it necessary to use wiggler insertions in order to shift the spectrum toward higher energies.

Wigglers are periodic arrays of magnets which can be located in the straight sections of storage rings[4]. They accelerate the electrons transversally and periodically. The spectrum of photons emitted by wigglers extends to higher energies when a magnetic field stronger than that of bending magnets is used. The photon flux may also be increased for all photon energies, by using multipole wigglers. The increase factor due to the multipole effect is approximately equal to (N - 2), N being the number of poles. Figure 1 shows plots of the flux spectra of photons on the axis of a 2 Tesla normal magnet 12-pole wiggler and of a 5 Tesla 5-pole superconducting

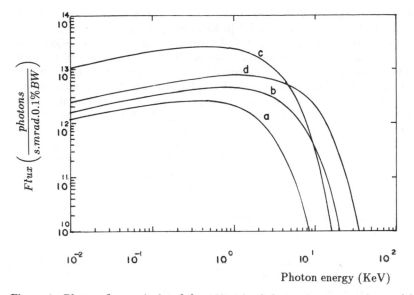

Figure 1: Photon flux, calculated for 100 mA of electronic current, from: (a) Bending magnets of VUV-III (1.15 GeV); (b) Bending magnets 2 GeV ring; (c) Normal wiggler (2 Tesla - 12 poles) in VUV-III; (d) Superconducting wiggler (5 Tesla - 5 poles) in VUV-III.

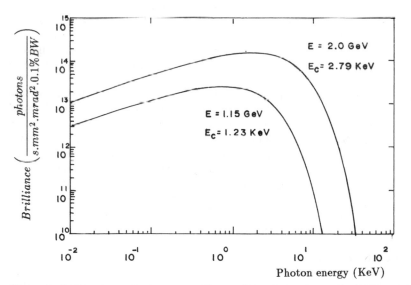

Figure 2: Brilliance spectra corresponding to the emission from the middle of the bending magnets of the VUV-III (1.15 GeV) and of the 2 GeV storage rings, calculated for 100 mA of electronic current. The spectrum of the VUV-III storage ring corresponds to the mode of operation 3 (see reference 3).

wiggler installed in the VUV-III ring. The critical energies E_c for these insertions are, according to Equation 1, 1.76 and 4.40 KeV, respectively.

As it can be seen in Figure 1, a 2 Tesla normal magnet 12 pole wiggler produces a flux of 8 KeV photons (commonly used for X-Ray diffraction and scattering experiments) higher than that corresponding to the maximum flux of the emission spectrum from the bending magnets of the VUV-III ring. For applications needing a high flux of harder X-rays, the insertion of a superconducting wiggler will be necessary. In Fig. 1 the shifting effect on the flux spectrum of a 5 Tesla superconducting magnet 5-pole wiggler installed in the 1.15 GeV storage ring is apparent.

In order to put experimental stations for X-ray applications into operation from the beginning of user activities at LNLS, the construction of one normal magnet 12 pole wiggler has been decided upon. The critical energy value, $E_c = 1.76$ KeV corresponding to the emission from a 2 Tesla wiggler inserted in the VUV-III ring indicates that usable photons will be produced with energies up to about 9 KeV, including then the 8 KeV photon spectral range which is required for classical crystallographic applications.

The wiggler construction will be carried out in parallel with the construction of the VUV-III storage ring. The decision concerning the type of wiggler (having normal instead of superconducting magnets) took into account the present technical possibilities at LNLS and also in Brazilian industry for constructing this type of device. The construction of a second wiggler for the VUV-III ring is an open question. Its particular features (type of magnet and number of poles) will be decided upon later.

If should be pointed out that the design of the electron optics for the VUV-III ring straight sections has not been optimised for wigglers [3]. The optical quality of the light beam generated by the planned wiggler may be improved by the addition of focussing magnets. This possibility is now being discussed. Studies on the influence of high magnetic-field wigglers on the VUV-III storage ring electron optics are in progress[9].

The spectral brilliance of light generated by the multipole wigglers which are planned to be installed on the VUV-III ring, has not yet been quantitatively evaluated. Experimental stations needing generally high flux but not very high energy resolution, like SAXS and powder diffractometry, will probably benefit to a greater extent from wiggler beam-lines. The work-station dedicated to "perfect-crystal" crystallography (e.g. X-ray topography, interferometry, $\theta = \pi/2$ diffraction and others), which requires high energy resolution but not necessarily very high photon flux, will be installed on a bending magnet beam line[7]. These types of experiments and all those requiring soft X-rays (2 KeV $< E < 5$ KeV) will still be possible under good conditions in the bending magnet work-stations.

3. CONCLUSIONS

The basic conclusions concerning the consequences of the revision of the LNLS construction schedule on the scientific program are:

1. The ultraviolet and soft X-ray beam lines to be installed at the VUV-III storage ring will cover most of the needs of the potential user groups which are at present building or planning experimental ultraviolet and soft X-ray work stations.

2. The insertion of wigglers (first a conventional wiggler and probably a superconducting one later on) will permit the installation of classical crystallography work-stations in the VUV-III storage ring.

3. Though the photon flux and brilliance associated with synchrotron light from the VUV-III bending magnets will be lower than that of the 2 GeV ring, they are comparable to those of many other existing and successfully operating rings around the world.

4. The possibility of a light source to be available at LNLS within a relatively short time (approximately four years) is expected to enhance the involvement of external users in instrumentation projects.

5. The low number of X-ray beam work-stations which it will be possible to install on the wiggler line of the VUV-III ring, as compared to that which could be accomodated in the 2 GeV storage ring, will be a probable limitation during the first years of operation, depending on the concrete demands of users. If the number of X-ray work-stations installed at VUV-III turns out to be insufficient to satisfy the actual user needs, an acceleration of the construction chronogram of the 2 GeV storage ring may be decided upon.

In short, the decrease in electron energy associated with the VUV-III ring will not seriously affect the current planning for developing the future work-stations of LNLS. The insertion of wigglers in the straight sections becomes necessary to allow for a number of X-ray diffraction, scattering and absorption experiments. The plans related to experiments using ultraviolet light and soft X-rays do not require any major modification.

REFERENCES

[1] A.R.D. Rodrigues, Project I, PRS Report (1985).

[2] D. Wisnivesky, The LNLS Project, Proceedings of the I Workshop Synchrotron Light: Applications and Related Instrumentation, World Scientific, pp. 259-278 (1989).

[3] L.Jahnel, Liu Lin & A.R. Rodrigues, A VUV electron ring for LNLS, these Proceedings.

[4] H. Winnick & S. Doniach, Synchrotron Radiation Research, Plenum Press (1980).

[5] A. Craievich & A.R.B. de Castro, Scientific Instrumentation at LNLS, Proceedings of the I Workshop Synchrotron Light: Applications and Related Instrumentation, World Scientific, pp. 279-291 (1989).

[6] G.G.B. de Souza, A gas phase work-station for the Brazilian National Synchrotron Light Laboratory, Proceedings of the I Workshop Synchrotron Light: Applications and Related Instrumentation, World Scientific pp. 292-302 (1989).

[7] C. Cusatis & C. Giles, An X-ray beam line for the LNLS, these Proceedings.

[8] A.R.B. de Castro, Optics for a VUV beam line at LNLS, these Proceedings.

[9] L. Lin, Effects of wigglers on the equilibrium emittance and energy spread of the LNLS VUV-III lattice, LNLS Internal Report-MP03 (1989).

A VUV ELECTRON STORAGE RING FOR LNLS

L. Jahnel, Liu Lin and A. R. Rodrigues [*]

Laboratório Nacional de Luz Síncrotron/CNPq
Caixa Postal 6192
13085 - Campinas, SP - Brasil
[*] on leave from IFQSC/USP

ABSTRACT

The preliminary design of a 1.15 GeV electron storage ring for the production of VUV and soft X-rays is presented.

The original plans for the LNLS equipment included a 2-3 GeV storage ring, with an injection system consisting of a 100 MeV LINAC and a booster [1]. These plans have been changed, under the recomendation of the Board of Directors, with the inclusion of a low energy storage ring to be injected, initialy, directly from the LINAC.

A six-fold-symetric lattice is proposed [2], with Chasman-Green type double bend achromat optics. Three meters of each of the six straight sections are free for machine components or insertion devices (Figure 1). Table I shows the main parameters of the ring.

Three operating points were investigated, with different emittances (49, 79 and 130 nm.rad; Figure 2), allowing for different compromises between lifetime and brightness. The flux and the brightness for each mode, are presented in Figure 3 and the optical functions (for mode 1) in Figure 4. All calculations for linear lattice optimization used the code MAD [3].

The PATPET code [4] was used to correct the chromaticity and minimize the tune dependence on momentum. Chromaticity correction is achieved with two families of sextupoles in the dispersive straight sections. The maximum tune shift is less then 0.1 for 3% momentum deviation and up to 25 and 35 mm vertical and horizontal amplitudes, respectively.

The dynamical apertures were also calculated with PATPET. Particles were tracked for 500 turns under various circumstances of multipole, strenght and alignment errors and momentum deviations up to 3%. Table II gives the multipole errors used. All random errors are considered to follow a gaussian distribution truncated at two standard deviations. The standard deviations for alignment are 0.2 mm and 0.02 degrees while, for strength is 0.1%. Figure 5 shows the dynamic aperture for the perfect machine and with systematic multipole errors only. The worst case, with no physical limits, is shown in Figure 6, including systematic and random errors, strength and alignment errors and momentum deviation of 3% (the hatching

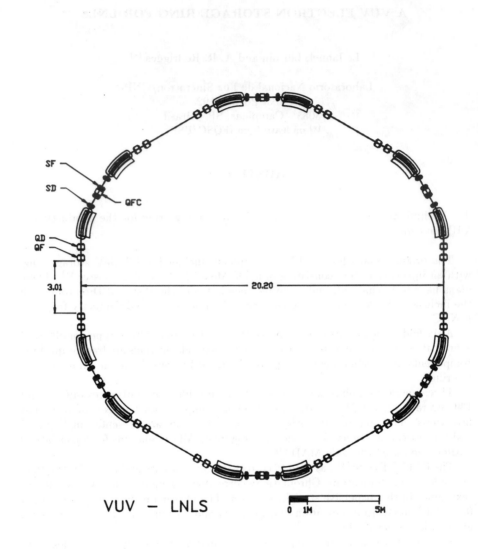

Figure 1: Layout of the 1.15 GeV storage ring lattice.

	MODE 1	MODE 2	MODE 3	
Energy		1.15		GeV
Current		100		mA
Circumference		65.928		m
Magnetic structure	Chasman-Green, 6-fold symmetric			
Revolution frequency		4547.27		kHz
Harmonic number		110		
RF-frequency		500		MHz
Natural emittance	130.	79.	49.	nm.rad
Horizontal betatron tune	4.24	4.75	5.22	
Vertical betatron tune	2.14	1.85	2.15	
Synchrotron tune		4.1		(1/1000)
Momentum compaction factor		0.012		
Natural energy spread		0.059		%
Natural bunch length		17.9		mm
Nat. horiz. chromaticity	-7.0	-7.6	-11.1	
Nat. vert. chromaticity	-5.7	-5.8	-6.0	
Horiz. betatron damping time		9.4		ms
Vert. betatron damping time		8.9		ms
Synchrotron damping time		4.4		ms
Dipoles				
Bending radius		2.735		m
Bending field		1.4		Tesla
Number		12		
Quadrupoles				
Max. gradient		4.38		m^{-2}
Max. field at pole tip		0.57		Tesla
Number of families		3		
Number of quadrupoles		30		
Sextupoles				
Max. int. strenght *	9.5	6.9	6.7	m^{-2}
Max. field at pole tip *	0.21	0.15	0.15	Tesla
Number of families		2		
Number of sextupoles		24		
Injection energy		100		MeV

* Values for zero chromaticity.

Table I: Main parameters of the storage ring.

16

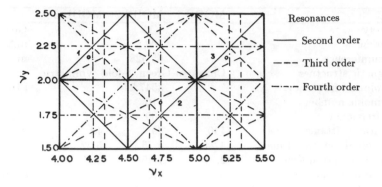

Figure 2: Working points on the resonance diagram.

indicates the dispersion obtained in the results for five different sets).

Further studies are under way to improve the dynamical aperture and evaluate the effect of insertion devices.

$$B(x) = B\rho \sum_n \frac{k_n x^n}{n!} = \sum_n B_n$$			
n	Dipole $B_n/B_o{}^*$		Quadrupole $B_n/B_1{}^*$	
	Systematic	Random	Systematic	Random
1	-	5×10^{-5}	-	1×10^{-3}
2	2×10^{-5}	1×10^{-4}	-	5×10^{-4}
3	-	2×10^{-5}	-	2×10^{-4}
4	2×10^{-6}	1×10^{-5}	-	6×10^{-5}
5	-	-	1×10^{-4}	1×10^{-5}
9	-	-	1×10^{-9}	1×10^{-8}

* Values at x = 1 cm.

Table II: Magnetic multipole errors.

REFERENCES

[1] Gonçalves da Silva, C. E. T., Rodrigues, A. R. D. and Craievich, A. F.; Synchrotron Radiation News, 1, 28 (1988).

[2] Liu, L., Jahnel, L.; LNLS-MP 009/89.

[3] Iselin, F. C. and Niederer, J.; CERN/LEP-TH/88-38.

[4] Emery, L., Wiedemann, H. and Safranek, J.; SSRL ACD-NOTE 36.

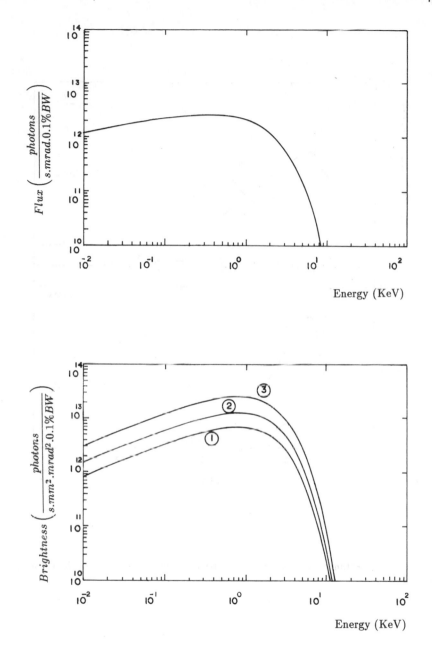

Figure 3: Photon flux and brightness from the bending magnets at 1.15 GeV and 100 mA for the three operating modes.

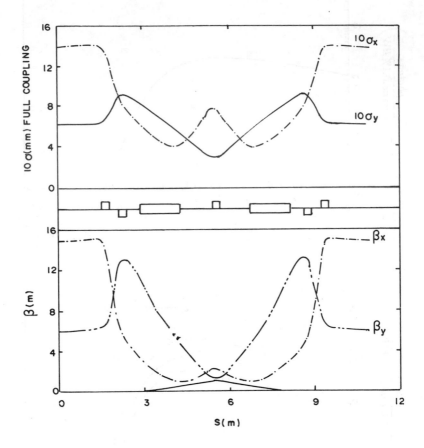

Figure 4: Optical functions and envelope (top) along one superperiod of the lattice (mode 1).

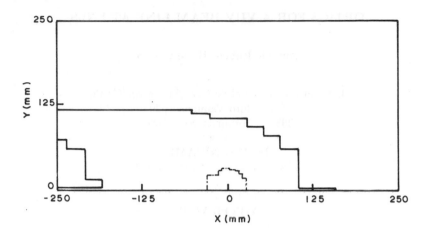

Figure 5: Dynamic aperture for the perfect machine (top) and with systematic multipole errors only (mode 1).

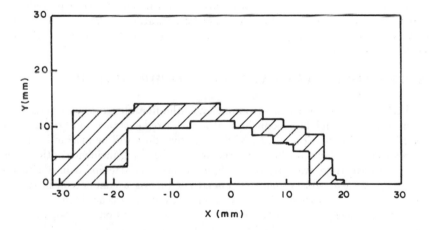

Figure 6: Dynamic aperture with systematic and random errors, strength and alignment errors and momentum deviation of 3% (mode 1).

OPTICS FOR A VUV BEAM LINE AT LNLS

Antonio Rubens B. de Castro

Laboratório Nacional de Luz Síncrotron/CNPq
Rua Lauro Vanucci, 1020
13085 - Campinas, SP - Brasil
and
IFGW/UNICAMP
13081 - Campinas, SP - Brasil

ABSTRACT

A 2.5 m TGM for the range 12 310 eV is discussed, with emphasys on its optical, vacuum and mechanical aspects. The optical design of pre-focussing and post-focussing toroidal mirrors for this instrument is described.

1. INTRODUCTION

Beam line 1 in the ring VUV-III will have a TGM monochromator preceded and followed by focussing mirrors. It is designed for operation in the range 12 eV thru 310 eV, with an entrance angular acceptance of 7 hor mrad X 3 vert mrad. Figure 1 shows this beam line.

2. THE TOROIDAL GRATING MONOCHROMATOR

A TGM, due to its mechanical simplicity, is the first choice when considering a medium resolution, high flux monochromator with fixed entrance and exit directions [1]. A 2.5m TGM is being built at LNLS since this effort will be instructive in very many respects (specially in what concerns design of grazing incidence optics), since we seem to have time available before first injection is attempted in a Brazilian storage ring, since it will be much cheaper than buying a commercial instrument and since, due to its mechanical simplicity, chances of success are high.

Preliminary design of an instrument of this type started on Nov 88, with a set of specifications suggested by the first scientific proposals presented to LNLS. The instrument would employ commercial aberration-corrected gratings of the highest quality and computer control for wavelength selection.

Figure 2 shows an outline of the monochromator.

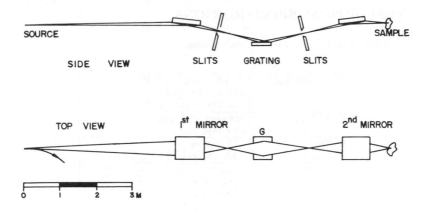

Figure 1: Outline of a VUV beam line.

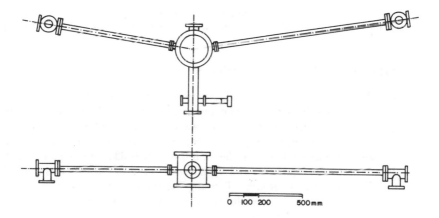

Figure 2: Outline of the TGM vacuum chamber.

3. TGM OPTICAL SPECIFICATIONS

Table I lists the TGM optical specifications.

Wavelength range:	40 120 A (310 100 eV)
	120 360 A (100 35 eV)
	360 1000 A (35 12 eV)
Focal distance:	entrance 1000 mm
	exit 1414 mm
Deviation:	162 degrees
Dispersion:	30.2 A/degree (1800 g/mm)
Gratings:	Jobin Yvon 540 00 200/2103220
Spectral resolution:	better than 0.1 A (40 to 120 A)
	better than 0.3 A (120 to 360 A)
	better than 1.1 A (360 to 1000 A)
angular acceptance:	30 hor mrad X 14 vert mrad

Table I: Optical specifications for the 2.5 m TGM.

Ray tracings (supplied by Jobin Yvon [2]) show that the specified spectral resolution of item (5) can be obtained with entrance and exit slit widths of about 200 micra, at a substancial loss in flux. On the other hand, slit widths of 600 micra will reduce the loss to negligible values, while increasing the bandpass to about 0.5 A and 1.5 A, as shown in figure 3.

These gratings are ion milled and hence they can have a blaze. Jark and Neviere [3] have measured, for a clean gold ruled surface with 1200 g/mm, an efficiency of 0.3 @ 100 A.

4. TGM MECHANICAL ASPECTS

a) Choice of angular range for grating rotation: normal operation in order -1 is from 10.5 to 13.0 degree. However, one must include order 0 for purposes of alignment and calibration. Hence, one wants to scan from 9.0 to 13.0 degree. So, settle on a 75 mrad range (4.3 degree), which can be conveniently scanned with a 25 mm course micrometer head, if the lever is 333 mm long. In order to maintain accuracy, clearances and backlash in bearings must be less than (333 mm)x(0.05 mrad) = 17 micra. The angular increment for grating rotation, given the limiting spectral resolution of 0.1 A and dispersion of 30.2 A/deg should be 3 mdeg = 0.05 mrad.

b) Motor scan: assuming a lead screw with a pitch of 0.5 mm a stepping motor of 50 steps/turn will allow an angular resolution of 0.03 mrad, which meets the requirements of item (a) above.

c) Testing mechanical accuracy: A full scale model of the grating craddle and rotation mechanism was built, in order to assess various aspects of bearing and angular adjustment design. A test jig was built, which allows shining a HeNe laser beam on the center of the grating and measuring the beam deflection. As a detector of the light beam center position, a Reticon RL1024S was used. If the goal is to resolve angular displacements of 0.05 mrad, and since the RL1024S sensor size is 25 micra, the Reticon must be placed at a distance of 500 mm from the grating center. Spot size at the surface of this detector is about 1 mm, which covers 40 sensor sites. With Reticon software presently available at LNLS, the line center can be found easily. Preliminary results give a RMS uncertainty of .02 mrad in the angular position. The test was, however, made over a limited range only.

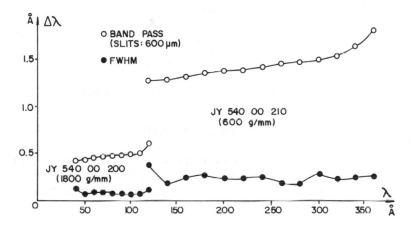

Figure 3: Calculated resolution of the TGM.

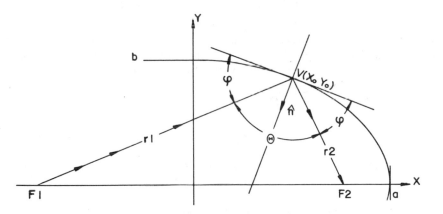

Figure 4: Geometrical definitions related to the collimating mirrors.

5. TGM VACUUM CONSIDERATIONS

It is realized that, since Carbon contamination of the grating surface reduces reflectivity sharply at photon energies above 277 eV, a clean vacuum with pressure in the 1E-10 Torr range is needed [4].

Table II lists the parameters used for vacuum calculations.

Internal area:	9000 cm² for chamber shown in fig. 2
	3000 cm² estimated area for grating and slit mechanisms.
	12000 cm² total area
Design base pressure:	5 X 10^{-10} Torr.
Degassing rate:	1 X 10^{-11} Torr. 1/sec. cm²
Pumping speed:	240 1/sec

Table II: Parameters used for TGM vacuum calculations.

6. PRE-AND POST-FOCUSSING MIRRORS

For grazing incidence optics, the ideal shape for collimating a point source is an ellipsoid with foci F_1 F_2 at the source and image points. Figure 4 shows the geometry. Let the entrance and exit distances to the mirror vertex V be r_1 and r_2. The semi-axes are then given by

$$2a = r_1 + r_2$$

$$2b = \sqrt{\{4a^2 - (F_1 F_2)^2\}} = 2\sin(\phi)\sqrt{\{r_1 r_2\}}$$

Ellipsoidal surfaces are difficult to grind; it is worthwhile to try to replace them with simpler surfaces. A convenient choice is a toroidal surface with principal radii of curvature equal to those at the vertex V of the ellipsoidal mirror.

For the ellipsoid, the principal radii of curvature are given by

$$R = \frac{1}{ab}\{r_2 r_1\}^{(3/2)}$$

$$r_o = \frac{b}{a}\{r_2 r_1\}^{(1/2)}$$

The physical space limitations for beam line construction either suggest or dictate, for physical placement of the mirrors, the parameter values given in Table III.

Notice that the angle ϕ limits the reflectivity at the short wavelength end of the spectral range. For gold, the reflectivity at 300 eV and at grazing incidence angle of 4.5 degrees was calculated to be only 0.4 [5].

The calculated radii of curvature are given in Table IV.

PRE-FOCUSSING	POST-FOCUSSING
r_1 = 4500 mm	r_1 = 1000 mm
r_2 = 1000 mm	r_2 = 1000 mm
ϕ = 4.5 degrees	ϕ = 4.5 degrees

Table III: Geometrical parameters for positioning collimating mirrors.

PRE-FOCUSSING	POST-FOCUSSING
R = 20.856 mm	R = 12.746 mm
r_o = 128.4 mm	r_o = 78.46 mm

Table IV: Optimum radii of curvature for toroidal mirrors.

It is intended that these mirrors be used with a TGM of constant deviation 162 degrees, built for gratings of dimensions 30 x 90 mm^2, with max angular acceptance 30 Hor mrad x 14 Vert mrad. Then, in order to match the angular acceptances of the exit mirror to the grating, the mirror dimensions must be approximately 30 x 180 mm^2. The choice of dimensions for the pre-focussing mirror could be made following several different criteria, and we will for simplicity just assume the same dimensions as the post-focussing one.

Figure 5 shows the aberrated focal spots of the collimating toroidal mirrors illuminated with a point source, obtained using SHADOW [6]. The tangential aberration (of circa 600 micra) in the pre-focussing mirror matches the grating aberration (which sets the practical width of the exit - and hence also of the entrance - slit). The tangential aberration in the post-focussing mirror (of circa 70 micra) matches the exit and entrance slit width for conditions of "highest resolution".

The aberration spot sizes for these mirrors can be somewhat reduced by optimization of R ro. This is done by performing a numerical search in space R ro. A steepest descent routine was used to find the minimum spot size, but the improvement was slight.

An estimate for the required angular accuracy delta of the mirror surface figure is obtained in the following way. If the normal to any given surface element deviates from the optimal direction by delta, the ray incident on this element deviates by 2*delta and the spot size increases by udel = 2*delta*L, where L is the exit focal distance. Taking L = 1000 mm in both cases, and udel as given by the ray-tracings, we are led to the estimates of delta given in Table V.

The heat load on the pre-focussing mirror can be estimated. The power radiated by VUV-III (@1.15 GeV and 0.4 A) would be 3.6 Watts/hor mrad. This mirror accepts 7 mrad, which results in a flux of 25 Watts. Most photons will be absorbed by the pre-focussing mirror, since its cut-off energy (about 300 eV) is way below the critical energy (about 1 keV) for VUV-III. Assuming uniform flux, and given the silica thermal conductivity of 0.014 Watt/cm.deg C, the thermal gradient across a

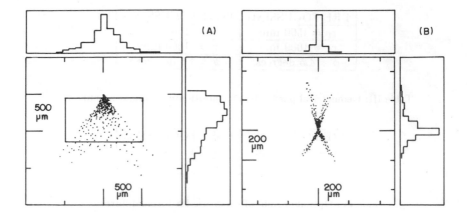

Figure 5: Aberrated focal spots of collimating toroidal mirrors; angular acceptance is 7 hor X 3 vert mrad^2 for pre-focussing and 30 hor X 14 vert mrad^2 for post-focussing.

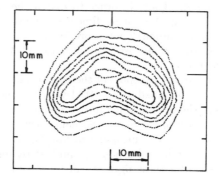

Figure 6: Calculated energy deposition contours on the pre-focussing mirror illuminated with VUV-III synchrotron source (1.15 GeV, 0.4 Amp, sigmax = 0.5 mm, sigmaz = 0.06 mm). The outermost contour corresponds to 1.1W/cm^2, while the two innermost ones correspond to 7.7W/cm^2. The mirror collects 14 hor mrad.

PRE-FOCUSSING	POST-FOCUSSING
udel = 600 micra	udel = 70 micra
delta = 300 microrad	delta = 35 microrad

Table V: Surface figure tolerance for collimating mirrors.

mirror silica substrate would be more than 33 deg C/cm. The flux is, however, not uniform. A more detailed study of the heat load was made ray-tracing the mirror with a synchrotron light source [6]. The resulting energy deposition contours are shown on figure 6. A detailed study of the temperature and thermal strain fields has not yet been made. All of this discussion assumed a pre-focussing mirror placed downstream of the LNLS standard front-end. This requires a distance $r_1 = 4500$ mm, as assumed in Table III. However, one might consider inserting the mirror chamber between elements of the front-end, in order to insure a closer approach to the source. There are many advantages in that: (i) The symmetrical mount $r_1 = r_2$ results in much tighter focussing (150 instead of 600 micra FWHM), which improves flux and allows for smaller entrance slit width settings. (ii) A mirror with the same size would collect 2.14 times more photons. (iii) Furthermore, these photons will now underfill the grating surface, improving spectral resolution.

There are disadvantages as well: (i) Reduced system safety, since an optical element would be inserted upstream of the complete front-end; and (ii) much increased heat load on the first mirror. Both of these disadvantages can however be rendered unimportant by adequate engineering.

Expert Latex file processing by Ms. E. Tarchiani is gratefully acknowledged.

It is the author's wish that no agency should derive military benefit from this paper.

REFERENCES

[1] Craievich, A. F. and de Castro, A. R. B., Proc. I Workshop Synchrotron Light: Applications and Related Instrumentation, ed. Craievich, A., 279 - 291, World Scientific Publishing, Singapore (1989).

[2] ISA division Jobin Yvon, 16 - 18 Rue du Canal, Longjumeau Cedex, France.

[3] Jark, W. and Neviere, M., Appl. Opt., 26, 943 - 948 (1987).

[4] Saile, V. and West, J. B., Nucl. Instr. and Meth., 208, 199 - 213 (1983).

[5] Yanagihara, M., Yamaguchi, S., Niwano, M., Iguchi, Y., Yagishita, A., Koide, T., Sato, S. and Sasaki, T., Photon Factory Activity Report 1983/4, VI-106, KEK Japan (1984).

[6] Lai, B. and Cerrina, F., Nucl. Instr. and Meth., A246, 337 - 341 (1986).

PHOTOELECTRON SPECTROSCOPY OF SOLIDS

PIERO PIANETTA and PAUL KING

Stanford Synchrotron Radiation Laboratory
Stanford, CA 94309, USA

ABSTRACT

The study of solids has advanced significantly in the past 20 years through the use of photoelectron spectroscopy. Synchrotron radiation has made important contributions to photoelectron spectroscopy through both its tunability and high fluxes in otherwise inaccessible photon energy ranges. This paper will discuss recent synchrotron-based instrumental developments which have brought high spatial resolution to photoelectron spectroscopy. Such developments will ultimately allow photoemission investigations of sub-micron areas. Applications of these new techniques to micro-chemical analysis and micro-EXAFS of surfaces are demonstrated.

1. INTRODUCTION

The use of synchrotron radiation to perform photoemission spectroscopy has resulted in a very powerful technique for studying a wide variety of problems in surface physics. We will illustrate the utility of the synchrotron radiation photoemission techniques with a number of examples ranging from core level spectroscopy to photoelectron microscopy.

The type of information that can be obtained from photoelectron spectroscopy is to a large extent dependent on the incident photon energy. Low photon energies between 15 and 50 eV are most useful for studying the band structures of solids while those above 50 eV can reach many core levels and are very useful in measuring chemical shifts of these levels. For example, for the case of the III-V compounds, both of these ranges are interesting since both the valence bands and core levels from the gallium and arsenic can be observed at high resolutions on the order of 0.1 eV. In Figure 1, we show a typical electron energy distribution curve (EDC) for the clean, cleaved GaAs (110) surface for a photon energy of 240 eV.[1] The spectral features of interest in this spectrum are the arsenic and gallium core levels located at 19.0 and 40.8 eV below the valence band maximum as well as the valence band (s-p derived levels) which occupy the top 12 eV of

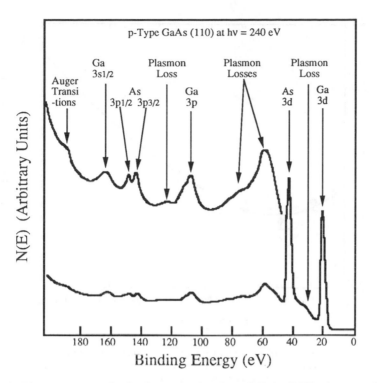

Figure 1. Electron energy distribution curve for cleaved GaAs (110) taken at a photon energy of 240 eV showing the core levels and many-electron lines that are accessible in photoemission studies

the spectrum. In addition to these one-electron lines, we are also able to see Auger transitions and plasmon losses.

One of the strengths of synchrotron radiation is the ability to continuously tune through any given photon energy range. In the case of the GaAs described above, by tuning through the available photon energies we are able to adjust the kinetic energies of the various core levels to be roughly between 20 and 200 eV. This is significant because the escape length of electrons in solids is strongly dependent on the electron kinetic energy. The tunability of synchrotron radiation thus allows the escape depth to be tuned from the minimum of 5 Å all the way up to 20 Å when photon energies on the order of 1 keV are used.[2] Figure 2 shows the escape depth of electrons in GaAs with kinetic energies from 20 to 200 eV. It shows the escape depth going through a minimum at 60 eV and increasing for energies both higher and lower than this point. The escape depth

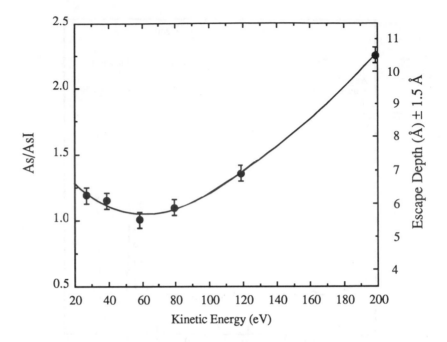

Figure 2. Plot of the ratio of the unshifted (As) to shifted (AsI) arsenic-3d levels as a function of electron kinetic energy for the GaAs (110) surface covered by a monolayer of oxygen. The scale on the right gives the escape depth in angstroms calculated using a simple two layer model (see text).

was determined by first measuring the As-3d core level of an oxygen covered GaAs surface as a function of photon energy. The surface arsenic atom (AsI), since it is bonded to an oxygen atom, is shifted to a higher binding energy by 2.9 eV.[1] This serves as a marker for the surface atoms. The bulk atoms are unshifted and serve as the reference. The escape depth can be easily calculated by assuming a two layer system in which the topmost GaAs layer (with the chemisorbed oxygen) forms one layer and the remainder of the crystal forms the second layer. The escape depth, L(E), can be written to first order as

$$L(E) = x_1/[1 + 1/\ln(As/AsI)] \tag{1}$$

where x_1 is the thickness of the top layer which can be estimated to be approximately 4 Å. This allows us to put an escape depth scale on Figure 2. At the minimum, the escape depth is 5.8 Å ± 1.5 Å or approximately 1.5 molecular layers. By choosing an appropriate photon energy, we are able to concentrate on what is happening just at the surface of the sample.

Experimental techniques such as low energy electron diffraction, Auger electron spectroscopy (AES) and ultraviolet photoelectron spectroscopy (UPS) also have high surface sensitivity. However, they lack the chemical information which can be obtained from x-ray photoelectron spectroscopy (XPS) studies of core level shifts. AES can be used to study chemical shifts in some materials, but the use of an electron beam as the excitation source can desorb the oxygen or destroy the integrity of some surfaces. This damage is minimized when using ultraviolet light or x-rays. Conventional XPS using Mg or Al Kα (1253.6 or 1486.7 eV, respectively) lacks the necessary surface sensitivity. With synchrotron radiation, not only can we study the chemical shift of core levels upon forming a chemical bond, but we can also perform these studies at submonolayer coverage due to the inherent surface sensitivity of the technique.

A limitation to the use of photoemission and photoabsorption measurements for analytic purposes has arisen from the relatively poor lateral resolution inherent in conventional instrumentation. The area probed by standard laboratory UPS and XPS systems is typically on the order of square millimeters. Even in more advanced systems the area probed is rarely smaller than 100 μm on a side being limited largely by the technological barriers that exist to producing focussed beams of photons of sufficiently high flux. A similar limitation exists in synchrotron-based photoabsorption measurements such as absorption fine structure measurements (XANES and EXAFS), where conventional beamline optics result in probes that generally exceed 100 μm.

A number of laboratories applying a variety of techniques are presently active in efforts to improve the lateral resolution of photoemission measurements. Some of these efforts have been reported on recently[3] while the entire field of small area and imaging photoemission and photoabsorption techniques have been reviewed in a number of other publications.[4, 5, 6] These next-generation techniques will extend photoemission and photoabsorption applications to the study of small samples as well as to the study of heterogeneous surfaces showing variations in surface chemistry in the range 0.1 to 100 μm. Applications in the basic sciences in studies ranging from electronic properties to biological structure and technical applications in the semiconductor, magnetic media, and catalysis industries have been targeted.

The most promising techniques being pursued for surface microanalysis can be classified as either microprobe techniques where a small focussed spot of x-rays limits the area probed and selected area techniques where photoemitted electrons are imaged using electrostatic or magnetic lenses, or a combination of both. Synchrotron-based microprobes are being developed to produce small spots of x-rays using advanced optical components.[7, 8, 9, 10] The lateral resolution of these systems is set by the size of a tightly focussed x-ray spot and ultimate resolution is expected to be on the order of 0.1 to 0.5 μm. Some designs make it cumbersome or impractical to scan the incident photon energy and so small area photoelectron spectroscopy is emphasized rather than photoabsorption studies. Other microprobe designs can be applied to both.

A second approach applicable to small area and imaging photoabsorption measurements is the secondary emission or photoemission microscope modified for use with synchrotron radiation. In this technique the surface of interest acts as an optical element in an electrostatic lens. Photoemitted electrons are not energy analyzed although lens aberrations generally filter out all but the low energy secondary electrons from the image. Variations in this low energy photoyield from the sample acting as photocathode are proportional to the absorption cross-section and when quantified result in photoabsorption spectra. This approach has been demonstrated performing small area XANES on a region 10 μm square.[11, 12] Ultimately a lateral resolution on the order of 0.1 μm may be achieved using undulator generated radiation.

A third technique, the magnetic projection photoelectron microscope is described in this paper. This instrument, a MicroESCA™ from Surface Science Instruments, has the ability to image and energy analyze high energy electrons while retaining quantitative spectroscopic capabilities.[13, 14, 15] That is, the position and intensity of specific core level photoemission can be measured with moderate to high spatial resolution. In addition, the ability to image electrons with arbitrary kinetic energies gives the possibility of readily varying electron escape depth as described above and enhancing the surface sensitivity. The current version of this photoelectron microscope gives spatially resolved images with a lateral resolution down to 1 μm and an energy resolution of better than 0.1 eV for electrons below 100 eV.[15, 16]

2. MAGNETIC PROJECTION PHOTOELECTRON MICROSCOPY

The MicroESCA™ is a development of the direct imaging magnetic projection method first used by the group of D. W. Turner at Oxford University.[13, 14] The heart of this photoelectron microscope is a superconducting solenoid which surrounds the sample. Photoelectrons produced by monochromatic photons are confined by the strong field to a helical path along the magnetic field lines. As the magnetic field lines diverge away from the solenoid, the electron paths diverge and the electrons are projected onto a detector as a magnified image. Figure 3 shows a schematic of the experimental arrangement. The image detector is of the resistive anode type[17] and is approximately 1.5 meters from the solenoid. The strength of the field at the sample, B_0, is 7 T, and at the detector plane, B_d, is 1.5 mT. Lateral magnification of the photoelectron microscope is equal to $[B_0/B_d]^{1/2}$. Given the parameters of the current instrument, the magnification is approximately 70, limited on one side by the highest magnetic field readily attainable in a large bore, air-core superconducting solenoid and on the other side by the need to avoid the disturbing effects of exogenous fields such as the earth's magnetic field, storage ring bending magnets and ion pumps. The magnification gives a field of view on the sample of 200 X 200 μm^2 consistent with a 14 X 14 mm^2 detector area.

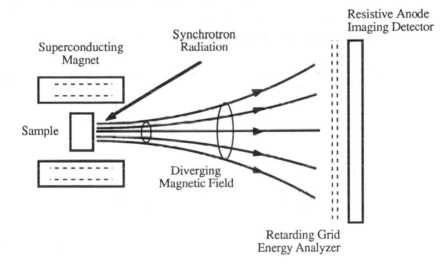

Figure 3. Schematic of the MicroESCA™ magnetic projection photoelectron microscope.

The physical limit on the spatial resolution of this instrument is determined by the electrons which are emitted with a large component of momentum perpendicular to the axis of the magnetic field.[13] If we define the photoelectron emission angle to be zero parallel to the magnetic field, it is the photoelectrons with large emission angles that significantly degrade the spatial resolution. These photoelectrons experience a Lorentz force which causes them to follow a helical path to the detector. The maximum radius of the helical path followed by the off-axis electrons is the cyclotron radius which is

$$R_{max} = (2\,m\,E_0)^{1/2} / e\,B_0 \tag{2}$$

where E_0 is the kinetic energy of the emitted photoelectron. The values of spatial resolution reported in the literature depend on the definitions which are used and vary from $(0.1)R_{max}$[13] to $(2.2)R_{max}$[18]. We use the more conservative measure of $(2.2)R_{max}$ for our estimates and predict spatial resolutions of 3, 10 and 30 μm for photoelectrons with kinetic energies of 10, 100 and 1000 eV, respectively. Figure 4 is a graph of calculated resolution for various monoenergetic electrons following arguments similar to those outlined by Kruit and Read which assume isotropic emission of electrons.[18] The electron emission is typically not isotropic so that the actual resolutions will be somewhat better than what we have shown in Figure 4.

Although these spatial resolutions are quite good, it may be possible to improve the

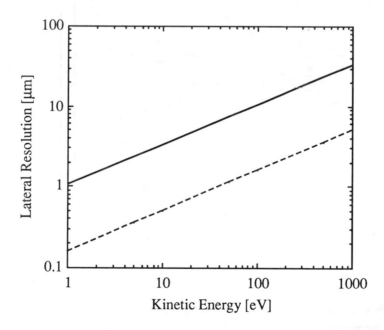

Figure 4. The lateral resolution versus electron kinetic energy is plotted for the magnetic projection photoelectron microscope. The solid line assumes that all electrons emitted from the sample are imaged. The dashed line assumes that only those electrons within a $10°$ cone centered about the axis of the magnetic field are imaged.[18]

resolution by allowing only those electrons which are emitted close to the axis of the magnetic field reach the detector.[19] In this method, electron optics are placed within the solenoid and would "skim" off electrons emitted from the sample at angles greater than, for example, 10° from the field axis and would result in spatial resolutions of 0.5, 1.5 and 5 μm for photoelectrons with kinetic energies of 10, 100 and 1000 eV, respectively. This will be a tremendous improvement since submicron XPS would then be a possibility. Total count rates are, of course, decreased when skimming is used as only 2% of the emitted electrons are in the 10° forward cone (assuming isotropic emission) and a high intensity source such as an undulator would be required.

A critical element in reaching the physical limits of spatial resolution is the imaging detector and its associated electronics. The present instrument uses a detector which consists of a pair of microchannel plates which produce a cascade of electrons for each incident electron, followed by a resistive anode plate with pickup electrodes at each of its four corners.[17] Signals proportional to the charge pulses received at each corner are converted into X and Y positions by an analog to digital converter and summed in a buffer memory. The contents of this buffer are then transferred to an Hewlett-Packard workstation which records and displays the image. Our position computer allows us to divide a 200 μm wide field of view into a 64 X 64 or 256 X 256 array thus giving a pixel size of better than one micron. The present electronics system is able to process position data at a rate of 100 kHz. This count rate capability has proved adequate for bending magnet fluxes, however operation on undulator beam lines must be able to record electron arrivals at count rates approaching 1 MHz.

The decreasing magnetic field between the solenoid and the detector has the effect of converting the off-axis momentum of the electrons at the sample to forward momentum at the detector.[13] Consequently, the angular distribution of the photoelectrons leaving the sample is collimated along the field lines while energy is conserved. It is this aspect of electron motion in a diverging magnetic field that is responsible for the excellent spectroscopic capabilities of this instrument. A simple retarding field analyzer performs as an efficient high pass energy filter of the projected image without angular distortion. The fact that the electrons are so well collimated results in a resolution of 0.1 eV at 100 eV which is more than adequate for chemical shift studies in solids. We note here that retarding field analysis yields an integral spectrum which must be differentiated numerically. In practice electron energies of interest are imaged by subtracting two images obtained at retarding potentials that bracket the kinetic energy of interest. However, signal to noise ratios and overall sensitivity would be dramatically improved if an imaging band pass analyzer were employed.

In practice we often perform small area analysis because small area analysis offers a compromise between the limits set by mechanical stability of the our present sample manipulation system and the count rate ceiling in our resistive anode imaging system. The count rate limitation is particularly troublesome while performing imaging spectrometry with a high pass energy filter due to the poor signal to noise inherent in retarding field analysis. Total yield photoabsorption measurements do not suffer from this effect and we expect to emphasize this advantage in the future. In addition the shapes of photoyield spectra are weighted such that the majority of the emitted electrons are secondary electrons with energies below 20 eV.[20] Total yield imaging can therefore be performed with relatively high lateral resolution, typically having better lateral resolution than core-level electron analyzed images. An exact calculation of resolution in total yield images and small area analysis can only be made if the total yield spectrum including the secondary tail has been determined. In small area analysis, we first perform imaging to identify, orient, and define areas of interest. An aperture is used to define the region of interest and a single characteristic spectrum is collected from that region. We have performed such analyses on regions as small as 20 μm in diameter

3. IMAGING PHOTOEMISSION MEASUREMENTS

We have worked with a number of material systems and have demonstrated the microscope's ability to analyze surfaces with microscopic variations in surface chemistry. When performing imaging photoelectron spectroscopy a number of images are collected at slightly different retarding potentials. By subtracting the images formed at any two retarding potentials, a differential image can be generated that represents the photoelectron intensity over a narrow energy window. Certain differential images (e.g. 10 eV wide and covering all shifted Si-2p peaks) provide largely elemental contrast reflecting variations in total silicon coverage on the surface. Other differential images (e.g. 3 eV wide and covering the shifted Si-2p peak in SiO_2) can be used to identify chemically shifted surface structures. Each set of images can be processed in a more sophisticated manner to give a conventional XPS analysis of selected surface features. We are using software techniques, similar to those developed for LANDSAT-type remote sensing,[21] which make it is possible to improve the signal to noise ratio in our small area XPS spectra. These methods, namely principle component analysis and scatter plot diagrams, have also been successfully applied to multispectral Auger images.[22, 23] Details of our image processing procedures are beyond the scope of this paper and are discussed elsewhere.[24] Keep in mind that our analysis results in an integral photoelectron spectrum which must be differentiated to give the XPS spectrum of a defined area. For both the differential images and the differentiated XPS spectra, spectral information is actually a relatively small difference above a large background and as such has the potential for being noisy. An imaging band pass analyzer that could record differential images directly, would give a much better signal to noise ratio than presently achievable and is under discussion.

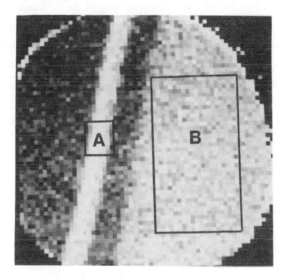

Figure 5. Photoelectron image of an aluminum line and pad on a silicon substrate with $h\nu = 170$ eV and $V_r = 85.5$ V. Field of view is 300 µm.

The first samples imaged with synchrotron light consisted of patterned aluminum on silicon. In Figure 5, we show a photoelectron image of a 25 µm aluminum line and an aluminum pad on a silicon substrate. This is one of nineteen images taken at different retarding fields from 85.5 to 94.5 volts, 0.5 volts apart. This particular image was taken with a photon energy of 170 eV and a retarding field of 85.5 volts. Under these conditions of photon energy and retarding field, the photoelectrons from the Al-2p level ($E_B = 72$ eV) have kinetic energies above the retarding field and will reach the detector. The photoelectrons from the Si-2p level ($E_B = 99$ eV) have kinetic energies below the retarding potential and are rejected. Therefore, in Figure 5, the aluminum shows up as a high intensity area and the silicon is dark (black = 0, white = 1). The signal intensities from a 30 X 50 μm^2 region on the Al line and a 100 X 200 μm^2 region on the Al pad were calculated for each of the nineteen images and the derivative of this signal per unit area is plotted in Figure 6. This clearly shows that the Al-2p core levels are shifted by 1 eV with respect to each other. The Al 2p core level from the aluminum line peaks at a retarding field of 90.25 volts while that from the aluminum pad peaks at 91.25 volts. This result is significant because it both shows that spot analysis can be done on areas as small as 30 X 50 μm^2 and that the retarding field analysis has sufficient energy resolution to detect the shift which in this case is due to charging of the Al line with respect to the pad. It should also be noted that since the area contributing to the signal coming from the aluminum line is over 12 times smaller than that from the pad, the signal from the line would have been too small to have been observed without using the high spatial resolution of this system.

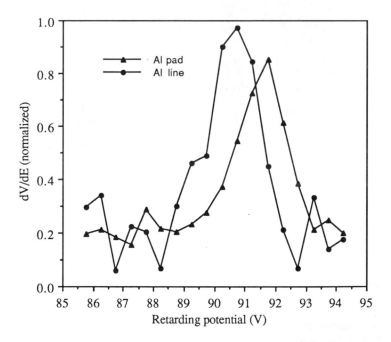

Figure 6. Al-2p core level for the areas of the aluminum line and pad shown in Figure 5. The magnitudes of the core levels have been normalized to the measured areas.

The information contained in Figure 6 is complemented by Figures 7A and 7B. Figure 7A shows a differential image obtained by subtracting the image taken at a retarding field of 93.5 volts from the image taken at 90.5 volts. The high intensity regions are clustered mostly on the aluminum pad and emphasize the surface features associated with the 91.25 volt retarding potential peak. Figure 7B shows a differential

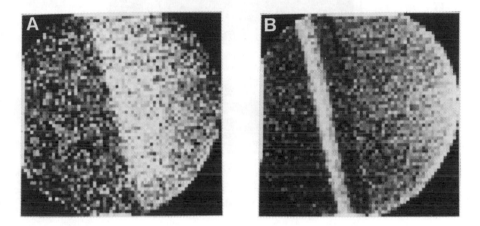

Figure 7. Differential images emphasizing the spectral regions between 91.5 and 94.5 volts (7A, left) and 85.5 and 91.5 volts (7B, right). Field of view is 300 µm.

image obtained by subtracting the image taken at a retarding field of 90.5 volts from the image taken at 85.5 volts. In this case, the contribution from the pad is removed and the areas associated with the 90.25 volt retarding potential peak (the aluminum line) is enhanced. The intensity on the far right of this image is an artifact due to spatial non-uniformity in the photon beam and can also be seen in Figure 5. This type of artifact can easily be removed for more detailed analyses.

4. SMALL AREA PHOTOABSORPTION MEASUREMENTS

The procedure followed when measuring the photoabsorption spectrum from a small area is best demonstrated by example. As stated earlier, the imaging mode is first used to identify, orient and define the sample. Figure 8 is a total yield image taken at a photon energy of 300 eV. The image is of a field of 50 µm square holes etched into a 1 µm thick resist over the native oxide on a silicon wafer. The sample was lightly

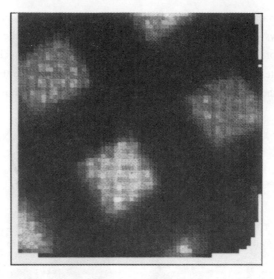

Figure 8. A total yield image of a field of 50 μm holes etched through a 1 μm thick photoresist. hν = 300 eV. Image contrast arises from differential charging of the sample. Field of view is 200 μm and the retarding field is set to 10 V.

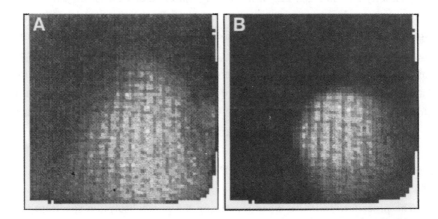

Figure 9. (9A, left) Same sample as in Figure 8 at a slightly larger magnification. (9B, right). Same field of view as Figure 9A but with an aperture now limiting the electrons to those originating from the bottom of the hole. hν = 300 eV. The field of view is 75 μm and the retarding potential is set to 0 V for both images.

sputtered prior to imaging. Contrast mechanisms in total yield imaging can arise from a variety of absorption and emission phenomena including absorption cross-sections, photoelectron or Auger emission, work function variations and differential charging. The photoyield from the holes is more than twice that from the resist and the origin of this contrast is thought to be differential charging. With contrast as high as this, single images with sufficient signal to noise to classify individual pixels as belonging to the hole and the resist areas can be recorded in a matter of seconds. Figure 9A is an image of one of the holes magnified so that the entire field of view now covers only 75 μm. Each image consists of a 64 by 64 array of pixels which at this magnification translates into a hardware limit on resolution of about 1 micron. A 5 mm aperture on the low magnetic field side of the instrument is used to define a 40 μm diameter area at the bottom of the hole as the area to be analyzed. The aperture is shown in place in Figure 9B. The positioning of this aperture is straightforward as it is done on the low magnetic field side of the instrument where the image has already been magnified.

Prior to the near-edge photoabsorption (XANES) scan, the incident photon flux is optimized to get the maximum signal from the feature of interest now that the aperture excludes unwanted electrons. This is the major payoff from moving to small area analysis; unneeded signal that would contribute to the total count rate in photoabsorption imaging is excluded so that the count rate in the area of interest can be increased without overloading the detector. At present any lateral variations within the aperture defined region are ignored and a single near edge absorption spectrum is collected for the entire 40 μm diameter region. XANES spectra over the carbon 1s edge from within the hole and from the resist outside the hole are shown in Figure 10. The similarity in the spectra indicate that the bottom of the hole has retained a significant residue of resist through the end of the etch process.

In another study we collected the XANES spectrum from a 20 μm diameter region on a clean cleaved single crystal BiSrCaCuO (2122) superconductor and compared this spectrum with that obtained from a 200 μm square region which is our usual field of view forgoing additional magnification or apertures. These near edge spectra are shown in Figure 11 with the O-1s absorption edge resolved. They do not differ significantly indicating that lateral variations, if they exist at all, exist on a scale smaller that that accessible with this instrument. The minor differences that do appear in these spectra arose when the monochromator resolution was adjusted (from about 0.3 eV to 0.6 eV) to increase the flux for the small area application. These spectra and those shown in Figure 10 were recorded in a matter of minutes using a spherical grating monochromator on a

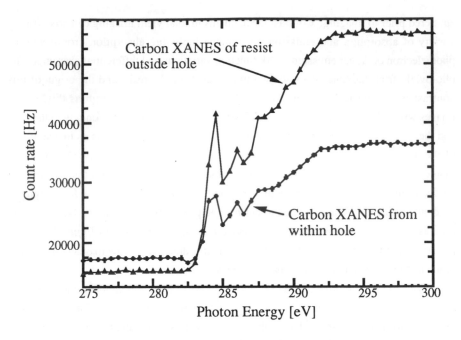

Figure 10. Carbon 1s XANES spectra taken from the bottom of a hole in a film of photoresist and from the surrounding resist. The area within the hole was selected by placing a 5 mm aperture in front of the detector which gave a 40 μm region at the sample.

bending magnet station (Beamline 8-2) at SSRL. A detailed analysis of this and other near edge spectra collected on this material will be the subject of a future paper.

As stated earlier, the limit to the lateral resolution in our total yield photoabsorption measurements is a function of the energy distribution curve (EDC) making up the total yield signal. In the geometry of our apertured small area analysis we arbitrarily define lateral resolution as the diameter of that disc from which 90% of the signal originates. The remaining 10% of the signal comes from outside this disc but gets through due to the helical path followed by the drifting photoelectrons. Electrons with higher kinetic energies follow larger helical paths and so are detrimental to high resolution imaging.

This is demonstrated in Figure 12 where we have estimated the limits to the small area analysis for a variety of EDC's. We have assumed EDC's where the fraction of the total yield made up of low energy secondaries is varied from fifty to one hundred percent while the remaining electrons have energies distributed between 250 and 300 eV. An example EDC for the case where 90% of the yield is in the secondary tail is presented in

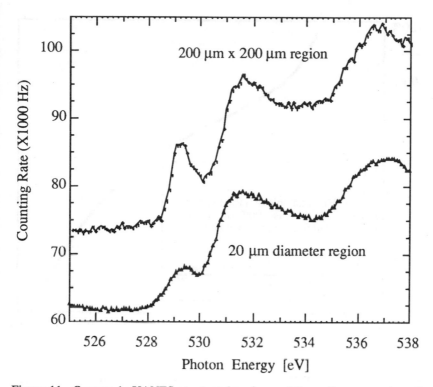

Figure 11. Oxygen 1s XANES spectra taken from a 20 μm diameter region of a clean cleaved BiSrCaCuO (2122) single crystal superconductor and from a larger 200 μm square region on the same sample.

the inset to Figure 12. The structure of the secondary tail follows the "universal curve" described in the work by Henke, Smith and Atwood[20] and assumes a work function of 3.7 eV. In the most conservative case where fifty percent of the total yield is found in the secondary tail, a lower limit on resolution is around 10 μm. By 100% the resolution has improved to 2 μm. One of the strengths of retarding field analysis is the ability to resolve the structure of the low energy secondaries without aberrations. In future photoabsorption measurements we intend to resolve the entire photoyield spectrum in order to better quantify our working lateral resolution. A hemispherical band-pass analyzer appropriate for small area analysis will soon be added to the instrument. Set to pass only low energy electrons, say below 2 eV, band pass analysis will allow us to achieve a lateral resolution near 1 μm independent of the nature of the total yield EDC.

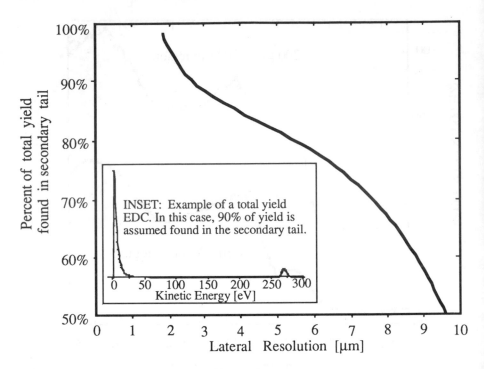

Figure 12. Estimate of the lateral resolution in small area total yield photoabsorption measurements assuming varying amounts of the total yield found in the secondary tail. The inset is an example of the EDC's used. In this case 90% of the yield is made up of low energy secondary electrons while the remaining 10% is distributed around 275 eV.

5. CONCLUSIONS

Our first results show the ability of the magnetic projection photoelectron microscope to image surfaces with 5 μm lateral resolution. The results demonstrate the ability of this instrument to image chemically shifted surface features and its potential for small spot XPS analysis. In addition they point out the additional work that needs to be done. Improvements in the quality of the current images will come with improved normalization procedures. Variations in the synchrotron beam intensity over time contribute to image to image variations and must be kept below a few percent for quantitative XPS analysis. In addition, we have demonstrated a practical technique capable of measuring surface sensitive photoabsorption spectra from areas as small as 20 μm in diameter. The procedure relies on the imaging properties of the photoelectron microscope to help identify and isolate features of interest. Small area photoabsorption measurements of areas selected by apertures is then carried out. Photoabsorption measurements are particularly attractive with this instrument due to its high collection efficiency and excellent lateral resolution when imaging low energy secondary electrons. In the photoabsorption mode, a lateral resolution on the order of 5 μm is readily achievable and with the addition of a band-pass analyzer, small area XANES or EXAFS analyses nearing 1 μm will be possible.

6. ACKNOWLEDGEMENTS

This work was supported under Air Force Contract No. AF 49620-86K-0019. This research was performed at SSRL which is operated by the Department of Energy, Office of Basic Energy Sciences, Division of Chemical Sciences. That Office's Division of Materials Sciences has provided support for this research. We would also like to thank Lawrence Livermore National Laboratory for the use of the torroidal grating and spherical grating monochromators on Beamline 8 at SSRL.

7. REFERENCES

1. Pianetta, P., Lindau, I., Garner, C. M. and Spicer, W. E., Phys. Rev. B 18, 2792 (1978).

2. Lindau, I. and Spicer, W. E., J. Elect. Spectrosc. 3, 409 (1974).

3. For the latest reports on photoelectron microscopy see the proceedings from the Fourth International Conference on Electron Spectroscopy held July 10-14, 1989 at the University of Hawaii which will be published in the Journal of Electron Spectroscopy and the proceedings of the Ninth International Conference of Vacuum Ultraviolet Radiation Physics held July 17-21, 1989 at the University of Hawaii which will be published in Physica Scripta.

4. Griffith, O. H. and Rempfern, G. F., in Advances in Optical and Electron Microscopy (Academic Press, London, 1987).

5. Seah, M. P. and Smith, G. C., 11, 69 (1988).

6. Turner, D. W., Plummer, I. R. and Porter, H. Q., Phil. Trans. R. Soc. Lond. A318, 219 (1986).

7. Kunz, C., Moewes, A., Roy, G., Sievers, H., Voss, J. and Wongel, H., (HASYLAB Annual Report, 1987).

8. Cerrina, F., Margaritondo, G., Underwood, J. H., Hettrick, M., Green, M. A., Brillson, L. J., Franciosi, A., Hochst, H., P.M. Deluca, J. and Gould, M. N., Nucl. Instr. and Meth. A266, 303 (1988).

9. Nyholm, R., Eriksson, M., Hansen, K., Sairanen, O.-P., Werin, S., Flodstrom, A., Tornevik, C., Meinander, T. and Sarakontu, M., Rev. Sci. Instrum. 2168 (1989).

10. Ade, H., Rahrback, H. and Kirz, J., Physica Scripta (to be published).

11. Tonner, B. P. and Harp, G. R., Rev. Sci. Instrum. 59, 853 (1988).

12. Tonner, B. P. and Harp, G. R., J. Vac. Sci. Technol. A 7, 1 (1989).

13. Beamson, G., Porter, H. Q. and Turner, D. W., J. Phys. E: Sci. Instrum. 13, 64 (1980).

14. Beamson, G., Porter, H. Q. and Turner, D. W., Nature 290, 556 (1981).

15. Pianetta, P., Lindau, I., King, P. L., Keenlyside, M., Knapp, G. and Browning, R., Rev. Sci. Instrum. 1686 (1989).

16. King, P. L., Borg, A., Kim, C., Pianetta, P., Lindau, I., Knapp, G. and Keenlyside, M., Physica Scripta (to be published).

17. Lampton, M. and Paresce, F., Rev. Sci. Instrum. 45, 1098 (1974).

18. Kruit, P. and Read, F. H., J. Phys. E: Sci. Instrum. 16, 313 (1983).

19. Keenlyside, M. (private communication).

20. Henke, B. L., Smith, J. A. and Attwood, D. T., J. Appl. Phys. 48, 1852 (1977).

21. Canas, A. A. D. and Barnett, M. E., Int. J. Remote Sensing 6, 867 (1985).

22. Browning, R., MRS Bulletin 12, 75 (1987).

23. Browning, R., Smialek, J. L. and Jacobsen, N. S., Advanced Ceramic Materials 2, 773 (1987).

24. King, P. L., Browning, R., Pianetta, P., Lindau, I., Keenlyside, M. and Knapp, G., J. Vac. Sci Technol. A7 (6), 3301 (1989).

Soft X-Ray Spectroscopy

A.M. Flank and P. Lagarde

LURE Bat 209d Université Paris-Sud 91405 Orsay (France)

Abstract

This paper is a short review of the characteristics, in terms of experimental problems, theoretical analysis and results, of the soft X-ray spectroscopy within the domain 700 to 3000 eV by comparison with the more well-known hard X-ray domain. A definitely large expansion of this technique may be expected from the development of new synchrotron radiation machines : either small machines with an energy around 1 GeV like Super-ACO at Orsay or very powerful ones as ESRF using insertion devices.

INTRODUCTION

Soft X-ray spectroscopy has been used now for quite a long time : nevertheless, it appears less developped than the VUV region in one side, and than the hard X-ray one on another ; it could be because of some intrinsic difficulties in terms of monochromators, sample preparation and even theoretical background. This domain covers the range 700-3000 eV : at lower energies, monochromators are based on gratings, the experimental set-up's are UHV compatible. On the contrary, in the hard X-ray region a primary vacuum is sufficient in most of the cases while the radiation safety is much more difficult to handle. This paper will review the special features of the soft X-ray domain, first in terms of experimental apparatus, then with some examples of structural and electronic studies on solids.

I - THE EXPERIMENTAL CASE

Within the energy domain 700-3000 eV most of the elements beyond fluorine have an absorption edge, either a K-edge or an L or M edge. Depending on the core level which is excited, either structural (using

EXAFS) or electronic structure (3d elements, rare earths, actinides) studies will be possible. Therefore, it is a very wide range of physical and chemical informations which can be extracted from such a spectroscopy.

1 - Crystals and monochromators

While the whole hard X-ray region can be covered, on synchrotron radiation machines with only one type of crystal (for instance a Si(311) channel-cut or double crystal), this becomes no longer true on the soft X-ray range since the 2d-spacing of the crystal has to match, because of the Bragg law, the wavelength one wants to isolate. Therefore, as it has been gathered in Table I, different crystals have to be used depending on the element of interest. And, for instance, on new synchrotron machines with an high flux, aluminum K-edge EXAFS is only possible with quartz (1010) crystals, whose range of energy ends at the silicon edge some 300 eV beyond : the use of the couple multilayer-KAP can also be used at these energies but at the price of a poorer resolution and a lower flux while with beryl crystals the transmission function of the monochromator is strongly affected by the aluminum and the silicon K-edges of the crystals. As a result, the monochromator design must provide an easy way to change the crystals in order to cover all the energy domain from 700 eV to 3 keV.

Because the crystals listed in Table I are difficult to obtain in large dimensions, all the soft X-ray spectrometers are based on the two-crystal (1,-1) design. The exit beam is kept fixed in position using different mechanical systems, starting from the simplest one used at LURE [1] where a special cam drives a translation stage supporting the second crystal , to a more complicated one like Jumbo [2] at SSRL where the two crystals are independently rotated from outside the ultra-high-vacuum chamber through bellows. Differences also come from the type of vacuum which is allowed inside the monochromator, from UHV to conventional high vacuum by means of a thin beryllium window at the front of the monochromator. A sketch of the beam line used on SA72 of Super-ACO is shown in Fig. 1 as an example.

49

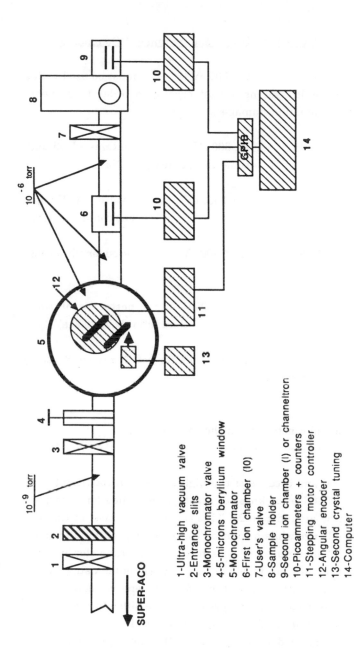

SUPER-ACO

1-Ultra-high vacuum valve
2-Entrance slits
3-Monochromator valve
4-5-microns beryllium window
5-Monochromator
6-First ion chamber (I0)
7-User's valve
8-Sample holder
9-Second ion chamber (I) or channeltron
10-Picoammeters + counters
11-Stepping motor controller
12-Angular encoder
13-Second crystal tuning
14-Computer

Fig.1 : Scheme of the SA72 line on Super-ACO

Crystal	2d (Å)	Useful energy range	Comments
KAP	26.63	E > 500 eV	must be used with a multilayer as a first crystal in order to prevent radiation damage
Beryl (1010)	15.95	E >800 eV	contains Al, Si and some impurities (Mg, Na)
Quartz (1010)	8.51	E > 1500 eV	good for Al K-edge but contains silicon
InSb (111)	7.48	E > 1800 eV	good for silicon edge
Ge (111)	6.53	E > 1950 eV	better resolution than InSb above 2000 eV

Table I - Characteristics of the usual crystals for soft X-ray spectroscopy on synchrotron radiation machines.

2 - Experimental constraints on the samples

Around 2 KeV and because of the high absorption coefficient of all the elements, the effective thickness of a sample designed for absorption spectroscopy must be around 1 to 2μ. This constraint is most of the time very difficult to challenge while a solution can be to deposit by filtration a very fine powder of material onto a carbonate membrane (for instance Nucleopore). This allows for transmission experiments, using an ion chamber as a detector with a very thin polypropylene window : a good signal to noise ratio is achieved at the price of severe difficulties to obtain a very homogeneous sample needed for spectroscopy. In cases where this sample preparation method is not possible, the detection of the total electron yield, which is proportional to the absorption coefficient [3] is the only alternative one : in this range of energy - let's say above 800 eV- the sampling depth amounts to 200 Å which makes the total yield not very surface sensitive. This is perhaps the detection method most widely used, specially when an UHV environment of the sample is needed while the X-ray fluorescence detection is far from being of a common use.

3 - Data reduction problems on EXAFS spectroscopy

The extraction of the EXAFS data, and the data analysis present some difficulties in comparison to the hard X-ray regime, for several reasons :

- the overall absorption coefficient decreases much more rapidly as a function of energy, making the background modelling much more difficult. This is just a consequence of the Victoreen variation of the absorption coefficient far from a characteristic edge.

- the energy domain of the EXAFS data is very limited, sometimes for experimental reasons (like in the case of aluminum), sometimes because the backscatterer atoms are also light elements whose backscattering amplitude dies off very rapidly (oxygen for instance).

Therefore, one wants to use an energy range as wide as possible by using the data up to the very near edge, where the EXAFS theory is supposed to be not well established, and where the modelling of the atomic absorption coefficient is sometimes difficult : this is typically the case of silicon compounds. This point will be developed below.

4 - Experimental counterpart : the energy resolution

Because the Bragg angles of the monochromator in this domain of energy are quite large (40 to 70° usually) and because the core hole width of the light elements is very narrow, the resolution of the experimental spectra in the soft X-ray domain is very high : for instance, the Ge(111) crystal allows at 7 keV a resolution of 2 eV while this figure approaches 0.1 eV at 2 keV. An example of this large difference appears just by comparing the two K-edges of indium and phosphorus within the same energy interval for crystalline InP (Fig. 2). It is obvious that almost no information can be extracted from the indium near-edge structure which is smoothed by the poor energy resolution and the wide core hole width while many details, related either to the electronic structure or to the environment, appear beyond the phosphorus K-edge.

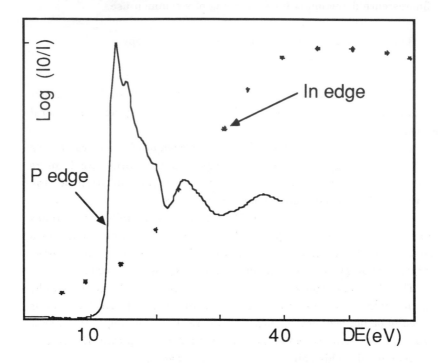

Fig.2- The K-edges of indium (crosses) and phosphorus (solid line) on the same energy range (70 eV) for crystalline InP showing the effect of the energy resolution.

II - EXAFS ANALYSIS ON THE LOW-K DOMAIN

Because the EXAFS energy range is limited on the high energy side, it can be fruitful to try to analyze the data very close to the edge in order to get as much information as possible. Such an analysis, using the conventional procedure for EXAFS but starting the Fourier transform (F.T.) of the data from values as low as 5 to 10 eV, has been first applied to crystalline silicon and silicon carbide [4]. The result (Fig. 3) appears to be the following : peaks on the magnitude of the F.T. extend up to 10 Å, each one compares well with the crystallographic value (within 0.05 Å) except the first two or three interatomic distances which present, between the measured value and the crystallographic one, the usual discrepancy of the order of 0.3 Å due to the slope of the phase shifts. The interpretation goes as follows : taking into account the very low electron energies, we use the domain where the elastic mean free path of the electron increases dramatically up to values of the order of 25-50 Å. The contribution to the EXAFS spectrum of the high distance shells appears therefore in this low photoelectron energy region and it is taken into account by the Fourier transform process since the high energy resolution of the experiment does not smooth their signature .

Assuming that, in this low energy region, the slopes of the phase shifts are independent of the wavevector, these contributions on the modulus of the F.T. have therefore no R-shift compared to the crystallographic value. On the contrary, for the first shells which originate from the whole energy range, the slope of the phase f(k) in the sin(2kR+f(k)) term of the EXAFS formula plays its usual role.

This type of analysis has been done in various crystalline compounds where a light element exists. Table II compares the known interatomic distances with the measured ones on the different F.T. It is worth noticing that these two sets of numbers coincide approximately beyond the third shell.

This high energy resolution of the spectra has allowed the extraction of information about the structure of amorphous silicon. Beside the peaks corresponding to the crystalline state (apart from a large decrease in intensity due to the structural disorder of the material), two new peaks at 4.1 and 5. Å appear while the peak at 5.43 Å sees its intensity considerably lowered [5]. If one calculates the five first interatomic distances in silicon as a function of the dihedral angle between two tetrahedron, one sees that the value 5.5 Å calculated for an angle of 0° does not appears in the F.T. : the interpretation could be that all dihedral angles do not have the same probability, the eclipsed position being less probable. An alternative interpretation [6] of these experimental results makes use of the multiple scattering theory applied to photoelectron paths involving the second shell of neighbours : the structures of the absorption coefficient close to the edge come from a partial ordering of this second shell.

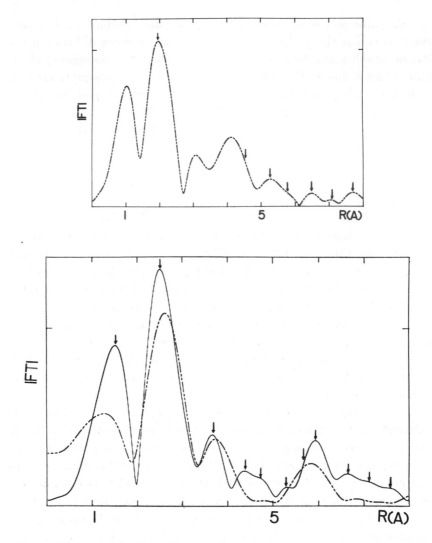

Fig.3 - Magnitudes of the Fourier Transforms of crystalline silicon (top) and crystalline silicon carbide (bottom) ; in this last case, the solid line corresponds to an analysis done over the range 10 to 300 eV while for the dotted line this analysis has been started at 50 eV showing the role played by the low-k domain.

Distances (Å)

GaP

measured	2.	3.36	4.44	5.44		6.60	6.90	7.68	8.1		8.9
crystallo.	2.35	3.85	4.5	5.45	5.92	6.67	7.06	7.89	8.04	8.6	8.9

InP

measured	2.35	3.7	4.4	5.1	5.9	6.49		7.84	8.38		9.14
crystallo.	2.53	4.14	4.84		5.87	6.4	7.18	7.8	8.3		9.26

Al

measured	2.3	3.6	4.52	5.2	6.35		7.45	8.09	8.6
crystallo.	2.86	4.05	4.96	5.72	6.4	7.01	7.57	8.1	8.61

Si crystal

measured	1.96	3.07	4.15	5.3	5.87	6.52	7.06	7.70
crystallo.	2.35	3.85	4.5	5.45	5.92	6.67	7.06	7.69

Table II : Comparison between the crystallographic values and the measured ones on the EXAFS Fourier Transform for various compounds.

As another example, we will see later that the use of the low k domain of the EXAFS spectrum has allowed us the structural interpretation of the ceramic compounds of the SiC-type since as in the crystalline silicon case most of the information on the long range order is confined into the firsts tens of eV beyond the edge.

III - NEAR EDGE STRUCTURE

Another approach of the XANES regime, complementary to the simple EXAFS analysis with a Fourier transform, uses the multiple scattering calculation[7] where all the electron paths are taken into account.

Soft X-ray experiments are good candidates for such theories, again because the energy resolution allows us to extract many spectroscopic details. As an example, the different edge structures of different silicon compounds are shown in Fig. 4 . The edge shifts by some 1.5 eV in coming

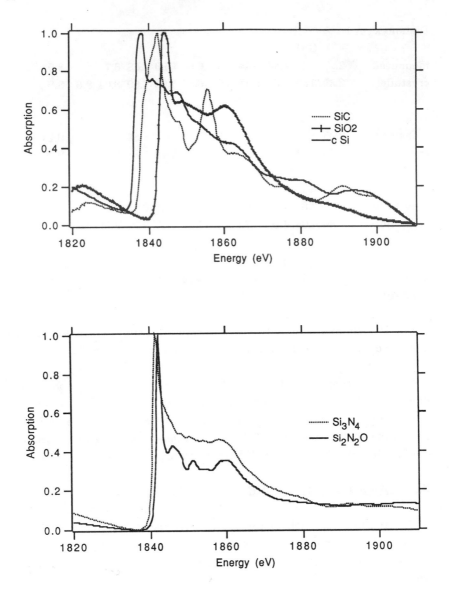

Fig.4 - Near edge structure of different silicon compounds.

from pure cristalline silicon to the silicon carbide, then to the silicon nitride and finally to silica : this shift is the classical one observed when the formal valency of the atom increases. Beyond the edge the structure of the absorption coefficient is a signature for each type of compound and the peak noted A has been interpreted as a shape resonance due to the second silicon shell of neighbors around one silicon atom [8].

Another now well known situation where the near edge structure is very sensitive to the local environment and can be used for structural studies is the case of aluminium four or six-fold coordinated in various aluminum oxides [9]. This sensitivity to the symmetry is therefore the starting point of the determination by X-ray spectroscopy of the composition of different kinds of aluminas.

On the framework of the full multiple scattering theory, an ab-initio calculation of the sulfur near edge structure on crystalline ZnS has been done taking into account up to the 8th shell of atoms around the central sulfur one [10] : the overall theoretical result agrees quite well with the experimental one (Fig. 5) and shows that, in this low electron energy region, most of the signal comes from the light element since the backscattering amplitude of the heavy one is very low. The same interpretation has been applied to crystalline silicon with the same success and these two calculations are the most representative of this theory.

IV - EXAFS STUDIES

In all cases of structural studies using EXAFS spectroscopy, a great use has been made of the low electron energy domain by starting the analysis very close to the edge. An example of such a procedure is found on the EXAFS determination of the microstructure of ceramic fibers of the SiC type [11]. On line with the analysis of pure silicon and pure silicon carbide, a low-k analysis has given informations beyond the first shells of atoms, showing therefore the microcrystalline structure of these samples.

Fig. 6 compares for instance the Fourier transform of one of the ceramic samples - a Nippon-Carbon Nicalon fiber - together with those of the two model compounds : pure SiC and silica. This comparison immediately shows the similitude of the local structure of the fiber with that of silicon carbide. A quantitative interpretation has started from the

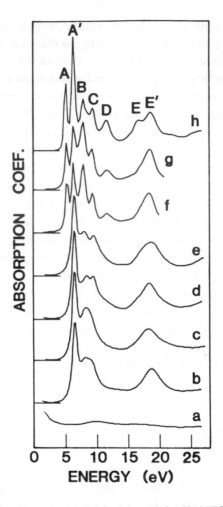

Fig.5 - Full multiple scattering calculations of the XANES region above the sulfur edge in crystalline ZnS showing the effect of the increase of the cluster size : from the bottom to the top each curve corresponds to the introduction of a new shell of neighbours (from ref.10).

analysis of the second shell which is a silicon first shell on the silicon fcc sub-lattice : an average size of the clusters is extracted from the coordination number of this first shell. Assuming that the outside silicon atoms of these clusters are linked to another SiC cluster via a silicon-oxygen bond, the calculated average coordination of the first shell compares well with the direct EXAFS analysis of the first peak of the F.T. Therefore a structural model of the material has been extracted which is in good agreement with other techniques (NMR, ESCA, WAXS).

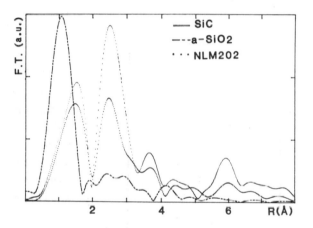

Fig.6- Fourier Transforms of the EXAFS data of crystalline SiC, amorphous SiO_2 and a Nippon Carbon serie 200 fiber above the silicon edge. The microcrystalline nature of the fiber appears from the existence of high coordination shells.

V - ELECTRONIC PROPERTIES

Soft X-ray spectroscopy is a very powerful technique for the determination of some electronic properties of solids. The main reason is that the 3d, 4d, 4f states for instance of most elements have an absorption edge (L_{II}, L_{III}, M_{IV}, M_V) which lies on that domain, and that the electronic properties of the element are strongly related to the filling of these states. Here again, the high energy resolution within the range 700-3000 eV plays a very important role. An example is found on the determination of the copper valence state of high Tc superconductors : the electronic structure of this element is determined by the filling of the 3d states and the L_{III} edge (transition from a core level of 2p symmetry to the 3d empty state) lies around 930 eV. The energy resolution of a double crystal monochromator equipped with two beryl crystals is close to 0.3 eV in this energy range. The spectra of the copper oxide CuO and of an yttrium superconductor with Tc close to 80K are shown in Fig. 7 together with the XPS results on the same energy scale.

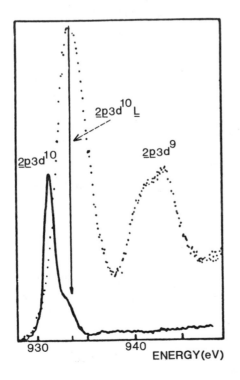

Fig.7- XAS on the copper L_{III} edge (solid line) and XPS (3d level, dots) results of the superconductor $YBa_2Cu_3O_{7-\delta}$ on the same energy scale showing at about one eV above the white line the $3d^9\underline{L}$ initial state (corresponding to a $3d^{10}\underline{L}$ final state) characteristic of the superconductor behaviour.

This figure evidences a shoulder on the high energy side of the main white line which has been interpreted [12] as an initial $3d^9\underline{L}$ charge transfer state where the hole induced by doping has been transferred to the oxygen ligand instead of being on the copper atom. The lack of any absorption with a final $3d^9$ state proves that the copper does not have an initial $3d^8$ configuration. The use of the polarisation of the synchrotron radiation has allowed the determination of the symmetry of this state whose intensity is closely related to the oxygen doping and to the critical temperature [13] (Fig. 8).

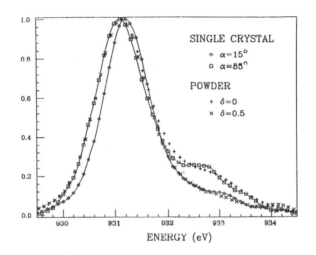

Fig.8- Polarized spectra of the copper L_{III} edge of the $YBa_2Cu_3O_{7-\delta}$ showing that the $3d^9\underline{L}$ state is z-polarized (α-dependence) and is a function of the oxygen doping. The z-polarized $3d^9\underline{L}$ state appears at high oxygen doping when the critical temperature reaches its highest value.

On bismuth compounds we have been able to show that the z-component of the copper white line lies at lower energy than the xy component [14] (Fig. 9). This splitting amounts to a few hundred meV, it depends - as well as the relative intensity of each line - on the class of material and also on the critical temperature inside each class.

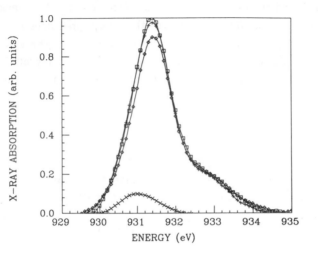

Fig.9- Copper L_{III} edge of a bismuth superconductor compound as a function of the polarization showing the energy splitting between the two components :
- crosses : E parallel to the z axis,
- diamonds : E normal to the z axis,
- plusses : sum of the two components,
- squares : magic angle result.

The interpretation of the atomic spectra of the L_{II}-L_{III} absorption edges of transition metals in compounds like nickel or copper oxides and halides has been developped the last few years on the basis of experiments performed at LURE-ACO [15]. Here again on this 1 keV domain the high energy resolution of the experiments has been of a considerable interest in order to carefully follow the dependence of the multiplet structure with the nature of the ligand. The same group has more recently [16] performed one of the first magnetic X-ray dichroism experiments on rare earth compounds by just using the linearly polarized part of the synchrotron beam. This field of magnetic experiments is expected to expand widely with the development of specially designed new insertion devices like the asymmetric wiggler which will deliver a very intense circularly polarized flux on this 1 keV energy range [17].

As a last example of electronic properties investigated with soft X-ray spectroscopy it is worth mentioning the study of the transition from the atomic to the solid state of rare earths on clusters of an increasing size. These clusters are made by co-deposition of the rare earth with a rare gas on a cold substrate, the size of the clusters depending on the relative fluxes of the two beams. The change of the valence state of the rare earth as a function of the size is very well evidenced by the shape of the M_{IV}-M_V absorption lines [18].

CONCLUSION

Between the ultra soft X-ray domain which ranges from a few tens of eV to about 700 eV, and necessitates ultra-high-vacuum grating monochromators, and the hard X-ray region beyond 4 keV, the soft X-ray domain plays a special role.

In terms of experimental set-up, it uses Bragg monochromators but with high vacuum (10^{-5} torr) capabilities because of the high absorption coefficient of air or helium. In terms of problems which can be addressed it belongs to both outside ranges of energy since structural investigations (EXAFS) can be performed as well as electronic properties of the elements can be determined through the edge structures.

This soft X-ray domain appears therefore to be a wide field whose development has only been limited up to now by some experimental difficulties which are mostly solved nowadays. The recent development of grating monochromators [19] with a very high resolution in the 600-800 eV range together with the use of good multilayers devices which withstand the photon beam will close this gap between the VUV and the X-rays.

The theoretical interpretation of the near edge structure which shows many details at low photon energies is making progress in the last few years although its use is still not as straightforward as the EXAFS domain. Nevertheless it can be hoped that interpretations of the radial distribution functions beyond the pair correlation will soon be possible on soft X-ray absorption edges. As a parallel development we must point out soft X-ray absorption spectroscopy as one of the best tools to study the electronic structure by looking at the L or M edges.

References :

1- M. Lemmonnier, O. Collet, C. Depautex, J.M. Esteva, D. Raoux
   Nucl. Instrum. Methods 152 , 109 (1978)
2- Z. Hussain, E. Umbach, D.A. Shirley, J. Stöhr, F. Feldhaus
   Nucl. Instrum. Methods 195 , 115 (1982)
3- J. Stöhr, C. Noguera, T. Kendelewicz
   Phys. Rev. B30 , 5571 (1984)
4- P. Lagarde, A.M. Flank
   J. Phys. (Paris) 47 , 1389 (1986)
5- A. Menelle, A.M. Flank, P. Lagarde, R. Bellissent
   J. Phys. (Paris) C8 , 379 (1986)
6- A. Filipponi, A. di Cicco, M. Benfatto, C.R. Natoli
   Proceedings of the 2nd European Conference on Progress in X-Ray
Synchrotron Radiation Rome, Sept. 1989
   A. Filipponi, A. di Cicco, M. Benfatto, C.R. Natoli
   Proc. of the 13th Int. Conf. on Amorphous and Liquid
Semiconductors,
   Asheville, NC (USA) Aug. 1989 J. Non-Cryst. Solids
   M. A. Paesler and R. Zallen ed.
   A. di Cicco, A. Bianconi, C. Coluzza, P. Rudolf, P. Lagarde, A.M.
Flank, A. Marcelli
   to be published in J. Non-Cryst. Solids (1990)
7- C.R. Natoli, M. Benfatto
   J. Phys. (Paris) C8 , 11 (1986)
   M. Benfatto
   Proceedings of the 2nd European Conference on Progress in X-Ray
Synchrotron Radiation Rome, Sept. 1989
8- C. Laffon
   Thèse Orsay (1990) unpublished
9- G.A. Waychunas, G.E. Brown, Jr.
   Proc. Int. Conf. "EXAFS and Near Edge Structure III"
   K.O. Hodgson, B. Hedman, J.E. Penner-Hahn ed.
   Springer-Verlag (1984) p. 336
10- Ph. Sainctavict, J. Petiau, M. Benfatto, C.R. Natoli
   Proc. of the "Vth Int. Conf. on X-Ray Absorption Fine Structure"

Seattle WA (USA) August 1988

J. Mustre de Leon, E.A. Stern, D.E. Sayers, Y. Ma, J.J. Rehr ed.

North-Holland (1989) p.347

11- C. Laffon, A.M. Flank, P. Lagarde, M. Laridjani, R. Hagège, P. Olry,
J. Cotteret, J. Dixmier, J.L. Miquel, H. Hommel, A.P. Legrand

J. Mat. Science 24 , 1503 (1989)

12- A. Bianconi, A. Congiu-Castellano, M. de Santis, P. Rudolf, A.M.
Flank, P. Lagarde, A. Marcelli

Sol. State Comm. 63 , 1009 (1987)

13- A. Bianconi, M. de Santis, A. di Cicco, A.M. Flank, A. Fontaine, P.
Lagarde, H. Katayama-Yoshida, A. Kotani, A. Marcelli

Phys. Rev. B38 , 7196 (1988)

14- A. Bianconi, M. de Santis, A. di Cicco, A.M. Flank, P. Lagarde, A.
Marcelli, C. Politis, H. Katayama-Yoshida, A. Kotani, Z.X. Zhao

Modern Phys. Lett. B 2 , 1313 (1988)

15- G. van der Laan, C. Vestra, C. Haad, G. A. Sawatztky

Phys. Rev. B23 , 4369 (1981)

G. van der Laan, J. Zaanen, G.A. Sawatzky, R. Karnatak, J.M. Esteva

Phys. Rev. B33, 4253 (1986)

16- B.T. Thole, G. van der Laan, J.C. Fuggle, G.A. Sawatzky, R.C.
Karnatak, J.M. Esteva

Phys. Rev. B32 , 5107 (1985)

Jeroen Goedkoop

PhD Thesis , Nijmegen (1989)

17- J. Goulon, P. Elleaume, D. Raoux

Nucl. Instrum. Methods A254 , 192 (1987)

18- C. Blancart

Thèse Orsay (1989) unpublished

19- C.T. Chen, F. Sette

Rev. Scien. Inst. in press (1989)

FRAGMENTATION OF MOLECULES BY USE OF SOFT X-RAY RADIATION

P. Morin

LURE

Universite Paris Sud

Bat. 209d

91405, Orsay Cedex

France

and

DLPC/SPP/SPER

CEA/CENSaclay

91191 Gif Yvette Cedex

France

ABSTRACT

Radiation damage induced on molecules is very dependent on the photon energy. Above 10 eV, the dominant process is ionization, eventually followed by fragmentation. The question of interest, especially for photochemistry, is to know how selectively this fragmentation can occur.

The use of X-ray radiation (now available in a continuous range with the use of synchrotron radiation and appropriate monochromators) allows us to do a selective excitation because inner shells are located very near the nucleus. Thus, one can excite a specific atomic site in a given complex molecule. Subsequent fragmentation is governed by electronic relaxation phenomena like the Auger process. In the case of deep inner shell excitation, one ends up with a highly charged ion (due to cascade Auger processes) which, of course, is not stable and gives rise to the so-called Coulomb Explosion. This strong effect makes the selective fragmentation unobservable. On the contrary, by use of soft X-ray radiation, one can excite shallow inner shells and the damage induced on the molecule is not so severe: the ionization degree of the residual ion is much less (one, two or three). In that case, selective fragmentation can occur, depending on the charge(s) localization in the final state.

We will discuss these various points by choosing available examples from several groups.

GLANCING ANGLE X–RAY ABSORPTION SPECTROSCOPY: APPLICATIONS TO THE STRUCTURAL CHARACTERISATION OF CONDENSED INTERFACES

S. Pizzini[1], K.J. Roberts[1,2], G.N. Greaves[2], N. T. Barrett[3],

I. D. Dring[4] and R. J.Oldman[4].

1) Department of Pure and Applied Chemistry, University of Strathclyde, Glasgow G1 1XL, UK.

2) SERC Daresbury Laboratory, Daresbury, Warrington WA4 4AD, UK.

3) LURE, Batiment 209D, Centre Universitaire, 91405 Orsay Cedex, France

4) ICI Chemicals and Polymers plc, Runcorn, Cheshire, WA7 4QE, UK.

ABSTRACT

Glancing angle X–ray absorption spectroscopy together with background theory and instrumentation requirements associated with this technique are described. Recent instrumentation developments on the Daresbury Synchrotron Radiation Source are presented together with experimental data which give an overview of applications to studies of the oxidation of metals, organic surface coatings, glass surface corrosion, semiconductor dopant coordination and interface properties, and adsorbed habit modifiers in ionic crystals. Potential future developments are outlined.

1. INTRODUCTION

Considerable advances have been made in recent years in the understanding of the structural and electronic aspects of clean single crystal surfaces through the use of surface sensitive electron spectroscopic techniques. However, the application of such techniques to elucidate the structure of interfaces, involves in most cases, 'post–mortem' examination in UHV systems following some interaction. It often requires removal of the sample from working conditions and in the case of solid–solid interfaces, sectioning or ion–etching is needed to expose the interface. The interfacial structure inferred from such an analysis may bear little relation to that of the undisturbed interface. A structural probe capable of examining solid interfaces in–situ and non–destructively, and providing information relating to 'real' conditions is clearly needed. Glancing angle X–ray absorption spectroscopy (XAS) offers a potential answer to this need.

In this paper we describe facilities developed for use at the Daresbury Synchrotron Radiation Source (SRS) for this kind of investigation   and present a number of recent case–studies which overview some recent applications of this technique.

2. GLANCING ANGLE X–RAY ABSORPTION SPECTROSCOPY

2.1. X–ray Absorption Spectroscopy

Over the past few years X–ray absorption spectroscopy has achieved increasing prominence in materials science due to its ability to give information on the local atomic environment of selected atoms in complicated systems which may not be easily amenable to conventional X–ray crystallographic analysis, e.g. glasses, alloys, surfaces and biological systems.

A typical X–ray absorption spectrum is shown in figure 1 and can be conveniently sub–divided into three regions:

(a) the edge region, which covers an energy range of ≈10 eV close to the absorption threshold. The physical origins of the absorption features are different in different classes of compounds [1], but these are essentially determined by the electronic structure of the material.

(b) the near–edge structure or XANES extends beyond the edge for 30–40 eV. It involves multiple scattering of the excited photoelectrons and is determined by the geometrical arrangement of atoms in a local cluster around the absorbing atom.

(c) the extended X–ray absorption fine structure (EXAFS), which extends from the XANES region to 600–1000 eV above the edge.

EXAFS refers to the oscillatory structure of the X–ray absorption coefficient μ above an absorption edge [2-4]. It was fully explained in the early 1970s in terms of a one-electron, single-scattering, short-range order theory [2]. The fine structures are due to changes in the final state wavefunction as a consequence of the interference between the outgoing

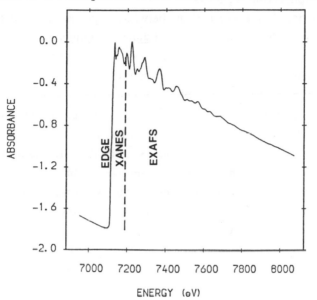

Figure 1: Fe K edge X-ray absorption spectrum of a Fe foil illustrating the main regions of interest in an absorption spectrum.

photoelectron wave ejected in the absorption process with the backscattered wave from neighbouring atoms. The normalised EXAFS spectrum is given by $\chi(E) = (\mu - \mu_0)/\mu_0$ where μ_0 is the smooth background term. The generally accepted formalism for EXAFS treats it as a sum of sinusoidal waves, each arising from a particular neighbouring shell. In the plane-wave approximation, we have:

$$\chi(k) = -\Sigma_i \left[N_i/(kR_i^2) \; F_i(k) \; S_0^2 \; e^{-2R/\lambda} \; e^{-2k^2\sigma^2} \right] \sin(2kR_i + \varphi_i(k)) \tag{1}$$

where R_i is the distance from the absorbing atom to shell i; k is the photoelectron wavenumber; $\varphi_i(k)$ is the total phaseshift experienced by the photoelectron; $F_i(k)$ is the backscattering amplitude of the neighbouring atoms; N_i is the coordination number of the ith shell; $S_0^2(k)$ and $e^{-2R/\lambda}$

are damping terms and $e^{-2k^2\sigma^2}$ is a 'Debye–Waller' type term, describing the structural and thermal disorder. σ^2 is the mean square average of the difference in atomic displacements.

From equation 1, the comparison between experimental and theoretical EXAFS spectra yields information on distances, number and chemical type of the neighbouring atoms, through the phase terms, and on the coordination numbers and disorder through the amplitude terms. By tuning the X–ray photon energy to that of a particular absorption edge, the local arrangement about each type of atom can be determined   separately. It is also important to note that long–range order is not required and thus non–crystalline and crystalline solids can be treated on the same basis.

Experimentally, the most widely used technique uses transmission geometry, in which the absorption is measured by monitoring the incoming (I_0) and transmitted flux (I_t). The absorption is then given by: $\mu t = \ln(I_0/I_t)$. The absorption coefficient can also be measured by monitoring secondary processes such as electron yield or X–ray fluorescence. The latter is particularly advantageous when the absorption is small, e.g. for diluted systems. When working in glancing angle geometry the X–ray absorption can be deduced from measurements of the reflected beams as well as by fluorescence detection.

2.2. Glancing Angle Geometry

A comparison of the scattering lengths of X–rays ($\approx 10\mu m$) and electrons ($\approx 1\mu m$) reveals that in a normal X–ray scattering experiment the contribution for the bulk material will dominate over that from a surface monolayer by about 6–7 orders of magnitude. However, surface sensitivity can be enhanced by using glancing angle geometries. At low angles of incidence the penetration of X–rays is naturally reduced. If the glancing angle is further reduced a critical angle (φ_c) is reached for which the angle of refraction is zero and the incident X–rays are 'totally' externally reflected. Whilst total external reflection only occurs at ideally flat, non–absorbing interfaces, reflectivity can be as high as 90% or more for real interfaces. External reflection is possible at the interface between air and a condensed medium because the refractive index of most materials is less than 1 in the X-ray part of the electro-magnetic spectrum [5]. The critical angle φ_C is related to the refractive index of the condensed medium (n_2) by Snell's law:

$$\cos \varphi_C = n_2 = 1 - \delta - i\beta \tag{2}$$

where $\delta = (4\pi N e^2/m)1/E^2$, $\beta = \mu\lambda/4\pi$; N is the surface atomic density (atoms/cm³), E is the X-ray photon energy and μ is the absorption coefficient of the medium. As β and δ are of the order of 10^{-5}-10^{-6} the numerical value of φ_C is small (typically of the order of a few mrads for most materials). Far from an absorption edge β can be neglected and $\cos \varphi_C$ can be expanded to give:

$$\varphi_C \approx (2\delta)^{1/2} \tag{3}$$

or in practical units:

$$\varphi_C(\text{mrad}) \approx 20\rho^{1/2}/E(\text{keV}) \tag{4}$$

where ρ is the density of the sample (g/cm³). From electromagnetic theory, for glancing angles $\varphi \ll \varphi_C$ the refracted wave does not penetrate the medium but propagates parallel to the surface, vibrating in a plane perpendicular to it, and is coupled to a standing wave generated by the interference of the incident and refractive waves [6]. The penetration depth of X-rays in the medium (z) is governed by the damping of the evanescent wave in the direction perpendicular to the surface. As φ decreases z falls to a minimum [6] such that:

$$z_{min} = \lambda/(4\pi\varphi_C) \tag{5}$$

z_{min} is typically $\approx$ 20-50Å for most materials for hard X-ray photons. As φ is increased beyond φ_C the penetration rapidly increases, approaching the limiting case for $\varphi \gg \varphi_C$ where $z = (\sin \varphi)/\mu$. This penetration is sample dependent, to some extent, and depends on the flatness of the reflecting surface. By varying the angle of incidence through the critical angle the X-ray beam can be 'depth-probed' from the surface and into the bulk material.   This surface-confined beam can then be analysed by X-ray absorption spectroscopy.

2.3. X-ray Absorption Spectroscopy Under Conditions of Total External Reflection

From the Fresnel equations, the X-ray reflectivity coefficient for photons of energy E incident on a perfectly smooth surface with glancing angle φ is given by [6]:

$$R(E, x) = \frac{h - x\,[2(h - 1)]^{1/2}}{h + x\,[2(h + 1)]^{1/2}} \tag{6}$$

where $x = \varphi/\varphi_C$, $h = x^2 + (x^2 - 1)^{1/2} + Y^2$ and $Y = \beta/\delta$. This equation shows that the reflectivity R(E) is related to both the real (δ) and imaginary (β) parts of the refractive index. Thus the reflected X-rays scattered from a sample at energies greater than a component absorption edge will contain extended absorption fine structures (ReflEXAFS) in both $\beta(E)$ and $\delta(E)$, related by the Kramers-Kronig equations. R(E) can be written [7] as:

$$R(\beta,\delta) = R(\beta - \beta_0) - \Delta R(\beta - \beta_0, \delta - \delta_0) \tag{7}$$

where β_0 and δ_0 refer to the non-oscillatory part of β and δ and $(\beta - \beta_0)$ and $(\delta - \delta_0)$ are respectively the $\beta-$ and $\delta-$EXAFS. The difference between these two components (ΔR) can be expressed by:

$$\Delta R(\beta - \beta_0, \delta - \delta_0) = (dR/d\beta)_{R=const}[(\beta - \beta_0) + (d\beta/d\delta)_{R=const}(\delta - \delta_0)] \tag{8}$$

The relative weights of the $\beta-$ and $\delta-$EXAFS are determined by the function $(d\beta/d\delta)$. Martens and Rabe [7] have shown that the latter approaches zero for glancing angles $\varphi \ll \varphi_C$. In this condition, the δ−EXAFS can be neglected and the ReflEXAFS is essentially β−EXAFS. By inverting equation 6, the relation between $\beta(E)$ (e.g. $\mu(E)$) and $R(E)$ can be extrapolated. In the case $\varphi \ll \varphi_C$ we obtain [7]:

$$\mu(E) = (4\pi\delta/\lambda) \; \frac{(1-x^2)^{1/2}}{x} \; \frac{1-R}{1+R} \tag{9}$$

Since the oscillations in δ are small compared with the oscillations in the function $(1-R)/(1+R)$, $\delta(E)$ can be approximated to a monotonic function beyond an absorption edge and the ReflEXAFS are therefore related to the EXAFS oscillations in the absorption coefficient.

The same treatment cannot be applied to the case $\varphi \geqslant \varphi_C$, where the oscillations in δ dominate [7]. In this case a Kramers−Kronig analysis must be applied to derive the δ−EXAFS from the experimental $R(E)$ [7]. The ReflEXAFS data presented in this paper were calibrated using the relation between $R(E)$ and $\mu(E)$ given in equation 9. All the experimental spectra were modelled using the curved−wave least−squares fitting programme EXCURV88 [9].

3. INSTRUMENTATION FOR GLANCING ANGLE X−RAY ABSORPTION SPECTROSCOPY AT THE DARESBURY SRS

Working at the small glancing angles required for total external reflection geometry imposes tight constraints on incident beam collimation and sample alignment. We have developed a dedicated instrument [10] for glancing angle XAS.

3.1. Mechanical Specifications.

The instrument is set up on station 9.2 [11] of the Daresbury Synchrotron Radiation Source (SRS) which uses a harmonically rejecting Si(220) double−crystal monochromator [12]. The instrument is shown schematically in figure 2, together with a sketch of the geometrical requirements for a glancing angle XAS experiment.

The experimental set-up comprises an optical bench, a collimation system, a sample stage, detectors and a computer control system. The whole instrument sits on a motorized table which can be adjusted with respect to the beam position.

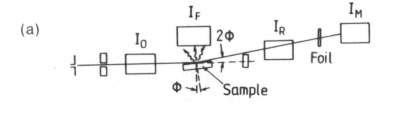

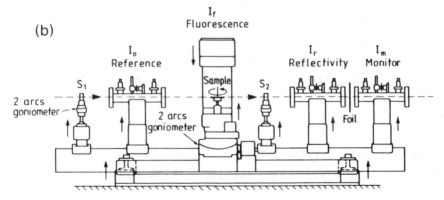

Figure 2: (a) Sketch showing the glancing angle geometry experiment; (b) Schematic representation of the glancing angle instrument used on the Daresbury SRS. The arrows indicate the motorized translations and rotations of detectors, slits and sample stages with respect to the beam direction.

Precise collimation is provided by two precision slits (S_1 and S_2) mounted either side of the sample stage. The slit assemblies consist of a pair of finely ground non-reflecting tungsten carbide blocks, separated by brass spacers and mounted on motorised goniometer heads. The sample stage is mounted on a large two-axis goniometer (incremental angular resolution 0.005 mrads) with the two axes of rotation defining the glancing angle (φ) and the transverse tilt angle. Samples are set on an Al coated steel disc mounted on a vertical traverse. When single crystals are being examined the sample holder can be rotated to enable any contamination of the EXAFS spectra due to Laue diffraction to be averaged out.

Ionisation chambers record the incident (I_o), reflected (I_r), fluorescence (I_f) and monitor (I_m) intensities. The latter monitors I_r through a reference foil to give a direct measure of any edge–shifts whilst the fluorescence ion chamber can be replaced by a multi–element solid–state detector when energy discrimination is necessary.

The motor control system consists of a PKS stepper motor drive system, interfaced to CAMAC via an EC724 multiplexer and controlled by an LSI 11/23 microcomputer. A versatile software package allows for motor movement control and calibration and enables individual axes and translations to be scanned.

3.2. Alignment Procedure

The instrument is first adjusted vertically so that the X–ray beam intercepts the focal point of the sample's goniometer. The beam path is defined by aligning the two slits S_1 and S_2 (typically $50\mu m$ wide) parallel to each other and the angular scale is calibrated by defining the angle $\varphi=0$, for which the sample is parallel to the beam. The latter is achieved iteratively by tilting the glancing angle (φ) in both directions around an approximate zero angle, and translating the sample vertically, until a sharp maximum, defining the angular zero ($\varphi=0$) is recorded. A similar procedure is applied to determine the zero angle in the transverse tilt. Once the angular scale is defined, the slit S_2 is used only as a beam stop. Finally the vertical position of the sample is finely adjusted to maximise the reflectivity.

When the sample is accurately aligned, a reflectivity profile is measured for a fixed photon energy close to the absorption edge of interest. From the resulting $R(\varphi)$ curve, suitable angular positions for XAS measurements are chosen.

The angular resolution $\Delta\varphi$ of a glancing angle experiment is particularly important, as critical angles for hard X–rays are typically of the order of a few mrads. $\Delta\varphi$ is determined by convoluting the source and slits size over the distance between the source and the sample ($\approx$20m). Beyond a certain factor the slits size has little effect on the angular resolution; for example $\Delta\varphi$=0.008mrads for 50μm slits and improves by only 7% in reducing the slits size to 5μm.

The non–perfect planarity of the sample has generally negligible effect on the penetration depth, compared with depth effects introduced by angular dispersion. With a planarity resolution of $\lambda/2$ (λ=5890A) and a sample 5cm long, the worst deviation in the glancing angle determination is 0.006mrads.

4. RECENT EXPERIMENTAL STUDIES AT THE DARESBURY SRS

4.1. Studies of the Surface Oxidation of Metals

4.1.1. Cu on float–glass substrates. Glancing–angle X–ray absorption measurements were carried out for 'as–deposited' Cu films ($\approx$1000Å thick) and for similar films after thermal oxidation for 30 minutes at 408K [13]. Figure 3(a) shows the reflectivity curves obtained for the Cu films before and after thermal oxidation. The 'as–deposited' film exhibits a critical angle (φ_C = 0.33˚) less than that expected for pure Cu (φ_C = 0.36˚) indicating that the surface is partially oxidised. The reflectivity curve obtained for the oxidised film reveas the presence of a thick oxide layer, with the two maxima associated with reflectivity from the air–oxide and oxide–substrate interfaces.

The change in the local environment around Cu is revealed in figure 3 (b) which compares the Fourier transforms of the ReflEXAFS spectra recorded before and after thermal oxidation at a glancing angle φ=0.18˚ ($z\approx$20Å). The parameters derived from least–squares fits of these data are given in table 1 together with the crystallographic parameters of some model compounds.

The data reveals the surface of the 'as–deposited' film to comprise of a macroscopic mixture of metallic Cu and oxide. This is evidenced by the strong coordination at $\approx$ 2.5Å, due to the first shell of fcc metallic Cu.

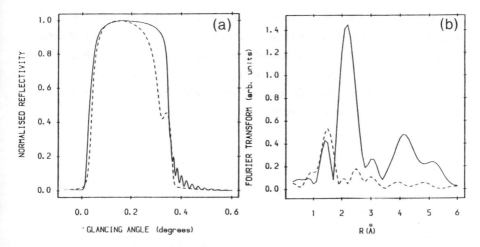

Figure 3: Experimental data for 'as–deposited' Cu film (full line) and thermally oxidised film (dotted line): (a) Reflectivity curves for E=8.79keV; (b) Fourier transforms of k^3–weighted Cu K edge ReflEXAFS spectra.

This shell has ≈50% of the amplitude expected for pure Cu and is complemented by an oxygen shell at ≈ 1.85Å. The Cu–O distance is close to that of the first oxygen shell in Cu_2O, and indicates that this is the dominant oxide phase at the surface. The Cu–Cu distances at 2.8–3.0Å are probably due to cation shells of the oxide phase. The splitting of this shell indicates that the surface oxide is more distorted then that expected for pure Cu_2O, where a single shell is present at 3.0Å. The weightings of the coordination numbers of the first (oxygen) and second (metallic copper) neighbour shells are consistent with a mixed metal–oxide surface layer with each phase giving a contribution of about 50%.

The surface layer of the thermally treated Cu film is completely oxidised with no metallic Cu correlations (see table 1). The surface oxide cannot be easily identified as one of the known stoichiometric Cu oxides. The presence of two Cu–O distances at around 1.8Å and 1.9Å may be indicative of a mixture of cation sites, presumably Cu^{1+} and Cu^{2+}. The two distances are in fact close to the first oxygen neighbour distances in

Cu_2O and CuO. Cu cation shells are present at distances which show some resemblance to Cu–Cu separations typical of the two stoichiometric Cu oxides. However, the overall coordination number (≈ 4) is much lower than that expected for a pure stoichiometric oxide phase (14 for CuO and 12 for Cu_2O). This is probably due to structural disorder introduced by the thermal treatment and is probably associated with the formation of a high cation vacancy concentration.

Table 1: Structural parameters obtained from least–squares fits of the ReflEXAFS spectra of Cu films deposited on glass, before and after thermal oxidation. The values of N and R(Å) for Cu, Cu_2O and CuO are also reported.

'as–deposited' Cu film				Oxidised Cu film			
atom	N	R(Å)	$2\sigma^2(Å^2)$	atom	N	R(Å)	$2\sigma^2(Å^2)$
O	1.2	1.85	0.010	O	1.8	1.90	0.010
Cu	6.6	2.52	0.018	O	1.9	1.81	0.010
Cu	2.6	2.77	0.015	O	1.2	2.60	0.010
Cu	5.0	2.98	0.027	Cu	1.0	2.85	0.012
Cu	1.3	3.45	0.029	Cu	3.1	3.52	0.030

Cu			Cu_2O			CuO		
atom	N	R(Å)	atom	N	R(Å)	atom	N	R(Å)
Cu	12	2.556	O	2	1.841	O	4	1.947
Cu	6	3.615	Cu	12	3.007	O	2	2.766
			O	6	3.526	Cu	4	2.884
						Cu	4	3.071
						Cu	2	3.159
						Cu	2	3.410
						Cu	2	3.727

4.1.2. Corrosive Oxidation of Polished Stainless Steels. The corrosive oxidation of polished AISI 304 stainless steel samples, oxidised at 1273K for up to 4' has been studied [14,15]. ReflEXAFS spectra were recorded above the Fe K edge for glancing angles $\approx 0.2°$ ($z \approx 35$Å). The results, summarised in figures 4 and 5, demonstrate the self–consistency that can be achieved by combining the near edge, EXAFS, edge height, chemical shift and reflectivity data obtained from a single series of measurements.

The normalised reflectivity curves measured for the steel surface after oxidation are shown in figure 4(a). After 1' the step in the reflectivity at $\varphi \approx 0.22^{\circ}$ is less evident than for the uncorroded sample, suggesting that any change in the surface layer, formed as a result of polishing, is removed with oxidation. With continuing oxidation the main reflectivity step, due to the steel, becomes less well–defined. This behaviour is typical of increased absorption of the X–ray beam [6] and is evidence for the creation of an absorbing layer on the steel surface.

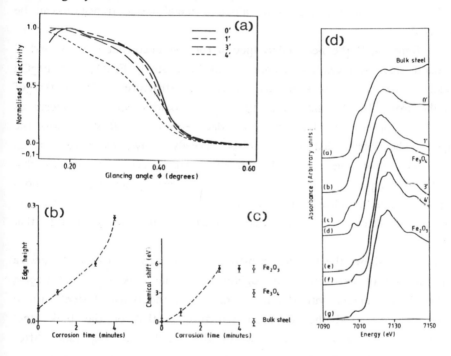

Figure 4: (a) Normalised reflectivity curves as a function of oxidation time; (b) the step height at the Fe K edge as a function of corrosion time; (c) The chemical shift as a function of corrosion time; (d) near–edge spectra of the Fe K edge for steel surfaces corroded for: (b) 0' , (c) 1' , (e) 3' , (f) 4' ; compared to the near edge spectra for: (a) the bulk steel, (d) Fe_3O_4 and (g) Fe_2O_3

Figure 4 (b) and (c) show the step height and chemical shift (measured with respect to metallic Fe) associated with the edge region of the absorption spectrum, as a function of oxidation time. From the edge height there is a clear increase in the Fe content near the surface, which probably relates to Fe diffusion through the protective Cr_2O_3 layer normally present on stainless steel. For steel measured in transmission the edge position coincides with that of metallic Fe. The increasing chemical shift with corrosion time indicates that the oxidation state is changing as corrosion proceeds. The edge position is shifted by 1 eV for 1' corrosion time and after 4' the shift is 5 eV, corresponding to that observed for Fe_2O_3. Thus from the edge shift alone a metal–oxide transition can be identified.

In figure 4(d) the near–edge spectra for the uncorroded, 1', 3' and 4' corroded steel surfaces are compared to bulk steel, Fe_3O_4 and Fe_2O_3 model spectra. The bulk steel has a near edge structure similar to that of metallic iron [16]. A white line, typical of oxides' spectra, appears as corrosion proceeds, as does the pre–edge feature $\approx$ 10eV below the edge. The uncorroded steel surface already shows evidence for an oxide–like white line. After 1' the pre–edge structure resembles that found for Fe_3O_4. As corrosion proceeds, Fe_2O_3 becomes the more dominant phase, as clearly indicated by the splitting of the pre–edge and main peaks. After 3' the near edge structure is virtually identical to that of Fe_2O_3.

Figure 5 shows the Fourier transforms of the raw ReflEXAFS spectra as a function of corrosion time together with the bulk steel and Fe_2O_3 spectra. In agreement with the near–edge data, the polished steel surface is metallic like, and the dominant structure is that of the bulk steel although there is some reduction of the first shell (fcc) amplitude. After 4' corrosion time the fcc crystal structure of the metallic steel has disappeared and the Fourier transform is virtually identical to octahedral Fe_2O_3. The transformation from metal to oxide can be traced by following the changes in the fine structure of the Fourier transforms.

Up until 1' there would appear to be a mixture of metal and oxide phases which may be indicative of an intermediate phase containing several oxides. Between 1' and 3' the weighting of the first two shells around 1.5Å and 3.0Å reverses, indicating the transition to an oxide–like local environment. In the fcc steel structure the first metal–metal distance is expected at 2.54Å with twelve nearest neighbours. In the mineral oxides there are two main coordination shells corresponding to Fe–O distances with the second mainly due to a spread of Fe–Fe distances from 2.90Å to 3.70Å. The change in the weighting of the main shells reflects the transition from a metallic to an oxide environment around Fe. The weighting of the first two shells in the Fourier transform suggests that, after 4' corrosion, the Fe is present chiefly as Fe_2O_3, at least in the top 35Å of the surface layer.

On the basis of these results the following model emerges for the very early stages of the corrosion process at the steel surface. The polished surface, although retaining its metallic character, shows signs of initial oxidation. As corrosion proceeds the surface content of Fe is enriched and the oxidation state increases. The first oxide phase to be formed on oxidation is probably similar to Fe_3O_4 but further reaction yields preferential oxidation as Fe(III) in the form of Fe_2O_3.

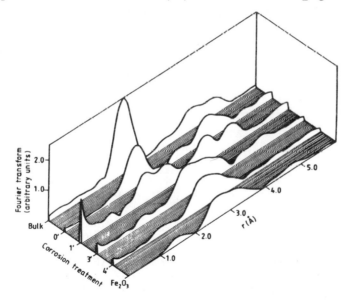

Figure 5: Fourier transforms of the raw ReflEXAFS spectra of stainless steels recorded at the Fe K edge as a function of corrosion time.

4.2. Studies of Organic Surface Coatings

4.2.1. The Local Structure of Zr and Co in Alkyl Resin Paints.

Popular household paints are commonly based on solutions of alkyl resins. The drying of these paints proceeds with solvent evaporation, followed by a curing process. The latter stage involves crosslinking reactions between unsaturated centres of adjacent polymer chains and can be accelerated by metal additives incorporated in the form of metallic soaps, $(Mn^+(OOR)_n)$ 17,18).

Two paints, one containing a Zr(IV) 2-ethyl hexanoate soap complex (0.5 wt% Zr) and the other a Co(II) 2-ethyl hexanoate complex (0.1 wt% Co) in the form of films 200 μm thick spread on glass slides, were investigated 19) using glancing angle XAS measurements in fluorescence mode. Glancing angles of 2˙ were used and wet films and films at two stages of the drying process (2 week and 2 month dried films) were examined. Data from 2 month dried Zr and Co paints are shown in figure 6. The results of the data analysis are given in table 2.

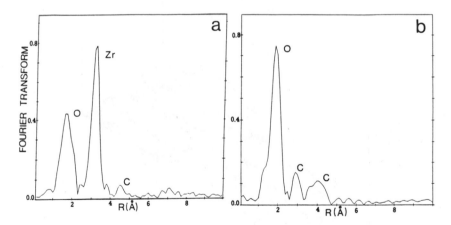

Figure 6: Fourier transforms of fluorescence EXAFS spectra: (a) Zr K edge of Zr–based paint showing a strong Zr–Zr correlation pointing to metal clustering; (b) Co K edge of Co–based paint for which metallic clustering is not observed.

The local structure around Zr shows two major shells, a broad O peak (3

O shells ranging from 2.08Å to 2.34Å) and a Zr shell at 3.15Å. If Zr was evenly dispersed in the paint, the nearest neighbour Zr distance would be around 30Å. The presence of Zr–Zr correlations is therefore an indication of the extensive clustering of the Zr additive. The clusters were observed both in the wet and the 2 week and 2 month dried films. An increase in the Zr and O nearest neighbour coordination numbers from the wet to the 2 week dried film suggests that the clusters agglomerate as the solvent evaporates. A comparison of the 2 week and 2 month dried films revealed no further changes.

In contrast the Co environment is dominated by a single shell (2 O shells ranging from 2.01Å to 2.17Å) and no evidence is found for any Co–Co correlations. The absence of such correlations confirms that no clustering occurs in the Co-based paint. The detailed analysis shows a variation in the average Co–O bond length with drying time. While the

Table 2: Structural parameters obtained from least–squares analysis of the Zr–and Co–based paints spectra.

Zr paint				Co paint			
atom	N	R(Å)	$2\sigma^2(Å^2)$	atom	N	R(Å)	$2\sigma^2(Å^2)$
O	2.4	2.08	0.006	O	3.2	2.01	0.012
O	3.8	2.21	0.006	O	2.6	2.17	0.012
O	2.2	2.34	0.006	C	4.3	2.97	0.014
C	0.5	2.50	0.006	C	4.6	3.24	0.014
Zr	2.3	3.51	0.006	C	3.8	4.02	0.016
C	1.8	4.28	0.009				

same distance (2.09Å) is calculated for the wet and the 2 month dried paint, a shorter distance (2.07Å) is found for the 2 week dried paint. The changes are consistent with a redox reaction [20] in which Co catalyses crosslinking. This is initiated by the reaction of atmospheric oxygen with methylene groups adjacent to unsaturated carbons thus forming hydroperoxides. Co(II) may then participate in a redox reaction to produce radicals which undergo crosslinking thus:

$$Co(II) + ROOH \rightarrow Co(III) + RO\cdot + OH^-$$

(10)

$$Co(III) + ROOH \rightarrow Co(II) + ROO\cdot + H^+$$

The bond distance variation can be explained by Co being predominantly Co(II) in the wet and 2 month dried film and Co(III) in the 2 week dried film. An octahedral oxygen coordination geometry was indicated in all cases by the EXAFS analysis, with the higher effective charge on the O ligands for the case of Co(III) resulting in a shorter average O nearest neighbour distance.

Thus, an interesting relation has been found between the clustering properties of the metallic additives and the curing rate of the paint. By showing the presence of clustering in Zr–based formulations and thus heterogeneous dispersion, it indicates why this is a poor additive for accelerating paint curing rates.

4.2.2. Surface Treatment of Copper with Benzotriazole.

Benzotriazole (BTA) is an efficient corrosion inhibitor for copper. Corrosion protection is believed to be due to chemisorption of BTA onto Cu leading to the formation of a protective film consisting of polymeric Cu(I)–BTA chains [21,22] (figure 7) when Cu is immersed in BTA solutions. The thickness of the complex depends on the pH of the solution but efficient protection can be obtained for coatings as thin as 10Å.

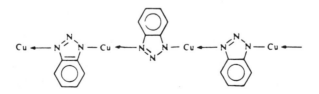

Figure 7: Sketch of the Cu–BTA complex, showing Cu atoms bonded to BTA molecules through N atoms of the triazole ring.

Cu films (1000Å thick), deposited on glass substrates, were dipped in 0.5wt% BTA in methanol for 30 minutes at 323K and then rinsed in methanol. ReflEXAFS spectra were recorded before and after this treatment for glancing angles (φ_1=0.10˚ and φ_2=0.24˚; z = 18A and 26A). The experimental results are presented in figure 8.

The data show that the average local environment of Cu probed at the larger glancing angle (φ_2) is only slightly modified by BTA treatment which reveals the BTA coating to be much thinner than the penetration depth. The neighbour distances (table 3) obtained from least–squares fits to the experimental spectra reveal the surface to be partially oxidised, with a significant residual metallic Cu present both before and after BTA treatment.

Important changes in the Cu environment, induced by BTA treatment, are detected when the X–ray penetration depth is decreased. The amount of metallic Cu decreases considerably after treatment, as indicated by the decrease in the coordination number of the (fcc) Cu shell from 5.2 to 3.1 (table 3). This is complemented by an increase of the total amount of oxygen in the surface layer. After BTA treatment, the oxygen shell splits in two shells at 1.84Å and 2.00Å.

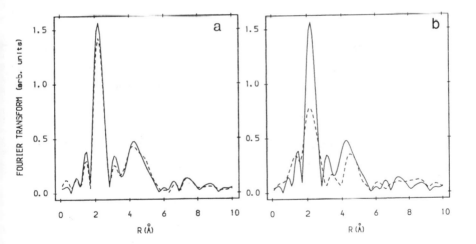

Figure 8: Fourier transforms of the experimental ReflEXAFS spectra for Cu films before (full line) and after (dotted line) BTA treatment for the two glancing angles φ_2 (a) and φ_1 (b) ($\varphi_1 < \varphi_2$)

Table 3: Structural parameters extracted from least–squares fits of the ReflEXAFS spectra of Cu films before and after BTA treatment. Only the data relative to the smaller penetration depth (angle φ_1) are given since very little changes are detected for the larger angle.

	no BTA				with BTA		
atom	N	r(Å)	$2\sigma^2(Å^2)$	atom	N	r(Å)	$2\sigma^2(Å^2)$
O	1.4	1.91	0.010	O	1.4	1.84	0.006
				O	1.1	2.00	0.010
Cu	5.2	2.53	0.018	Cu	3.1	2.49	0.018
Cu	3.9	2.81	0.015	Cu	2.1	2.92	0.027
Cu	6.1	3.05	0.027				
Cu	3.7	3.43	0.029				

As EXAFS cannot clearly distinguish between O and N backscattering atoms, one of the two shells assigned to O in table 3 may effectively be due to the correlation of Cu to the N atoms of the triazole ring of BTA. The change of the distance and the decrease in the coordination number for the metallic Cu shell at around 2.5Å may indicate that the residual metallic Cu on the outermost surface is involved in the formation of the Cu–BTA complex. More evidence for the formation of a surface Cu–BTA complex comes from the increased amount of oxygen (or nitrogen) coordinated to copper on the surface. Thus, whilst one of the two shells may be due to Cu–O coordination in the oxidised surface, the other may be related to correlations to the triazole ring of BTA.

4.2.3. Corrosion Inhibition of Mild Steel by 'Haloflex'.' Haloflex [24] is a water–based acrylate modified vinyl chloride/vinylidene dichloride copolymer emulsion which is used as a primer paint for steels. After application, initial evaporation of the water is followed by coalescence of the polymer particles into a coherent film which forms a low water vapour permeability barrier and hence is a very effective protection agent. During the film formation process there is some leaching of the substrate reaction products into the polymer, which manifests itself as a dark interfacial film. Examination of sections that run through the steel/polymer interfacial region using electron microscopy reveals that the dark material is amorphous and extends several microns into the polymeric material. Also present are small platelet crystallites, predominately at the interface. XRD showed that these comprise of two major phases: Fe_3O_4 and a Pyroaurite type compound [25]. The presence of the latter is thought to enhance the anti–corrosion properties of these systems.

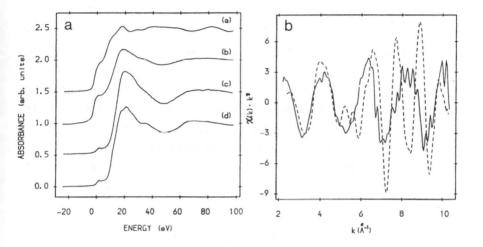

Figure 9: (a) Fe K near edge spectra of (A) Fe foil, (B) Haloflex film at 1.0˚, (C) Haloflex film at 0.5˚ and (D) Fe_2O_3. The zero in the energy scale corresponds with the edge position for metallic Fe. (b) Overlay of the experimental k^3–weighted Fe K edge EXAFS spectra for Haloflex film (0.5˚) (full line) and Fe_2O_3 (dotted line).

Investigations of the amorphous material in a $2\mu m$ thick polymer coating spread on a polished mild steel substrate were carried out using glancing angle fluorescence XAS. [19] Particular interest was concentrated on the determination of the oxidation state of the Fe ions in the Haloflex film. Glancing angle geometry enabled the measurements to be specific to the polymer region and the contribution of the steel substrate signal was avoided. The use of a multi–element solid–state detector allowed the Fe $K\alpha$ fluorescence signal to be discriminated from the radiation scattered by the polymer matrix.

Figure 9(a) shows the Fe K near edge spectra of the Haloflex film, recorded at glancing angles of 1.0˚ and 0.5˚, and compares them with Fe and Fe_2O_3 spectra recorded in transmission. The spectrum taken at 1.0˚ shows some similarities with the Fe spectrum, indicating a significant contribution of the steel substrate signal to the data. At the lower glancing angle X–rays no longer reach the substrate and the pre–edge spectrum closely resembles that of Fe_2O_3. It is therefore concluded that the oxidation state in the amorphous material is predominantly Fe(III).

Figure 9(b) overlays the Fe K EXAFS spectrum of the 'Haloflex' film (0.5˚) with the spectrum of Fe_2O_3. In table 4 the crystallographic parameters of Fe_2O_3 are compared with those obtained from least–squares fits of the Haloflex spectrum ($\varphi=0.5$˚). The data show the Fe ions in the Haloflex film to be overcoordinated to O with respect to Fe_2O_3 and the Fe–O first neighbour distance to be correspondingly longer. No significant Fe–Fe coordinations are found at higher distances and this could either indicate that the substrate reaction product migrating to the surface of the film is amorphous or could be related to a particle size effect. Electron microscopy results seem to favour the former possibility.

Table 4: Least–squares fits of the 'Haloflex' spectrum compared with the crystallographic parameters of Fe_2O_3.

Haloflex				Fe_2O_3		
atom	N	R(Å)	$2\sigma^2$(Å^2)	atom	N	R(Å)
O	3.5	2.00	0.006	O	3	1.95
				O	3	2.11
				Fe	1	2.90
Fe	0.8	2.97	0.020	Fe	3	2.97
				Fe	3	3.36

4.3. The Surface Corrosion of Borosilicate Glasses

The leaching of metallic ions through glass surfaces is of significant interest to the understanding of materials requirements for the vitrification processes associated with nuclear waste management [26].

Borosilicate glasses loaded either with Fe_2O_3 or UO_2 were examined [27,28] with the object of studying corrosion-induced transport of incorporated Fe and U ions. Glancing angle fluorescence XAS measurements were carried out at glancing angles above and below φ_c ($z \approx 50\mu m$ and $1\mu m$) immediately after leaching in H_2O at 373K thus with the sample surface still in the 'wet' state. Dramatic changes are observed in the edge structures and in the EXAFS spectra both as a function of depth and of the extent of leaching. These reveal and contrast the different transport properties of these cations through the glass network during corrosion. The results show the intermediate character of Fe^{3+} in borosilicate glasses i.e. a coordination typical of a network forming cation such as Si but with a bond length and mobility more characteristic of a network modifying cation such as Na. In contrast U^{6+} purely takes the role of a modifying cation.

4.3.1. The environment around Fe^{3+}. XAS provides a useful tool in identifying the structurally intermediate role of Fe^{3+} in silicate glasses. In contrast to most minerals where ferric sites are octahedral, in glasses Fe^{3+} is commonly tetrahedrally coordinated [29]. This configurational change can be readily recognised in EXAFS by a shortening of the Fe-O distance. The two different geometries can also be distinguished in the edge structure from the magnitude of the white line (peak A in figure 10) which is considerable for octahedrally coordinated Fe^{3+} but much reduced when the metal occupies tetrahedral sites. Converse behaviour is exhibited by the pre-edge feature (peak B in figure 10) which is prominent for tetrahedrally coordinated Fe^{3+} in oxide glasses, but diminutive for octahedral configurations in the corresponding crystals [29,30]. Both types of ferric coordination can be identified at the surface of borosilicate glass. The Fe K edges are displayed in figure 10 as a function of leaching time [28]. The most obvious effect at the edge is the increase in step height, I, as leaching progresses, demonstrating that ferric ions migrate to the glass surface - quadrupling in concentration over a period of $\approx 1h$. What perhaps is more interesting are the alterations in the white line (A) and pre-edge feature (B) as corrosion advances; these are detailed in the inset to figure

10. Initially the white line is weak and the pre–edge feature strong, indicative of extensive tetrahedral bonding. However after $\approx$1h leaching the converse is true pointing to a substantial fraction of octahedrally coordinated ferric ions. The same picture emerges from the glancing angle EXAFS data which is characterised by a single Fe–O distance at first followed by the appearance of a longer distance as corrosion continues. From what we know about the bulk structure of Fe^{3+} in aegerine glass and the mineral, the glancing angle XAS behaviour of the borosilicate glass surface strongly suggests that leaching promotes dissolution of Fe from the glass network and its transport towards the corrosion interface where it precipitates in a form similar to that of a ferric silicate.

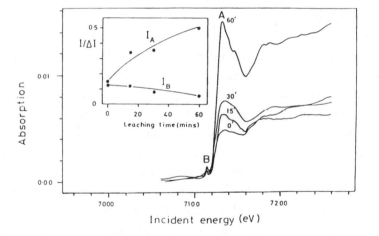

Figure 10: The changing near edge structure of Fe K edge measured in glancing angle fluorescence mode for borosilicate glass as a function of leaching. The inset shows the increase in the white line (peak A) and the decrease in the pre–edge feature (peak B) with advancing corrosion. Both are normalised to the step height I.

4.3.2. The environment around U^{6+}. Changes in the size of the uranium L_{III} threshold with leaching are less striking, amounting to a 10% increase in concentration at the surface over the first hour of treatment. Subsequent leaching is even less effective in drawing uranium to the surface. The uranium environments measured at the surface are given in the partial radial distribution functions (PRDF) shown in figure 11, where shells attributed to oxygen, silicon and uranium are indicated.

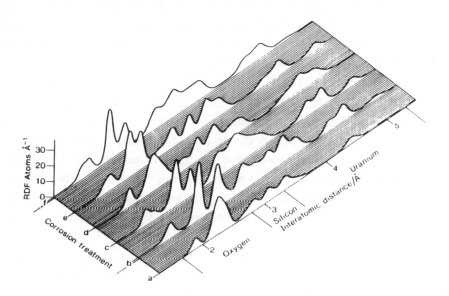

Figure 11: PRDFs for U in borosilicate glass obtained from L_{III} EXAFS measured at below φ_C (z = 40Å) as a function of corrosion treatment: (a) bulk structure (measured at 45° incidence), (b) as−received polished glass, (c) after 15 mins leaching, (d) after 15 mins leaching and subsequent drying under vacuum, (e) after 30 mins leaching and (f) after 90 mins leaching.

The changes in environment of uranium at the surface with aqueous corrosion (b − d) can be clearly seen and compared to the bulk structure (a). The most obvious characteristic of the PRDFs presented in figure 11 is the split shell of neighbouring oxygens. The analysed coordination number falls between 7 and 8. In the bulk structure (a) oxygens are divided into two subshells located at 1.9Å and 2.3Å , but at the surface (b−f) these are often further split into subsidiary shells at around 1.8Å and 2.4Å. Examination of the edge region reveals the leached uranium to be in the $U6+$ oxidation state and this together with the structured oxygen shell are hallmarks of the uranyl configuration in crystalline uranates 31). This local geometry promotes layered structures through the longer U−O bond.

The precise length of these equatorial bonds and the shorter axial bonds, that complete the uranyl configuration, are influenced by the types of cation neighbouring uranium and the degree of interlayer bonding. The 1.9Å and 2.3Å distances found in the bulk glass structure (a) closely correspond to the uranium environment in alkali uranates like Na_2UO_4 [31]. The other pairing of axial and equatorial distances, 1.8 to 2.4Å, found at the glass surface (c, e and f) closely match the uranium configuration in the layered hydroxide $UO_2(OH)_2$ [31]. This evidence strongly suggests water is intruding into the environment of uranium as a result of aqueous corrosion. Further confirmation comes from comparing PRDFs (c) and (d) in figure 11, which both correspond to glasses leached for 15 minutes. However, where glass (c) was measured in the 'wet' state, glass (d) was dried under vacuum for 12h. The $UO_2(OH)_2$ configuration disappears for glass (d) and the alkali uranate environment found in the bulk glass structure (a) is restored.

In addition to oxygen neighbours, the U PRDFs shown in figure 11 include U–U correlations, indicating a degree of clustering. Indeed if R is the equatorial U–O bond length, the principle U–U distances fall into two groups whose shell radii are approximately $\sqrt{2}R$ and 2R, suggestive of a square planar arrangement. A striking feature of figure 11 is the way this clustering is exagerated at the glass surface as the result of corrosion.

4.4. Studies of Semiconductors

4.4.1. The local structure around As and Ga in doped a–Si:H. Unlike crystalline silicon, the efficiency of doping amorphous silicon is low as most impurities alloy with the matrix and tetrahedral sites appear to form only under compensating conditions [32]. Street [33] proposed an Autocompensation Model where Group V's or Group III's acquire tetrahedral configurations through charge transfer either with silicon defects or by chemical compensation [34], with both models predicting dopant sites to be charged.

Glancing angle XAS has been used [35] to study Ga and As (0.5%) implants in n–type amorphous silicon containing 3% P. Changes in amplitude between Ga and As spectra have been calibrated by directly comparing Fourier filtered nearest neighbour spectra with the spectrum of substitutional As (0.04 wt %) thermally grown in crystalline silicon (figure 12).

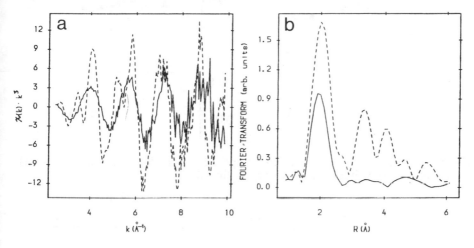

Figure 12: Overlay of As K k^3–weighted EXAFS spectra of 0.5% As doped a–Si (full line) and of substitutional As in crystalline Si (dotted line); (b) Fourier transforms of (a).

Ratioing fine structure amplitudes for Ga and As in amorphous silicon with those of substitutional As in crystalline silicon (figure 13) indicate more than one site is present. Assuming an alloying site (A) and a tetrahedral site (B), the two can be deconvoluted and the intercept of B reveals that the fraction of tetrahedral sites is quite small (5–10%). From the intercept of A the coordination of the dominant alloying site can be obtained. For Ga this is 4.8 and for As it is 3.5. The 8–N Rule [36] predicts coordination numbers of 5 for Ga and 3 for As. The slopes of the two contributions yield differences in Debye–Waller factor compared to dopants in crystalline silicon. Clearly in amorphous silicon alloying sites are poorly ordered whilst tetrahedral sites have a slightly better geometry compared to the crystalline state.

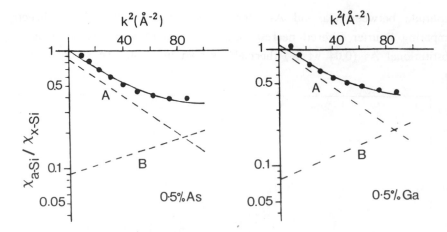

Figure 13: Ratio of fine structure amplitudes for As and Ga in a–Si:H with those of substitutional As in crystalline Si.

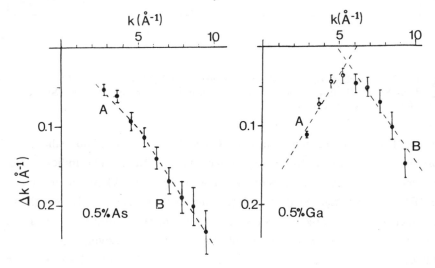

Figure 14: Difference of fine structure frequencies for As and Ga in a–Si:H with those of As in crystalline Si.

Nearest neighbour distances associated with alloying (A) and tetrahedral (B) sites obtained by comparing the fine structure frequency with that of As in crystalline silicon ($R = 2.42\text{Å}$) are shown in figure 14. For alloying sites:

$$R_{Ga} = 2.51\text{Å} \quad \text{and} \quad R_{As} = 2.37\text{Å}$$

whilst for tetrahedral sites:

$$R_{Ga} = 2.39\text{Å} \qquad R_{As} = 2.35\text{Å}$$

Accordingly tetrahedral sites are substantially shorter in amorphous silicon compared to crystalline silicon. This is consistent with the sites being charged (polaronic) as Street's model predicts [33]. Note that the differences in radii of the two alloying sites are consistent with the different coordination numbers.

4.4.2. Studies of the Structural Environment of Te in Doped GaAs. Studies of Te–doped GaAs [38] have shown that lattice super–dilation takes place for Te concentrations greater than 10^{18} atoms cm^{-3} resulting in a violation of Vegard's law [37]. Figure 15 compares the Te K edge fluorescence EXAFS spectrum of a 1" Te doped GaAs wafer (8×10^{18} atoms cm^{-3}) together with the transmission spectra of elemental Te and GaAs at the Ga and As K edges. The glancing angle data were recorded at an angle of $\approx 10°$ with the sample rotated to average out any diffraction effects.

The persistence of the zinc blende structure around Te in GaAs can be readily identified in figure 15. The structural parameters obtained from least–squares fits of the relative spectrum are compared with bulk GaAs in table 5.

Table 5: The local environment of Te in Te–doped GaAs (as obtained from least–squares fits) is compared with that of As in pure GaAs.

Pure		Doped	
N	R(Å)	N	R(Å)
4	2.45	4	2.58
12	3.99	11	3.52
12	4.58	12	4.58

It can be seen that the dopant environment of Te is quite distinct from that of elemental Te as well as from that of As (or Ga) in the

GaAs matrix. The first shell is dilated and the second shell is contracted for Te compared to As (or Ga) in GaAs. In particular the first shell radius of 2.58Å is 0.13Å longer than the As–Ga bond length, indicating considerable relaxation to accommodate the larger anion. The second shell radius of 3.52Å is 0.47Å shorter than the equivalent shell in the zinc blende structure, indicating the possibility of vacancies in this shell. The third shell also appears to be slightly contracted, although this change is outside the precision of the analysis.

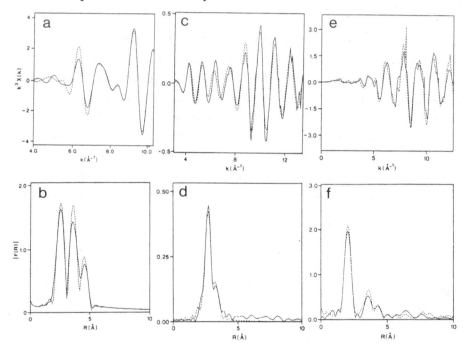

Figure 15: Experimental (full line) and calculated (dotted line) k^3-weighted EXAFS spectra and corresponding Fourier transforms of: (a–b) Te-doped GaAs at the Te K edge; (c–d) elemental Te. (e–f) Overlay of Ga K and As K edge spectra of bulk GaAs.

The data tend to support the model proposed by Sette et al. [39] for S doped GaAs, that incorporates Te on a Group V site with a strong dilation of the first (Group III) shell and the associated generation of As site vacancies in the second (Group V) shell. Sette's model proposed the first shell disorder to be greater than the second or third shells and hence a mixture of sites. However in this study narrow widths are observed for all three shells and indicate Te in GaAs in this concentration is related to a <u>single substitutional site</u>. These results do not support alternative models such as interstitial incorporation[40,41] which would generate non–zinc blende like bond lengths or Ga first shell vacancies.[41,42]

4.4.3. Surface Oxide on Polished GaAs(100).

The surface oxide structure of a polished 3" GaAs(100) wafer was investigated using glancing angle XAS [43,44]. ReflEXAFS spectra were recorded above the As K and Ga K absorption edges, for glancing angles $\varphi_1 = 0.08°$ and $\varphi_2 = 0.10°$ ($z \approx 25$Å and 30Å respectively). Figure 16 shows an overlay of the As K ReflEXAFS spectrum of the GaAs(100) wafer (angle φ_1) and the transmission spectrum of bulk GaAs.

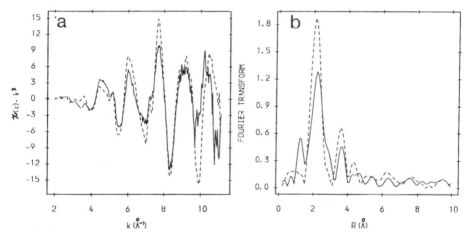

Figure 16: (a) Overlay of the As K edge k^3 weighted spectra for GaAs(100) wafer at angle φ_1 (full line) and bulk GaAs (dotted line); (b) Fourier transforms of (a).

The structural parameters obtained from least–squares fits of the ReflEXAFS data (table 6) show the surface of the GaAs(100) wafer to be partially oxidised with an oxide thickness of ≈ 7–9Å [43]. Ga and As atoms have different oxygen environments in the surface oxide. For both Ga and As atoms there is an oxygen neighbour shell at ≈ 1.7Å, close to that found for the tetrahedral coordination in $GaAsO_4$ or 3-fold coordination in As_2O_3. However, Ga atoms have an additional oxygen shell at $\approx 1.95\text{Å}$, which is typical of the octahedral coordination of Ga_2O_3. Thus while As in the surface oxide seems to be exclusively in a tetrahedral environment, Ga exists in both tetrahedral and octahedral coordinations.

Table 6: Coordination numbers and shell distances extracted from least-squares fits of the As K and Ga K edge ReflEXAFS spectra of the GaAs(100) spectra (angle φ_1).

Ga–O		Ga–O–M		Ga–As	
R(Å)	N	R(Å)	N	R(Å)	N
1.72	0.6	2.88	3.1	2.46	3.0
1.95	2.2	3.15	3.4		

As–O		As–O–M		As–Ga	
R(Å)	N	R(Å)	N	R(Å)	N
1.68	0.9	2.84	1.1	2.43	3.1
		3.09	1.0		

The two matched cation shells at the same distances ($\approx 2.8\text{Å}$ and $\approx 3.1\text{Å}$ for both Ga and As central atoms) are probably associated with the two different oxygen coordinations for Ga. The shell at $\approx 2.8\text{Å}$ possibly arises from a coordination between cations both in tetrahedral environment whilst the shell at $\approx 3.1\text{Å}$ shell is related to the coordination between octahedral Ga and a tetrahedral cation (As or Ga). The matching of these second shell distances for both Ga and As central atoms show the oxide to be a single phase which can be modelled as a <u>microscopically</u> random mixture of tetrahedral and octahedral sites, with Ga occupying both and As only the former 4-fold site. Figure 17 shows a schematic representation of the local coordination associated with this surface oxide.

Comparison between the Ga and As environments as a function of glancing angle shows no significant variation for As concentration while it indicates a distinct increase in Ga coordination at the surface [43]. Together with the angle dependence of the O shell amplitudes this trend indicates a greater association of Ga atoms to O in the outermost oxide layer and a corresponding As depletion.

A structural model [45] of this oxide based on a continuous random network (CRN) [46,47] with oxygens attached to the dangling bonds at the surface has been built up from a mixture of octahedral and tetrahedral Ga's, tetrahedral As's and bridging O's. The surface oxide so constructed resulted in an open structure. The presence of 2–fold coordinated oxygens and the variable cation coordination combine to encourage the formation of micro–voids (typical size $\approx 5 \text{Å}$) and fissures whose internal surfaces are oxygen rich.

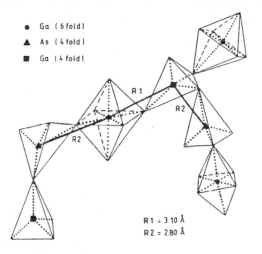

Figure 17: Sketch of the structure of the surface oxide on GaAs(100) wafer, showing tetrahedral Ga's and As's coordinated to octahedral Ga's via bridging O's.

4.4.4. Structure at the Cu/GaAs(100) Interface. Cu films deposited onto GaAs(100) exhibit markedly different properties to those of Cu films deposited on glass (see section 4.1.1). The near edge data (figure 18(a)) of 10Å and 100Å Cu films deposited on GaAs(100) reveal the surface layers to contain both Cu^{1+} and Cu^{2+} cations. For 100Å thick films, the ReflEXAFS spectra (figure 18(b)) show the Cu film to be completely oxidised and no evidence is found for significant long-range order. The degree of the oxidation of the Cu surface is much larger than that found for Cu deposited on glass, where a significant amount of metallic Cu was present at the surface. This result is consistent with a disordered oxide layer being formed from the amorphous oxide covering GaAs(100).

The Cu-O distances for the Cu oxide on GaAs(100) are longer than those observed for the Cu oxide phase on glass. These are typical of the 4-fold coordination in CuO. The more extensive Cu oxidation on GaAs compared to Cu on glass is probably catalysed by the open structure of the oxide layer on GaAs(100). The cracks and micro-voids in this layer will encourage mass-transport and hence the reactivity of this interface, Cu possibly bonding covalently via lone-pair electrons of the O's decorating the internal surfaces.

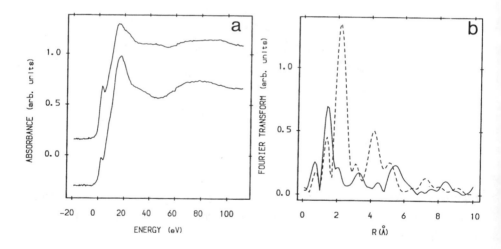

Figure 18: Comparison between the experimental data for 100Å Cu on GaAs(100) (full line) and Cu deposited on glass (dotted line): (a) near edge spectra; the zero in the energy scale corresponds with the edge position for metallic Cu; (b) Fourier transform of k^3 weighted ReflEXAFS spectra at the Cu K edge.

For thinner Cu coverages ($\approx$ 10Å) additional cation correlations are found at around 3.00Å [45], close to the cation-cation distance in the oxide coating on GaAs (see table 6). This suggests that Cu trapped in the voids in the surface oxide correlates with the surrounding cations. The open oxide structure on GaAs may well promote Cu interdiffusion into the oxide in a manner similar to that predicted for cation diffusion in chalcogenide glasses [48].

For 100Å Cu coverages the higher distance cation shells are not seen and the oxygen coordination number is smaller. This indicates that the reactivity of Cu in the structure of the thinner Cu overlayer catalyses the extensive oxidation when more Cu is present. Thus, whilst Cu passivates when deposited on glass, leaving approximately half of the Cu as metal, the opposite appears to be the case for GaAs(100) where all the Cu becomes oxidised. As the Cu coverage builds up it would appear that the surface oxide generated becomes increasingly disordered.

4.5. Studies of Ionically Adsorbed Habit Modifiers.

The shape and size of crystals is of significant importance in industrial crystallisation [49] and can often be controlled by habit modification. This usually involves the addition of micro–quantities of additives usually in the form of trace ionic impurities [50].

Glancing angle EXAFS has been applied [51] to investigate the local atomic environment around habit–modifying Fe^{3+} ions in nearly perfect single crystals of ammonium dihydrogen phosphate (or ADP) in order to understand the mechanism of modification. The structure of ADP [52] is tetragonal and comprises a three dimensional network of PO_4^{3-} tetrahedra linked by strong hydrogen bonds. The hydrogen bond protons occupy disordered sites between oxygens of two adjacent phosphate units. The addition of micro–quantities of Fe^{3+} ions results in an elongation of the crystal morphology along the [001] direction.

Fe K edge EXAFS data of 200ppm Fe^{3+} in ADP, recorded at a glancing angle of $\approx 10\mu m$ are shown in figure 19.

The least–squares fit to this data, summarised in table 7, reveals two coordination shells which are well fitted by two O atoms at 1.82Å and two P atoms at 2.85Å. The strong P coordination suggest an interstitial site near to two phosphate groups. The likely site [51,53] is at (0.25, 0.22,

0.125) for which the undistorted, near–neighbour crystallographic distances are given in table 7. For this site a dilation of 0.42A in the Fe–O distance is necessary and incorporation would cause a dilation of the lattice (from the Fe–P distance) and a rotation of the two PO_4^{3-} groups involved to produce the Fe–O measured separation.

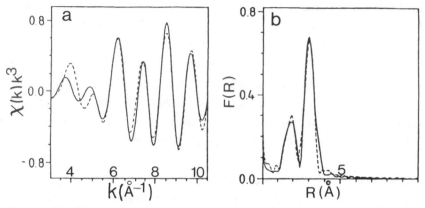

Figure 19: (a) Fe–K experimental (full line) and calculated (dotted line) Fourier filtered, k^3 weighted EXAFS spectra for Fe doped ADP (b) Fourier transforms of (a).

Table 7: Fe habit modifier environments in ADP as determined by the least–squares fit of the EXAFS spectrum.

	N	$R(\overset{\circ}{A})$	$2\sigma^2(\overset{\circ}{A}{}^2)$	$R_{xt\,al}(\overset{\circ}{A})$
O	2	1.82	0.004	1.36
P	2	2.85	0.006	2.67

Further evidence for the chemical bonding of Fe^{3+} into the ADP lattice is borne out by the size of the Debye–Waller factor for the Fe–P correlation. The structural model for this incorporation is shown in figure 20 and reveals the mixed oxygen/phosphorus local environment around Fe^{3+} along with the more distant nitrogens of the ammonia groups. The incorporation of Fe in this site will displace the proton shared between the two oxygens, breaking the strong O–H–O hydrogen bonds along <100>.

The breaking of the phosphate–linking hydrogen bonds generates lattice strain along <100> which in turn restricts growth [55,56] by lowering the surface attachment energy [54] of the prismatic {100} faces. The data thus shows that the mechanism of this habit modification is associated with modification of the bulk crystal structure in the {100} growth sections rather than by surface adsorption/surface terrace blocking or by modifying the growth environment.

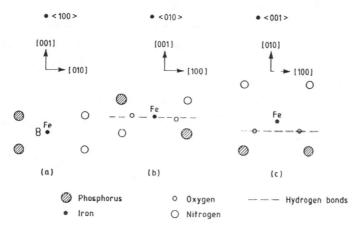

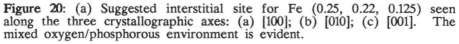

Figure 20: (a) Suggested interstitial site for Fe (0.25, 0.22, 0.125) seen along the three crystallographic axes: (a) [100]; (b) [010]; (c) [001]. The mixed oxygen/phosphorous environment is evident.

5. CONCLUSIONS

In this paper we have reviewed the development of glancing angle X–ray absorption spectroscopy on the Daresbury SRS over the past five years. Whilst the applicability of this technique to the structural characterisation of 'real' surfaces and interfaces is demonstrated, this technique is still very much in its infancy and significant further developments can be expected in the next few years:

(a) detectors: for glancing angles greater than φ_c collection of EXAFS data by total electron yield detection [57,58] will enable sub–surface structural information to be obtained from absorbers in concentrated form;

(b) diffraction studies: addition of a curved position–sensitive detector together with improved anti–scatter beam collimation to the existing set–up [59,60) will enable powder X–ray diffraction data to be collected at the same time as the absorption spectroscopy data;

(c) in–situ studies: the highly penetrating nature of synchrotron radiation coupled to the glancing angle geometry will enable buried interfaces such as electrode surfaces under liquid [59) or catalyst surfaces under dense gaseous environments to be studied;

(d) dynamic experiments: upgrade of data acquisition hardware by the provision advanced on–line computing, by fast angle scanning monochromators (for QEXAFS measurements [61,63) and by advanced position–sensitive detectors [64) will enable process–resolved experiments to be performed. Experiments such as potential–controlled surface electrochemical reactions or time/temperature–resolved studies can be anticipated.

This overall schematic forms an integral part of the development for the new integrated materials science station [60) being developed at the Daresbury SRS. It can be expected that this combination of techniques in a single series of measurements, will provide the same kind of capabilities, that routinely exists in surface science for the structural characterisation of interfaces and 'real' surfaces, but without the constraints of UHV.

ACKNOWLEDGEMENTS

We gratefully acknowledge the co–workers who have contributed to various aspects of the the work described here including, M. Antonini, R. Fabian, P. J. Halfpenny, N. Gibson, N. Harris, G. M. Lamble, P. A. Moore, E. Pantos, R. Thornley and M. Sacchi. Financial support from SERC, ICI Chemicals and Polymers plc, The Paint Research Association and EC research programmes on advanced materials and nuclear waste management is also gratefully acknowledged. SERC is further acknowledged for provision of beam time on the Daresbury SRS. One of us (KJR) also gratefully acknowledges the British Council and the Brasilian National Synchrotron Light Source (LNLS) for the travel funds which enabled this overview to be presented in Campinas.

REFERENCES

1) see for example: Bianconi, A., in 'X–ray Absorption, Principles, Applications, Techniques of EXAFS, SEXAFS and XANES, Ed. D.C. Koningsberger and R. Prins (J. Wiley and Sons, 1988), pag. 577

2) Sayers, D.E., Stern, E.A. and Lytle, F.W., Phys. Rev. Lett. 27, 1204 (1971)

3) Lee, P.A., Citrin, P.H., Eisenberger, P. and Kincaid, B.M., Rev. Mod. Phys. 53, 769 (1981)

4) Hayes, T.M. and Boyce, J.B., Solid State Physics, 37, 173 (1982)

5) James, R.W., The Crystalline State, Vol. II, The Optical Principles of the Diffraction of X–rays, (G. Bell and Sons 1969)

6) Parratt, L.G., Phys. Rev. 95, 359 (1954)

7) Martens, G., Rabe, P., Phys. Stat. Sol (a) 58, 415 (1980)

8) Bosio, L., Cortes, R., Defrain, A. and Froment, M., J. Electroan. Chem., 180, 265 (1984)

9) Gurman, S.J., J. Phys. C, 21, 3699 (1988)

10) Pizzini, S., Roberts, K.J., Greaves, G.N., Harris, N.,Moore, P., Pantos E. and Oldman, R.J., Rev. Sci. Instrum 60, 2525 (1989)

11) Greaves, G.N., Bennet, R., Duke, P.J., Holt R. and Suller, V.P., Nucl. Instr. and Methods 206, 139 (1983)

12) Diakun, G.P., Greaves, G.N., Hasnain, S.S. and Quinn, P.D., Daresbury Report DL/SCI/TM38E, 1984

13) Pizzini S. , Roberts K.J. , Dring I.S., Oldman R.J. and Greaves G.N., Physica B, 158, 676 (1989)

14) Barrctt, N.T., Gibson, P.N., Greaves, G.N., Mackle, P., Roberts, K.J. and Sacchi, M., J. Phys. D: Appl. Phys. 22, 542 (1989)

15) Barrett, N.T., Gibson, P.N., Greaves, G.N., Roberts, K.J. and Sacchi, M, Physica B 158, 690 (1989)

16) Grunes, L.A., Phys. Rev. B, 27, 2111 (1983)

17) O'Neil, L.A., Falla, N.A.R. and Judson, M.L., Paint Research Association Technical Report, TR/17/72 April 1972.

18) O'Neil, L.A., Falla, N.A.R. and Judson, M.L., Paint Research Association Technical Report, TR/32/72 July 1972.

19) Dring I.S., Oldman R.J., Stocks A. , Walbridge D.J. , Falla N., Roberts K.J. and Pizzini, S., Mat. Rec. Soc. Proc., (Boston, Dec. 1988) 143, 169 (1989)

20) Goodman, R.J. and Douek, J., Journal of Paint Technology, 43, 59 (1971)

21) Fleischmann, M., Hill, I.R., Mengoli, G., Musiani, M.M. and Akhavan, J., Electrochimica Acta, 30, 879 (1985)

22) Sastri, V.S. and Packwood, R.H., Werkst. Korros. 38, 77 (1987)

23) Pizzini, S., Roberts, K.J., Dring, I, Oldman, R.J. and Greaves, G.N., Proc. of XSR–89, (Rome, Oct. 1989), to be published in Il Nuovo Cimento

24) Humphries, R.G., J.O.O.C.C.A. 6, 150 (1987) 25) Moreland, P.J. and Padget, J.C., Proceedings of the ACS Division of Polymeric Materials, 53, 369 (1985)

26) Manara, A., Lanza, F., Ceccone, G., Della Mea and Salvagno, G., 'Scientific Basis for Nuclear Waste Management VII' (MRS:

Pittsburgh, 1985) p. 85.

27) Greaves, G.N., Barrett, N.T., Antonini, G.M., Thornley, F.R., Willis B.T.M. and Steel, A., J. Amer. Chem. Soc. 111, 4313 (1989)

28) Sacchi, M., Antonini, G.M., Barrett, N.T., Greaves G.N. and Thornley, F.R., Proc. 2nd Int. Workshop on Non-Crystalline Solids, San Sebastian (Spain), July 1989

29) Binsted, N., Greaves G.N. and Henderson, C.M.B., J. de Physique C8, 837 (1986)

30) Calas G. and Petiau, J., 'Structure of Noncrystalline Materials II' (Taylor & Francis: London, 1983) p.18

31) Weigel, F., "Chemistry of the Actinide Elements", Vol. 1 (Chapman and Hall: London 1986)

32) Spear, W.E. and LeComber, P.G., Solid State Commun. 17, 9 (1975)

33) Street, R.A., Phys. Rev. Lett. 49, 1187 (1982)

34) Robertson, J., Phys. Rev. B 31, 3817 (1985)

35) Greaves, G.N., Kalbitzer, S., Pizzini, S. and Roberts, K.J., Proc. of XRS-89, (Rome, Oct. 1989), to be published in Il Nuovo Cimento

36) Mott N.F., Adv. Phys., 16, 49 (1967)

37) See, for example, 'New Developments in Semiconductors Physics', Eds. F. Beleznay, G. Ferenczi and J. Giber (Springer-Verlag, Berlin 1980).

38) Greaves, G.N., Halfpenny, P.H., Lamble and G.M., Roberts, K.J., J. de Physique, Colloque C8, 47, 901 (1986)

39) Sette, F., Pearton, S.J., Poate, J.M., Rowe J.E., and Stohr, J., Phys. Rev. Lett. 56, 2637 (1986).

40) Fewster, P.F., J. Phys. Chem. Sol. 42, 883 (1981).

41) Mullin, J.B., Straughen, B.W., Driscoll C.M.H., and Willoughby, A.F.W., J. Appl. Phys. 47, 2584 (1976).

42) Hwang, C.J., J. Appl. Phys. 40, 4584 (1969).

43) Barrett, N.T., Greaves, G.N., Pizzini, S. and Roberts, K.J., Surface Science, 1990, in press

44) Barrett, N.T., Greaves, G.N., Pizzini, S. and Roberts, K.J., Proc. of XSR-89, (Rome, Oct. 1989) to be published in Il Nuovo Cimento

45) Pizzini, S., Roberts K.J., Greaves, G.N., Barrett, N.T., Dring, I.S. and Oldman, R.J., submitted for the Proc. of 'Structure of Surfaces and Interfaces as Studied Using Synchrotron Radiation', Manchester, UK, April 1990, to be published in 'Faraday Discussion n. 89 (1990)

46) Polk, D.E. and Boudreaux, D.S., Phys. Rev. 31, 92 (1973)

47) Greaves, G.N. and Davis, E.A., Phil Mag. 29, 1201 (1974)

48) Steel, A.T., Greaves, G.N., Firth, A.P. and Owen, A.E., J. of Non-Cryst. Solids, 107, 155 (1989)

49) Mullin, J.W., Crystallisation (Butterworths, London, 1972, 2nd ed.).

50) H.E., Buckley, Crystal Growth, Wiley, (1951).

51) Barrett, N.T., Lamble, G.M., Roberts, K.J., Sherwood, J.N. Greaves, G.N., Davey, R.J., Oldman R.J. and Jones, D., J. Crystal Growth 94, 689 (1989)

52) Tenzer, L., Frazer B.C. and Pepinsky, R., Acta Cryst. 11, 505 (1958)

53) Davey R.J. and . Mullin, J.W., Kristall. und Technik 11, 229

(1976)

54) Hartmann P. and Bennema, P., J. Crystal Growth 49, 145 (1980)

55) Bhat, H.L., Sherwood J.N. and Shripathi, T., Chem. Eng. Sci. 42, 609 (1987)

56) Ristic, R.I., Sherwood J.N. and Wojchiechowski, K., J. Cryst. Growth, 88, 385 (1988)

57) Shevchik, N.J. and Fischer, D.A., Rev. Sci. Instrum. 50, 577 (1979)

58) Long, G.G., Fisher, D.A., Kruger, J., Black, D.R., Tanaka D.K. and Danko, G.A., Phys. Rev. B. (1989), in press.

59) Barlow, N., Brennan, C., Doyle, S.E., Greaves, G.N., Miller, M., Nahle, A.H., Roberts, K.J., Robinson, J., Sherwood J.N. and Walsh, F.C., Rev. Sci. Instrum. 60, 2386 (1989)

60) Derbeyshire, G., Dobson, B., Greaves, G.N., Harris, N., Mackle, P., Moore, P.R., Roberts, K.J., Allinson, N., Nicoll, J., Doyle S. and Oldman R.J., Rev. Sci. Instrum. 60, 1857 (1989)

61) Frahm, R., Rev. Sci. Instrum. 60, 2515 (1989)

62) Frahm, R., Physica B, 158, 342 (1989)

63) Edwards, B., Garner, C.D. and Roberts, K.J., Proc. XSR-89, (Rome, Oct. 1989) to be published in Il Nuovo Cimento

64) Allinson, N.M., Baker, G., Greaves G.N. and Nicoll, J.K., Nucl. Ins. and Methods A 266, 592 (1988)

Applications of Synchrotron Radiation in Protein Crystallography

Richard Garratt

Instituto de Física e Química de São Carlos

Departamento de Física e Ciencias dos Materiais

Universidade de São Paulo, Caixa Postal 369

13560 – São Carlos – SP, Brasil

Abstract

Synchrotron radiation, through the provision of a high intensity, naturally collimated, tunable source of X-rays is providing new opportunities for the protein crystallographer. The natural intensity of the radiation has allowed the study of smaller, more weakly diffracting crystals, crystals with large unit cells and the advent of kinetic crystallography. The broad spectral range has facilitated the rebirth of the Laue technique and the tunability, the possibility of minimising the undesirable effects of absorption and maximising the benefits of anomalous dispersion.

1 INTRODUCTION

Several comprehensive reviews of the applications of synchrotron radiation (SR) in protein crystallography (PX) have appeared in the literature over recent years[1--3]. The paper by Helliwell[1] provides an excellent background to the relevant properties of SR, instrumentation for PX and the physical phenomena underlying the applications to protein structure determination. Lindley[3] has placed PX within the context of other techniques currently being applied to biological macromolecules at SR sources including the use of X-ray absorption spectroscopy and small angle scattering. Aspects of the synchrotron source itself and related instrumentation have been covered in other chapters of this volume and its companion in the series. This paper will focus on the reasons for the need for SR in modern protein crystallographic research and on some of its recent sucessful applications.

2 PROTEIN STRUCTURE

It is the three-dimensional or *tertiary* structure of proteins together with their intramolecular mobility which is ultimately responsible for their mechanisms of action. For example, catalytic sites of enzymes and metal-binding sites of metal activated proteins frequently involve several parts of the structure which are disperate in terms of the covalent or *primary* structure of the molecule but brought together as a consequence of the tertiary fold. Similarly, the complimentarity determining regions (CDR's) of the hypervariable loops of immunoglobulins are brought into appropriate proximity for antigen recognition by the three-dimensional structure of the variable domains. DNA and receptor binding regions of proteins are also believed to involve extensive regions of a protein's surface whose nature is defined by its three-dimensional architecture.

The tertiary structure of a protein, however, is only indirectly encoded in the DNA which houses the genetic information. At present we only fully understand the code which relates the *linear* sequence of nucleotides in the DNA (or RNA) into a *linear* sequence of amino acids (the protein's primary structure). We do not understand how this sequence then folds to adopt the tertiary structure of the mature protein. For this reason, experimental techniques, paramount amongst them X-ray diffraction, are required for the elucidation of structure in three-dimensions.

3   PROBLEMS OF PX

3.1   The Phase Problem

The electron density (ρ) at a point in the unit cell with fractional coordinates xyz is given by the following expression,

$$\rho(xyz) = \frac{1}{V_{cell}} \sum_{hkl} |\mathbf{F}_{hkl}| e^{i\alpha_{hkl}} e^{-2\pi i(hx+ky+lz)}. \tag{1}$$

Thus, in order that an electron density map can be calculated and interpreted in terms of atomic positions knowledge of both the amplitude ($|\mathbf{F}|$) and phase (α) of each reflection hkl must be known. Whilst the structure amplitudes can be derived directly from the intensities of the measured reflections all information of the phases is lost. This is the classical *phase problem* of crystallography. All methods for the resolution of the phase problem rely on the elucidation of phases from amplitude data alone. The classical solution for novel protein structures utilises the method of isomorphous replacement (§6).

3.2   Further Obstacles

The energy of the hkl'th diffracted beam from a crystal rotated at constant angular velocity ω is related to the incident X-ray intensity I_0, the wavelength of the radiation λ, the volume of the crystal V_x, the volume of the unit cell V_{cell}, the structure amplitude $|\mathbf{F}_{hkl}|$, the Lorenz, polarisation and absorption corrections L, P and A and the physical constants e, m and c by Darwin's equation.

$$E_{hkl} = \frac{I_0 e^2}{m^2 c^4 \omega} \lambda^3 PLA \frac{V_x}{V_{cell}^2} |\mathbf{F}_{hkl}|^2. \tag{2}$$

It can readily be seen that for protein crystals, which generally have a small V_x and a large V_{cell} the energy of the diffracted beams will be correspondingly weak. In general $|\mathbf{F}_{hkl}|$ for proteins is also inherently small due to considerable crystal mosaicity as a consequence of a relatively high solvent content (often greater than

50%). Furthermore, due to the large volume of data to be collected and the fragility of the protein molecules themselves, which are susceptible to radiation damage, the time for data collection can be substantial.

3.3   Advantages Of Synchrotron Radiation

The disadvantages of the small values for V_x and $|F_{hkl}|$ and the large value of V_{cell} can be overcome by an increase in I_0 such as that provided by synchrotron sources. Alternatively, at the expense of a loss in photon flux, the high intensity of the synchrotron source may be used to produce a more finely collimated beam often resulting in an improvement in resolution. This is attributable to a reduction in spot size giving rise to statistically significant data for the weaker reflections at higher resolution[1].

The high I_0 may also be used to reduce $\Delta\lambda/\lambda$ for experiments which demand a particularly well-defined wavelength such as those employing the effects of anomalous dispersion (§6), or together with the natural forward collimation of the beam may be used to increase the crystal-to-detector distance in order to improve the signal-to-noise ratio. The latter arises as a consequence of the rapid (inverse square) decay of the background scattered radiation with distance.

Since synchrotron sources provide high intensity X-rays over a broad spectral range, potentially longer wavelength radiation could also be employed as a means to increase E_{hkl}. However, protein crystals have a finite lifetime due to the effects of radiation damage and this too is λ-dependent. Helliwell[1] has argued that in general we would expect the lifetime of the crystal to have a λ^{-3}-dependence due to the effects of absorption. E_{hkl} is in reality λ^2-dependent and not λ^3-dependent (equation 2) due to a λ^{-1} term in the Lorenz correction and as a consequence we would anticipate the collection of a greater volume of diffraction data from a given crystal by using a shorter rather than a longer wavelength. This appears to have been borne out by experience at Daresbury, UK, where a reduction from 1.488Å on station 7.2 to 0.88Å on the wiggler-line station 9.6 is generally considered to have been beneficial.

The high photon flux may itself help to reduce the problem of radiation damage by delivering a given number of photons to the sample in a shorter time period. Thus the data may be collected before the damaging effects of free radicals have accumulated. The benefits of reduced radiation damage are twofold. Firstly, the amount of data recordable from a single crystal is increased thus reducing errors introduced in data processing by inter-crystal scaling. Secondly, the resolution of the data is improved since it is these data which attentuate most rapidly with time of exposure.

4   FOOT AND MOUTH DISEASE VIRUS

The recent determination of the structure of the Foot and Mouth Disease Virus (FMDV)[4] adequately exemplifies the use of SR for small, radiation sensitive crystals with large unit cells.

The FMDV belongs to the family of picornaviridae which includes also the viruses responsible for polio[5] and the common cold[6]. The crystals are space group I23, $a = 345$Å, with 1/12th of the virus particle in the asymmetric unit. The crystals were small (of average dimension $0.12 \times 0.12 \times 0.06 mm^3$) and were very radiation sensitive. At the Synchrotron Radiation Source (SRS) at Daresbury the group of David Stuart from Oxford was able to collect only a single 0.4-0.5° oscillation photograph from each crystal. The majority of the data was collected using the so-called 'American' method[7] in which crystals are aligned by eye and then randomly orientated for data collection. Using a wavelength of between 0.85 and 1.0Å together with a collimator of $300\mu m$ diameter, data were collected on 500 crystals of which 135 were useful and 106 processed, yeilding an almost complete dataset (87% to 2.9Å resolution). The feasibility of the data collection was attributed to the extreme parallelism of the beam, its intensity and the use of a short wavelength. All of the above led to an improvement in the yeild of data from a single crystal. The parallelism and intensity of the beam also facilitated the use of fine collimation reducing the problem of the overcrowding of reciprocal space present for crystals with large unit cells.

The elucidation of the structure of FMDV and its comparison with other picornaviridae[5--6,8] has enabled Acharya et al.[4] to propose explanations for several viral properties. In particular they have broadened the concepts behind the mechanisms by which viruses attach to host cells. Embedded in the so-called canyon hypothesis of Rossmann et al.[6] is the idea that the cell attachment sites of picornaviruses lie buried within clefts in the viral coat proteins thus protecting them from surveillance by the host's immune system. However, the cell attachment site of FMDV is a highly exposed and mobile loop poorly defined in the 2.9Å electron density map. This apparent contradiction is resolved by Acharya et al. by noting the considerable genetic variability between different viral strains in the vicinity of the cell attachment site. This, together with the mobility of this region is thought to camouflage the virus from recognition by immunoglobulin.

The structures of several of the recently solved viruses are currently being used for the rational design of anti-viral drugs.

5   ENZYME KINETICS

There is considerable interest in being able to directly visualise the mechanisms of action of proteins. Until recently, however, the long timescale for crystallographic data collection (usually several days) compared with that of biological events (picoseconds to kiloseconds) has rendered such studies impossible. However, by reducing the time for data collection SR is bringing *kinetic crystallography* into the realms of possibility.

Many enzyme crystals show catalytic activity and contain large solvent channels

114

through which substrates or cofactors may be diffused. If the kinetics of the system is such that the reaction is not limited by this diffusion and intermediates whose half-lives are long compared with the time for data collection can accumulate to dominate the population of molecules in the crystal then direct visualisation of these intermediates is theoretically possible using conventional monochromatic diffraction techniques[9].

5.1 An Example - Glycogen Phosphorylase

Glycogen phosphorylase is a central enzyme of energy metabolism. The interconversion of the *a* and *b* forms of the enzyme is the final step in a cascade of reactions initiated by extracellular stimuli and resulting in the phosphorylytic breakdown of glycogen to produce glucose-1-phosphate[10] (Fig. 1).

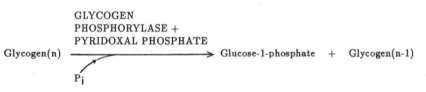

Figure 1: Action of glycogen phosphorylase.

Pyridoxal phosphate is required as a cofactor for the reaction and was believed to act by donation of a proton to the inorganic phophate, P_i, but no direct evidence for this was available prior to the kinetic crystallographic experiments of Hajdu *et al.*[11]. The artificial substrate, heptenitol, was used in place of glycogen as under these circumstances the rate-limiting step in the reaction is the breakdown of the enzyme-substrate complex into products. 'Snapshots' were taken at defined time intervals after initiating the reaction by pumping substrate over a crystal mounted in a flow-cell. At the SRS, Daresbury, the time for the recording of an individual 'snapshot' was on the order of one hour compared with approximately one week on a conventional laboratory source. Difference Fourier maps were utilised to reveal the sequence of events in substrate binding and showing for the first time the phosphate interacting with both the heptenitol and phosphate moiety of the pyridoxal phosphate cofactor.

The limitations of the technique were identified as its relatively poor time resolution and the need for a new crystal for each 'snapshot'.

5.2 Laue Diffraction

Conventional X-ray diffraction data collection such as that described in §4 and §5.1 employs monochromatic radiation. In order that different sets of lattice planes (d_{hkl}) can be brought into the diffracting position in accordance with Bragg's Law

$$\lambda = 2d_{hkl} \sin \theta_{hkl} \tag{3}$$

the crystal must be rotated. Generally, for protein crystals, an oscillation about an axis perpendicular to the X-ray beam on the order of a few degrees is employed for each photograph. However, the spectral range of SR allows a broad band of incident radiation to be used in place of monochromatic radiation thus simultaneously recording reflections from a much larger percentage of lattice planes, each of which selects its own appropriate λ for the given crystal orientation, without the need for crystal rotation. This is termed Laue diffraction. Fig. 2 shows an Ewald sphere construction for the Laue case for a crystal diffracting to a maximum resolution of d_{min} using a wavelength range $\lambda_{min} - \lambda_{max}$. The advantage of recording such a high percentage of the data simultaneously is the dramatic reduction in the number of photographs necessary for a complete dataset. Furthermore the intensity of the white beam reduces the time necessary for each photograph to the order of seconds or less. By this means data accumulaton rates of greater than 100,000 reflections/second are possible[12]. The Laue method is thus ideal for kinetic studies on short timescales but is also highly attractive for radiation sensitive crystals whose lifetime in the X-ray beam is short[13]. The principal problems with the method are

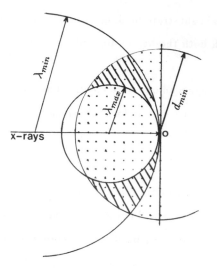

Figure 2: Ewald sphere construction for Laue diffraction.

those of overlapping reflections and the need for a λ-dependent intensity correction curve (wavelength normalisation curve).

Overlapping reflections fall into two catagories. Energy overlaps and spatial overlaps. The former arise from the superposition of different orders of reflection, eg. 111, 222, 333 etc. which will be recorded as a multiple spot due to diffraction from X-rays of wavelengths λ, $\lambda/2$, $\lambda/3$, etc. respectively. Cruikshank *et al.*[14] have shown this to be only a limited problem since even for an infinitely broad spectrum the energy overlaps only constitute 27% of the data and for a more realistically restricted λ-range this is further reduced to the order of 17%.

Spatial overlaps arise from the proximity of diffraction spots from unrelated lattice planes as a consequence of the density of reflections recorded simultaneously on the film. This problem demands fine collimation of the incident X-rays and is aided by the natural low divergence of SR.

The λ-normalisation curve. As different reflections in a Laue dataset have arisen from different wavelengths of radiation several λ-dependent corrections to the data need to be applied in order to obtain a self-consistent set of relative intensities. Variation as a function of λ results from a number of factors including the incident X-ray spectrum, sample absorption, detector response and the polarisation and Lorenz effects[15]. The λ-normalisation curve can be determined either by reference to a monochromatic dataset or internally, by reference to symmetry related reflections recorded at different wavelengths[16]. The problems of determining the λ-normalisation curve can be alleviated by the use of a *difference* technique as exemplified by the work of Hajdu et al.[12].

Difference technique. Hajdu *et al.*[12] have collected Laue diffraction data before, during and after the binding of maltoheptose to the glycogen storage site of glycogen phosphorylase. Three photographs at different orientations of the crystal were taken at each stage of the reaction using a $200\mu m$ unfocussed white beam (effective λ-range 0.2 – 2.1 Å) on the wiggler-line station 9.7 at the SRS. The crystal was wedged in a thermostatically-controlled flow-cell which was pumped with 50mM maltoheptose to initiate the reaction. The intermediate dataset showed signs of disorder in the crystal and has not been processed further. The final dataset was scaled to the initial dataset and difference Fouriers with coefficients of the form,

$$\frac{|\mathbf{F}_{ld}| - |\mathbf{F}_{ln}|}{|\mathbf{F}_{ln}|} \times |\mathbf{F}_{mn}| \qquad (4)$$

calculated using phases from the structure previously solved using monochromatic radiation. $|\mathbf{F}_{ld}|$ is the final Laue structure amplitude, $|\mathbf{F}_{ln}|$ the initial Laue structure amplitude and $|\mathbf{F}_{mn}|$ the monochromatic structure amplitude. In this way the need for both λ-dependent and position-dependent (eg. polarisation and Lorenz) corrections can be circumvented.

After rejection of energy and spatial overlaps and the statistically poorest data, the remaining 9,029 unique reflections represented 25% of the complete dataset. The difference map clearly showed the position of the bound maltoheptose and was superior in quality to a map calculated using the same reflections from the monochromatic dataset. This improvement was attributed to a reduction in radiation damage, identical data collection conditions for all datasets and to the *difference* technique itself.

6   ANOMALOUS DISPERSION

In protein crystallography, the phase problem (§3.1) is most commonly solved by preparing heavy atom derivatives of the crystal by soaking in a solution of an appropriate heavy atom compound. The structure factor of the derivative, $\mathbf{F}_{PH}$ is then given by the vector sum of the components from the native crystal, $\mathbf{F}_P$ and the heavy atom, $\mathbf{F}_H$

$$\mathbf{F}_{PH} = \mathbf{F}_P + \mathbf{F}_H. \tag{5}$$

Once $|\mathbf{F}_{PH}|$ and $|\mathbf{F}_P|$ have been derived from experimental measurement and $\mathbf{F}_H$ has been determined by Patterson or other methods then the phase α_P can be calculated by use of the Harker construction (Fig. 3). For a single heavy atom derivative there is an ambiguity in the phase (A or B) which can be resolved by preparing one or more further derivatives. This method is termed multiple isomorphous replacement (MIR)[17].

At wavelengths approaching an absorption edge of the heavy atom *anomalous* scattering starts to become significant. Under these circumstances the atomic scattering factor for the anomalous scatterer becomes modified by the dispersion (f') and absorption (f'') terms in the following manner,

$$f = f_0 + f' + if'' \tag{6}$$

As a consequence there is a breakdown in Friedel's Law, ie. the intensity of reflection hkl ($|\mathbf{F}^+|$) is no longer equal to that of $\overline{hkl}$ ($|\mathbf{F}^-|$) (Fig. 4a). Fig. 4b shows how this effect can be used to resolve the phase ambiguity in a similar manner to MIR. This method is termed single isomorphous replacement with anomalous scattering (SIRAS).

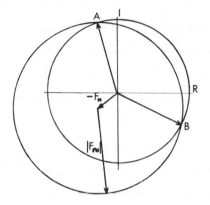

Figure 3: Isomorphous replacement.

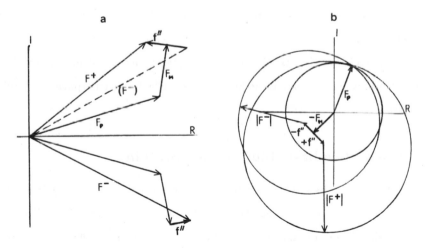

Figure 4: Single isomorphous replacement with anomalous scattering.

SR has greatly increased the use of the anomalous dispersion effect by providing a source of wavelength tunable radiation allowing access to the L-absorption edges of many elements used in the preparation of heavy atom derivatives and the K-absorption edges of naturally occuring metals in metalloproteins and enzymes. The use of a narrow bandpass can be exploited by benefitting from XANES features on the absorption edge which enhance the anomalous effect further. However, in general the effect is small. For example, an isomorphous derivative of the iron transport protein transferrin ($\sim$ 6500 atoms) involving a single Hg atom (Z=80) at a single fully occupied site would be expected to produce an average *isomorphous* intensity change of 20% but an *anomalous difference* of only 5% at 1.54Å, although the latter could be enhanced by appropriate choice of λ [3].

For a metalloprotein which naturally contains an anomalously scattering atom, no dataset equivalent to $|F_P|$ of Fig. 4b can be collected. This problem can be overcome, however, by collecting data at at least two different wavelengths (to modify f') and using the differences in f'' at at least one such wavelength. Generally wavelengths are chosen to maximise the dispersion and absorption effects seperately as shown in Fig. 5. More commonly, more than two wavelengths would be employed. This technique is termed multi-wavelength anomalous dispersion or MAD and benefits greatly by avoiding the problems of the lack-of-isomorphism in derivative crystals.

6.1 Cucumber basic blue copper protein

The structure of the basic blue copper protein from cucumber seedlings is one example of a structure solved using the MAD technique. Guss *et al.*[18] utilised the anomalous signal from the single copper atom in a protein of M_r 10,000. Data were collected over a period of 8 days on station 1-5AD at the Stanford Synchrotron Radiation Laboratory, using a Si(111) double crystal monochromator and an area detector system built specifically for this type of application. Four wavelengths were

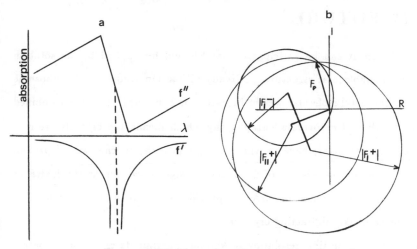

Figure 5: Multiwavelength anomalous dispersion.

used, one maximising f'', one minimising f' and two offset by approximately $1KeV$ either side of the absorption edge. The absorption spectrum was directly monitored using a fluorescence detector at $90°$ to the incident beam and used to recalibrate the monochromator after each new injection. This was observed to be stable to within $1eV$. Attempts were made to record Bijvoet pairs (F^+ and F^-) simultaneously and the data for each image was recorded sequentially for each of the four wavelengths thus rendering the crystal condition effectively constant for equivalent reflections in each dataset.

The structure is a considerable achievement representing a solution to a problem which had resisted both isomorphous and molecular replacement techniques and over a decade of research effort. It has provided considerable insite into the nature of blue copper proteins in general and served to explain several of their spectroscopic and electrochemical properties.

7 THE FUTURE

In the near future it can be anticipated that SR will be applied to the solution of ever larger biomolecular structures. Already diffraction studies of the ribosome and its subunits (total molecular weight in excess of 2 million) using the combined advantages of SR and cryocrystallography (by which means the crystals are rendered effectively immortal) have provided insight into the mechanism of protein synthesis[19]. The next generation of dedicated storage rings such as the ESRF at Grenoble and the APS, Argonne, USA will provide access to the study of smaller, less stable, more weakly diffracting crystals.

Improvements in the time resolution of kinetic experiments can be anticipated. Szebenyi and coworkers have already suceeded in recording a Laue photograph from a single X-ray pulse in 100ps at CHESS. To benefit from such rapid data collection times substrates will need to be prediffused into the crystal and then activated immediately prior to the analyser X-ray pulse. Hajdu *et al.*[9,12] have suggested photoactivation amongst others as a means by which this could be acheived.

Anomalous dispersion is expected to become routine for the solution of structures containing metal centers. Hendrickson's group at Columbia is extending the applicability of the technique by replacing naturally occuring cysteine residues by seleno-cysteine and then employing the selenium anomalous scattering for phasing. The structure of strepavidin has already been solved using the anomalous scattering from a selenium atom substituted into the biotin molecule[20].

Finally, it is hoped that the use of the non-Bragg diffuse scattering from protein crystals can be used to provide information on protein mobility. The weak nature of the diffuse scattering demands the use of SR and has already been applied to the study of the motions of crystalline lysozyme[21]. It is to be hoped that such studies will provide an experimental test for theoretical simulations of protein motion[22].

Acknowledgements

The author wishes to thank FAPESP for financial support and the Instituto de Estudos Advançados, Universidade de São Paulo under whose auspices his visit to the IFQSC was arranged.

References

[1] Helliwell, J.R., "Synchrotron X-radiation protein crystallography: Instrumentation, methods and application", Rep. Prog. Phys. 47, 1403–1497 (1984)

[2] Helliwell, J., "Laue, Bragg and all that", Phys. World 2, 29–32 (1989)

[3] Lindley, P.F., "Crystallographic Studies of Biological Macromolecules using Synchrotron Radiation", in *Chemical Crystallography with Pulsed Neutrons and Synchrotron X-rays* (Carrondo, M.A. & Jeffrey, G.A., eds.), pp 509–536, Reidel (1988)

[4] Acharya, R., Fry, E., Stuart, D., Fox, G., Rowlands, D. & Brown, F., "The three-dimensional structure of foot-and-mouth disease virus at 2.9Å resolution", Nature 327, 709–716 (1989)

[5] Hogle, J.M., Chow, M. & Filman, D.J., "Three-dimensional structure of polio virus at 2.9Å resolution", Science 229, 1358–1365 (1985)

[6] Rossmann, M.G., Arnold, E., Erickson, J.W., Frankenberger, E.A., Griffith, J.P., Hecht, H-J., Johnson, J.E., Kamer, G., Luo, M., Mosser, A.G., Rueckert, R.R., Sherry, B. & Vriend, G., "Structure of human common cold virus and functional relationships to other picornaviruses", Nature 317, 145–153 (1985)

[7] Rossmann, M.G. & Erickson, J.W., "Oscillation Photography of Radiation-Sensitive Crystals using Synchrotron Radiation", J. Appl. Cryst. 16, 629–636 (1983)

[8] Luo, M., Vriend, G., Kamer, G., Minor, I., Arnold, E., Rossmann, M.G., Boege, U., Scraba, D.G., Duke, G.M. & Palmenberg, A.C., "Atomic Structure of Mengo Virus at 3.0Å resolution", Science 235, 182–191 (1987)

[9] Hajdu, J., Acharya, K.R., Stuart, D.I., Barford, D. & Johnson, L.N., "Catalysis in Enzyme Crystals", TIBS 13, 104–109 (1988)

[10] Stryer, L., Biochemistry (third edition), Freeman, New York (1988)

[11] Hajdu, J., Acharya, K.R., Stuart, D.I., McLaughlin, P.J., Barford, D., Klein, H.W., Oikonomakos, N.G. & Johnson, L.N., EMBO J. 6, 539–546 (1987)

[12] Hajdu, J., Machin, P.A., Campbell, J.W., Greenhough, J.J., Clifton, I.J., Zurek, S., Gover, S., Johnson, L.N. & Elder, M., "Millisecond X-ray diffraction and the first electron density map from Laue photographs of a protein crystal", Nature 329, 178–181 (1987)

[13] Moffat, K., Szebenyi, D.M.E. & Bilderback, D.H., "X-ray Laue diffraction from protein crystals", Science 223, 1423–1245 (1984)

[14] Cruikshank, D.W.J., Helliwell, J.R. & Moffat, K., "Multiplicity Distribution of Reflections in Laue Diffraction", Acta Cryst. A43, 656–674 (1987)

[15] Clifton, I.J., Cruikshank, D.W.J., Diakun, G., Elder, M., Habash, J., Helliwell, J.R., Liddington, R.C., Machin, P.A., & Papiz, M.Z., "Synchrotron X-radiation Protein Crystallography: CEA Film Absorption Factor as a function of wavelength $0.3 \leq \lambda \leq 2$Å", J. Appl. Cryst. 18, 296–300 (1985)

[16] Campbell, J.W., Helliwell, J.R. & Moffat, K., Inf. Quart. Prot. Crystallography, CCP4 Newsletter 18, Daresbury Laboratory (1986)

[17] Blundell, T.L. & Johnson, L.N., Protein Crystallography, Academic Press, New York (1986)

[18] Guss, J.M., Merritt, E.A., Phizackerley, R.P., Hedman, B., Murata, M., Hodgson, K.O. & Freeman, H.C., "Phase determination by Multiple-

Wavelength X-ray Diffraction: Crystal Structure of a Basic 'Blue' Copper Protein from Cucumbers", Science 241, 806–811 (1988)

[19] Yonath, A.& Wittmann, H.G., "Challenging the three-dimensional structure of ribosomes", TIBS 14, 329–335 (1989)

[20] Pahler, A., personal communication (1989)

[21] Doucet, J. & Benoit, J.P., "Molecular dynamics studied by analysis of the X-ray diffuse scattering from lysozyme crystals", Nature 325, 643–646 (1987)

[22] Karplus, M. & McCannon, J.A., "The dynamics of proteins", Sci. Amer. 254, 42–51 (1986)

SYNCHROTRON RADIATION ACTIVITIES AT FRASCATI
AND THE RELATED INSTRUMENTATION

E. Burattini

Consiglio Nazionale delle Ricerche
and
Istituto Nazionale di Fisica Nucleare
Laboratori Nazionali di Frascati, 00044 Frascati, Rome, Italy

ABSTRACT

In this paper, a brief description is given of the characteristics of the radiation emitted from an Adone bending magnet, from a conventional six-pole wiggler, and the radiation expected from a one-pole NbTi superconducting wiggler. The beamlines, the monochromators and some of the experimental stations in operation are also described. Some results of the research activities in progress are presented together with some future developments.

1. HISTORICAL REMARKS

The beginning of the work on synchrotron radiation at Frascati dates back many years. In fact, in 1961 a group of Italian researchers, who were involved in pioneering work on the first storage ring in the world, managed to study the injection efficiency of the apparatus, which was used at the time for injecting electrons into the vacuum chamber of ADA, by using an RCA6342 photomultiplier to monitor the synchrotron radiation emitted by less than 100 electrons circulating inside the storage ring. Based on an Italian-French scientific collaboration, the first experiments began in 1962, using the synchrotron radiation emitted from the 1.1 GeV electrosynchrotron operating at Frascati at the time, shown in Fig. 1.

The experiments were based on a research programme of far ultraviolet absorption spectroscopy in the spectral region (50-500) eV to determine the absorption coefficients of thin films of Ta, Pt and Bi[1].

The success of these early activities was such that by 1970 two beam lines dedicated to research on synchrotron radiation were already

Fig.1 The 1.1 GeV electrosynchrotron in operation at Frascati up to the end of 1975.

in operation at Frascati, as shown in Fig. 2. The experimental activities[2,3,4] concerning the two lines continued until the end of 1975 when all the electrosynchrotron research work on the accelerator was halted.

In 1976 a vast research programme was started, using the synchrotron radiation emitted from the Adone storage ring that up to the time had been used exclusively for high energy physics experiments. The first X-ray beam emitted from a bending magnet of Adone was utilized in 1979 for absorption spectroscopy experiments inside a dedicated laboratory named PULS.

A conventional transverse wiggler magnet was installed in a straight section of the Adone storage ring at Frascati during 1980 to enhance the critical energy and to obtain a photon flux higher than the one emitted from a bending section. A first experimental station was equipped inside the Adone hall and made available for preliminary work[5,6].

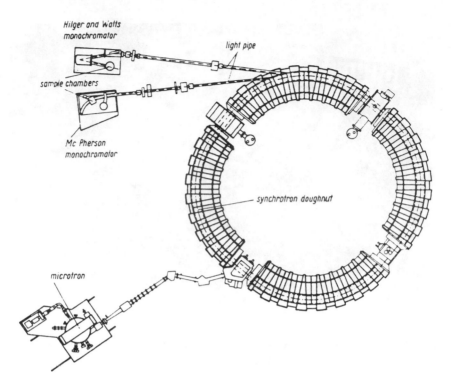

Hilger and Watts monochromator

light pipe

sample chambers

Mc Pherson monochromator

synchrotron doughnut

microtron

Fig.2 Layout of the two beam lines connected to the electrosynchrotron.

A new laboratory, outside the Adone building, is presently in operation. In this laboratory, known as the PWA Laboratory, the radiation emerging from the wiggler is exploited by means of three X-ray beam lines. A 6 Tesla, one-pole wiggler with NbTi superconducting windings will finally be installed in a straight section of the Adone storage ring at the beginning of 1991.

2.   THE ADONE STORAGE RING

Since 1976 the Adone storage ring has been partially dedicated to synchrotron radiation research. Presently, there are eight beam lines in operation, covering the energy range from 10 eV to 33 keV. The most important characteristics of Adone as a synchrotron radiation source are listed in Table I.

TABLE I

Characteristics of Adone as a synchrotron radiation source

Maximum energy	$E=1.5$ GeV
Maximum current	$I = 100$ mA
Number of bunches	$N_b = 1\text{-}3\text{-}18$
Bending radius	$R = 5$ m
Critical energy	$\epsilon_c = 1.50$ keV
Critical wavelength	$\lambda_c = 8$ Å
Radio frequency	$\nu = 51.8$ MHz
Spectral flux at critical energy	$N = 2\times10^{12}$ phot/s.mrad
(E 1.5 GeV; I = 100 mA)	0.1% band pass
Spectral brilliance at the critical energy	6×10^{14} phot.s.mrad^2.cm^2
(E = 1.5 GeV; I = 100 mA)	0.1% band pass
Spatial distributions*	$\sigma_x = 0.8$ mm
	$\sigma_z = 0.4$ mm
Vertical angular deviation*	$\sigma'_z = 40$ μ rad
Total Power	$P = 8.97$ kW
*one standard deviation	

It can be seen from the data given in Table 1 that the high brilliance of Adone as a synchrotron radiation source is due to the reduced dimensions of the electron beam, $\sigma_x = 0.8$ mm, $\sigma_y = 0.4$ mm, and to the small vertical standard deviation of $\sigma'_y = 40$ μ rad.

3. THE WIGGLER MAGNET

A conventional transverse wiggler magnet was built according to the characteristics listed in Table II.

The magnet length was chosen in order to fit the Adone straight section (2.50 m). The design specifications in terms of the field integral, at all fields, and the average multipole field coefficients in the transverse plane were met when proper correcting coils were used. The effects of the wiggler field on the optical parameters of the accelerator have been measured and found acceptable for the machine performance.

Maps of B_z on the magnet midplane were made for various supply currents: the relative accuracy in field values was better than 0.1% for B>1 T and 0.05% for B≤1 T.

TABLE II

Wiggler magnet characteristics

Magnet period	654 mm
Number of poles	5 full + 2 half
Total length	2100 mm
Gap height	40 mm
Pole length at the gap	196 mm
Pole height	100 mm
Pole width at the gap	280 mm
Maximum field on axis	1.85 T
Excitation turns per pole	7
Copper weight	270 kg
Current	4500 A
Current density	18 A/mm^2
Total power	230 kW

The spectral distribution of the radiation emerging from a single pole of the wiggler is shown in Fig. 3 (full line); the one emitted from a bending magnet section of Adone is also reported (dotted line).

As expected, a comparison between the two distributions shows that the critical energy ϵ_c of the wiggler is higher by the ratio of the wiggler magnetic field B_W to the bending magnetic field B: in our case $B_W/B = 1.85$.

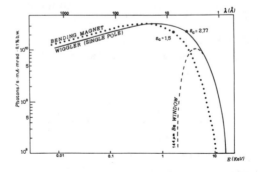

Fig.3 The spectral distribution of the radiation produced by a single pole of the wiggler compared with the one emitted from a bending magnet. The dashed line gives the spectral distribution after a 144-μm-thick window.

TABLE III
Characteristics of the radiation
emitted from the wiggler

Critical energy	$\epsilon_c = 2.77$ keV
Critical wavelength	$\lambda_c = 4.3$ Å
Spectral flux at the critical energy	$N = 1.4 \times 10^{13}$ phot/s.mrad
(E = 1.5 GeV; I = 100 mA)	bandpass 0.1%
Total radiated power	P = 1.3 kW
Horizontal angular emission	O = 70 mrad
Spatial distribution*	$\sigma_x = 1.4$ mm
	$\sigma_z = 0.24$ mm
Vertical standard deviation	$\sigma'_z = 80$ μrad

*one standard deviation

In Table III the most important characteristics of the wiggler radiation are listed.

The dashed line in Fig. 3 shows the spectral distribution of the radiation transmitted by a 144-μm-thick Be window. The total power transmitted by the Be window has been computed to be 78 mW/mA in good agreement with the experimental value of 77 mW/mA measured by a calorimetric method.

4. PULS LABORATORY

The PULS Laboratory utilizes the radiation emitted from 10 mrad of orbit from a bending magnet via five beam lines that enter a laboratory annexed to the main building of Adone. Each beam line is equipped with optics and with a monochromator that allows the use of the radiation in a particular photon energy range.

The main characteristics of the beams are given in Table IV.

The experimental stations installed on the different beam lines make it possible to carry out the following experiments:

X-ray beam line:
a) X-ray absorption spectroscopy (EXAFS, XANES) and X-ray fluorescence spectroscopy.
Grasshopper and Jobin-Yvon beam lines:
a) integrated photoemission;
b) angularly-resolved photoemission.

Hilger-Watts beam line:
a) absorption, reflectivity and luminescence;
b) two-photon spectroscopy.

TABLE IV
Monochromators

Line	Energy Range	Monochrom.	Grating	Res. Power	Pho/s.mA ...Adone
X-ray	2.4-12 keV	double crys.	Si (111)	1.3×10^{-4}	5×10^9
Grasshopper	40-800 eV	1m graz. ang.	conc. 600 lines/mm	2×10^{-3}	3×10^9
Jobin-Yvon	15-80 eV	320mm ang. 20°	toroid. 550 lines/mm	6×10^{-3}	3.5×10^8
Hilger-Watts	3-35 eV	1m norm. inc.	conc. 600 lines/mm	10^{-3}	10^8

4.1   X-ray Beam Line

The X-ray beam line, in operation since 1979, uses the radiation emitted by 1 mrad of orbit in the spectral range 2 keV - 12 keV. It comprises a double crystal, a channel-cut monochromator, and a chamber for measuring X-ray absorption and fluorescence in solid state, liquid or gaseous systems, at temperatures between 15°K and 300oK.

The activities regarding this line are mainly devoted to performing EXAFS and XANES measurements on different compounds. The two abbreviations stand for two different areas of the X-ray absorption spectrum, near the absorption edge: one covers the region between the edge and 40 eV (XANES), the other ranges from 30 eV to 1000 eV (EXAFS), as shown in Fig. 4.

With regard to EXAFS, a current general theory of the phenomenon allows the measurement, in an absorption spectrum, of the distance between the absorbing atom and its neighbours and of the number of atoms surrounding the absorbing one. Thus, the structural situation of the system around the absorption centre can be reconstructed. EXAFS is tending towards becoming increasingly a structural investigation which is complementary to the classic X-ray diffraction, and is particularly useful in experimental situations where the X-ray diffraction is not sensitive, e.g., systems with high dilution (such as the active areas of metallo-proteins) and solutions or highly disordered or even amorphous systems (such as catalysts and glass alloys). Activities in this field are being carried out by many university research groups, research institutions and industries.

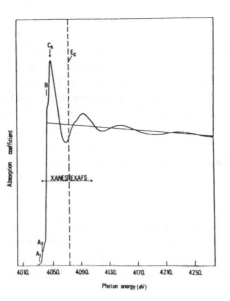

Fig.4 X-ray absorption spectrum in the energy region of Ca K edge. The two different regions EXAFS and XANES are also shown.

With regard to XANES, no general theory exists yet on the interpretation of spectra, even if it is generally known that, in a region passing from a few eV above the threshold to 40 eV, they can be interpreted as a multiple scattering effect of the photoelectrons by the neighbouring atoms and are thus sensitive to many-body correlations.

This spectroscopy is complementary to EXAFS in that it can indicate the relative angles existing between different bonds. This has been confirmed by the measurements and interpretation of XANES spectra of $K_3Fe(CN)_6$e$K_4Fe(CN)_6$ in terms of distortion of the octahedral coordination of a FeC_6N_6 cluster. The strong multiple scattering resonances in these systems depend on the shape resonances due to the CN group[7,8].

The study of solutions of $CrO4^=$, MnO_4^- and MnO_6^{++} ions has demonstrated that XANES is sensitive to correlation functions between three or more bodies, which contain direct information about the bond angles around the absorbing centre. This capability is unique to XANES as the many-body correlation function cannot be directly measured by other techniques. The Frascati research workers have made an important theoretical contribution to the interpretation of XANES spectra.

From the experimental point of view, the future of X-ray spectroscopy is mainly tied to the realization of a new apparatus that can register absorption spectra in a fraction of a second instead of tens of minutes. Therefore, an experimental apparatus for "dispersive EXAFS" has been constructed. In this device, the quasi-parallel X-ray beam is incident on a focalizing, curved crystal. As the radiant angle of the X-ray beam varies with continuity along the surface of the crystal, the reflected beam has a continual spectral distribution around the average value $\lambda = 2d \sin\theta$, with a width equivalent to 1000 eV (for a typical crystal of Si(111) of 10 cm length). Thus, if the sample is placed in the focal point, it is invested simultaneously by all the wavelengths typically measured in an X-ray absorption spectrum.

4.2   The Soft X-ray Beam line "Grasshopper"

The soft X-ray beam line, equipped with a Grasshopper monochromator, was made available to users in March 1985[9]. The useful energy range of the photons is 50-1000 eV. The ultra-high vacuum chamber for measurements allows photoemission and absorption threshold experiments to be performed using the partial yield technique.

During the first year activity, the experiments mainly concerned the following: 1) lamellar compounds; 2) Ni and Si oxides; 3) heterostructures with amorphous materials; 4) semiconductors; 5) silicides.

One of the first experiments carried out on the Grasshopper beam line involved the study of the absorption edges of different core levels in $FePS_3$ and $NiPS_3$. These materials (phospho-sulphates of transition metals) have a lamellar structure and intercalate alkaline ions. Their band structure is little known. Absorption spectra have been measured (relative to pure materials, i.e., not intercalated) of the $L_{2,3}$ edges of phosphorous and sulphur, of the sulphur L_1 edge, as well as the $M_{2,3}$ edges of Ni and of Fe.

The possibility of the Grasshopper to work at 500 eV (K edge of oxygen) has been exploited in the study of some oxides. For example, the structures near the oxygen K edge (XANES) have been studied for NiO.

4.3   The Photoemission Spectroscopy Beam Line "Jobin-Yvon"

The photoemission spectroscopy beam line for low energies consists of an ultra-high vacuum optic system, a high brightness 30 cm monochromator (spectral range 10-100 eV) and an ultra-high vacuum experimental chamber. The monochromatic beam from the monochromator hits the surface of the sample in the chamber and generates a current of photoelectrons that propagate in the vacuum with kinetic energies E_k given by the equation:

$$E_k = h\nu - E_I - \Phi$$

where E_I is the energy of the initial state of the electron inside the crystal and Φ is the potential barrier that the electron has to overcome in order to propagate in the vacuum (work function). The electrons emitted are collected by a cylindrical mirror analyzer (CMA), which selects their energy as a function of the voltage applied to the cylinders.

After excitation, the electron travels inside the crystal and may undergo inelastic collisions with the other electrons, thus losing information on the initial state and giving rise to a current of secondary electrons that constitute the "background" of the current of primary electrons that have not lost their energy and maintain information on the initial state. The occurrence of these inelastic processes, which at first sight seems to limit photoelectron spectroscopy, has in fact made this technique one of the most powerful for studying the surfaces of solids due to the small mean free path of the photoexcited electrons.

The possibility given by synchrotron light to vary the photon energy with continuity has allowed the development of new spectroscopic techniques, such as CFS (Constant Final State Spectroscopy) and CIS (Constant Initial State Spectroscopy). The first uses the continuity of the synchrotron radiation emission to couple all the full states in the crystal with only one state in a vacuum, which is simply obtained by keeping the voltage between the analyzer cylinders constant during the wavelength scanning. This reduces the effects due to the density of the final states which, for a kinetic energy lower than 20 eV, are not yet the "plane wave" type. If, during scanning, the monochromatic radiation should excite a transition from a deep level to one of the first vacuum states under the continuum, Auger recombination of the deep hole causes an increase of the current of the secondary electrons proportional to the density of the final vacuum states. This is equivalent to the process observed in optic spectroscopy on the absorption band of a deep shell. In addition, the possibility of being able to choose the energy of the secondary electrons allows a signal which is more or less sensitive to the surface of the sample.

The second technique consists in varying simultaneously both the photon energy and the CMA voltage analysis to ensure that the electrons collected by the analyzer always come from the same initial state. This technique is particularly useful for studying the resonance effects that occur when a transition from an occupied state to the continuous one is degenerate with a transition from a deeper state to a discrete one (Fano resonance).

These techniques have been applied to studying the electronic and the chemical properties of the surfaces of semiconductors and metals. A brief summary together with the most recent results follows.

a) Study of amorphous semiconductors and their interfaces

Studies have been made of the electron properties of silicon and amorphous germanium[10] (hydrogenated and non), and of silico-germanium and silico-carbon alloys. The effects of disorder on the localization of the electron states have also been investigated.

b) Study and control of the interface parameters in semiconductor-semiconductor and insulating semiconductor heterojunctions

It has been demonstrated that it is possible to change the alignment of the bands of two semiconductors of a heterojunction by operating on the chemical composition of the interface. This can be obtained by inserting a very thin metallic film at the interface. The results recently obtained lead to the conclusion that the alignment of the bands is governed by the microscopic dipole present at the interface due to the effects of the chemical bonds between the atoms of the thin film and those of the heterojunction components.

c) Study of the catalytic properties of copper

Investigations have been carried out on the copper-substrate[11] interface (Al_2O_3, MnO, TiO_2) in order to understand the catalytic properties of the system and the role of the substrate. The results have shown that there is a close relationship between the growth mechanism of the copper on the substrate and the catalytic properties of the system.

4.4   The UV Spectroscopy Beam Line "Hilger-Watts"

The "Hilger-Watts" beam line utilizes the visible and the vacuum ultraviolet regions (E = 4-35 eV).

The radiation is monochromatized by a 1 m normal angle monochromator and then focused in correspondence to the sample. There are basically two experimental devices connected to the monochromator.

The first device is set up for reflectivity, transmission and diffusion measurments, the second for luminescence measurements. The whole spectral range of 4-35 eV is covered by using two gratings and two photodetectors, optimized for the two distinct spectral regions: 4-12 eV and 10-35 eV, respectively.

In the first device, the photodetectors are installed on a rotating system. Even the "cold finger" of the cryostat can rotate, so it is possible to vary the angle of incidence of the radiation on the samples. Using this apparatus, reflectivity measurements have been performed on various materials (metal films of transition metals, semiconductors II-IV

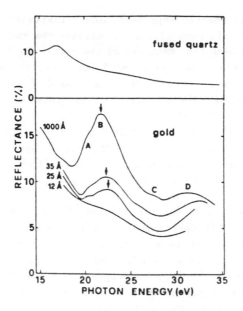

Fig.5 Reflectance in the (15-35) eV energy region of small particles of gold and its quartz substrate compared with the one of a gold thick film.

and their ternary mixtures, lamellar compounds, and insulating materials) over the whole spectral range of 4-35 eV. In addition, transmission and diffusion measurements have been made on small particles[12] of carbon, and transmission measurements on adenine vapour. As an example, Fig. 5 shows the reflectivity spectra between 15 and 35 eV carried out on small particles of gold deposited on quartz substrates. The variation of the spectra as a function of the sizes of the particles has, in this case, been attributed to the variation of the combined density of the gold states, caused by the decrease of the lattice constant, verified when the diameter of the gold particles decreases.

In the second device for luminescence measurements, the samples are placed on the cold finger of the cryostat with continuous control of the temperature from 10°K to 350°K. The luminescence radiation is collected at 90° in respect to the incident radiation via a quartz window[13]. A second monochromator analyzes the luminescence radiation over the range of 200-800 nm.

4.5   The Optical Spectroscopy Beam Line "Plastique"

The aim of this beam line is to utilize the radiation also in the 2-10 eV range. The beam line consists of two parts: the first in ultra-high vacuum runs from Adone to inside the laboratory, the second, made from polycarbonate and working in low vacuum conditions, goes up to the experimental apparatus. The two parts are separated by a LiF window whose cut-off is equal to 11.5 eV.

In the first section, an ultra-high vacuum chamber was installed to house a float-glass-type plane mirror with a special bending device to give it a cylindrical shape with its curvature in the horizontal plane. The radiation illuminates the mirror at a grazing angle of 2° and collects $(2.5{\times}7)$ $mrad^2$.

As just mentioned, the second part of the beam line is separated from the first by a $LiF.CaF_2$ window. It consists of a casing composed of various polycarbonate sections, where it is possible to create a vacuum by using a mechanical two-stage pump and thus it can work in both vacuum conditions and in an inert gas atmosphere. Ultimately, the pipe could end with a window like the one used to separate the first from the second part, or be directly connected to the experimental apparatus if it operates in low vacuum conditions.

5.   THE PWA LABORATORY

Since 1980 a conventional transverse wiggler magnet has been utilized at Frascati as a source of synchrotron radiation.

Until 1984 only one beam line, called BX1, was connected to the magnet, and the experimental apparatus for X-ray absorption spectroscopy was sited inside the Adone hall, with strong limitations in space and working conditions. Recently, a new laboratory has been built; the BX1 line has been lengthened and new experimental stations have been installed. Moreover, two new beam lines called BX2-S and BX2-L have been constructed. Experimental apparatus for "time resolved X-ray spectroscopy" and for "temperature resolved fluorescence spectroscopy" are in operation at the BX2-S line, and special devices for X-ray lithography and X-ray microscopy are connected to the BX2-L line.

The layout of the experimental area with the beam lines and experimental stations in operation is shown in Fig. 6.

The BX1 line collects the radiation emerging along the wiggler axis. The BX2-S and BX2-L lines are split from a common line, called BX2, making an angle of 1.7° with the wiggler axis. This angle was chosen as a compromise between the necessity of space and the conditions imposed

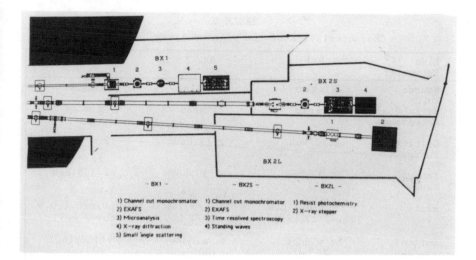

Fig.6 Layout of the experimental area, beam lines and experimental stations in operation at the PWA Laboratory.

by the optical properties of the source. The wiggler, indeed, is a particular source which emits the radiation in an overall forward angle of about 4.5° in the horizontal plane.

The beam of the BX2 line is split in two parts by a 1.5° grazing angle mirror: the straight fraction is utilized by means of the BX2-S beam line which collects one horizontal milliradian of radiation; the reflected part is utilized by means of the BX2-L beam line. The geometrical and spectral characteristics of the BX2-S line are similar to those of BX1 because BX2-S is obtained without crystals or mirrors.

The main characteristics of the three beam lines are reported in Table V.

5.1 The "Trace Element Analysis" Experimental Station

X-ray fluorescence (XRF) used for "Trace Element Analysis" has recently received renewed attention due both to the availability of strong beams of synchrotron radiation in the X-ray region and to the increasing interest shown by research and industry in this type of nondestructive analysis.

TABLE V

Characteristics of the wiggler X-ray beam lines

Line Parameter	BX1	BX2-S	BX2-L
Source	**Wiggler**	**Wiggler**	**Wiggler**
Horizontal Acceptance	1 mrad	1 mrad	2 mrad
Critical energy	2.77 keV	2.77 keV	2.77 keV
Energy range	(3-30)keV	(3-30)keV	(1-3.5)keV
Flux	10^{13}ph/s/0.1 b.w. (hv=2.77 keV)	10^{13}ph/s/0.1 b.w. (hv=2.77 keV)	10^{12}ph/s/0.1 b.w. (hv=2 keV)
Optical systems	Be window 75 μm 100 μm	Be window 100 μm	Cylindrical mirror Plane mirrors Be window 25 μm
Monochrom.	Channel-cut Si(m)-Si(220) Ge(200)	Channel-cut i(m)-Si(220) Ge(200)	Multilayer

Compared to conventional X-ray sources, the advantages of synchrotron radiation are basically tied to the linear polarization in the orbital plan of the electromagnetic radiation emitted by relativistic electrons circulating in a storage ring, to the high beam intensity, and to the reduced dimensions of the source, i.e., the electron beam.

In fact, the polarization permits the elimination of the Compton scattering in a direction which is orthogonal to that of the propagation of the X-ray beam and, therefore, the enhancement of the signal-to-noise ratio, with an improvement by a factor of between 3 and 4 for the Minimum Detection Limit (MDL).

The high spectral fluxes together with the reduced dimensions of the electron beam make synchrotron radiation one of the sources with very high brightness. Consequently, studies can be made using monochromatic lines with very reduced dimensions, which allows a further improvement in the MDL and the performance of high resolution microanalysis experiments.

A station for "Trace Element Analysis and Microanalysis" has been connected to the BX1 line and is now in operation[17]. The apparatus consists of:

1) a chamber for target irradiation, constructed so that it will be possible to work in an inert atmosphere, as well as in vacuum conditions, to reduce the X-ray beam absorption and Compton scattering;

2) a SI (Li) crystal detector to monitor the fluorescence emitted by the target;

3) a Si (Li) (or Ge-hp) crystal detector to monitor the beam striking the target;

4) a VME acquisition system comprising a crate, a Motorola 68000 microprocessor, an I/O control unit, and a computer for data acquisition;

5) a support for the irradiation chamber with an X-Y slide equipped with micrometric movements.

The schedule of research activity has been organized according to the following programme:

a) About a year will be devoted to data collection relative to the various experimental proposals regarding "Trace Element Analysis".

b) Finally, a system capable of carrying out high-resolution microanalysis (d<10 μm) with direct observation by means of an optical microscope of the areas under analysis will be used for:

1) analyses of biologically interesting elements present in traces on both liquid and solid targets;

2) analyses of traces of U and Th, responsible for the progressive damage of the silicon matrices used to realize high-density integrated circuits;

3) analyses of light elements such as B, P, Si and Al present in traces in industrial produces as a result of the manufacturing cycle;

4) multielement-type archeometric analyses to study the origin of statistically representative homogeneous findings, such as obsidians, ceramics, etc. The aim of these measurements is to trace the compositional profile of the elements present and, consequently, group the findings which have data in common, or which present trace element characteristics of a particular excavation or territory.

Fig.7 Diffraction apparatus with the drift chamber area detector.

5.2 The "Small Angle Scattering" Apparatus
5.2.1 The diffraction apparatus

The small angle scattering apparatus, shown in Fig. 7, has been installed on the BX1 beam line of the PWA laboratory and it is now in operation working in the 3-27 keV energy range. In order to obtain diffraction patterns of mechanically stretched, hydrated biological specimens, an additional chamber incorporating a fully automatic miniature tensometer can be utilized. The main vacuum specimen chamber contains micrometer movements for aligning the specimen. There is also a thermostatic cell to hold the specimen in the temperature range $(-30 \div +150)$°C. It is possible to change the specimen-detector distance to obtain small, medium and wide angle diffraction experiments on the same specimen because the detector is linked to the specimen chamber via a telescopic vacuum pipe[18].

Although the synchrotron radiation beam is highly collimated, a two-pinhole combination is used to cut down parasitic scattering. Using pin-holes of 0.3 and 0.5 mn diameter, placed 500 mm apart, a reduction of parasitic scattering of about two orders of magnitude has been achieved.

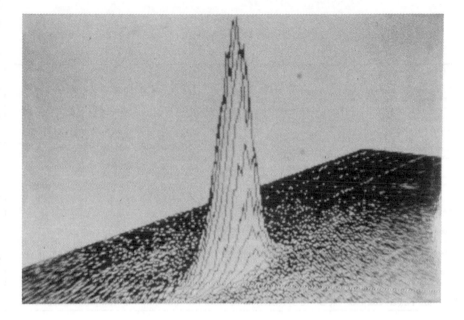

Fig.8 Profile of a 100 μm pinhole obtained using the drift chamber area detector.

A set of pin-holes with diameters ranging from 0.1 to 1.2 mm have been fabricated using gold disks having truncated conical shapes to avoid scattering at the grazing angle. The holes can be aligned by the provision of micrometer screw movements.

The apparatus is equipped with a beam stopper (2 mm width) made of gold, moveable by remote control for its alignment, and is placed in front of the entrance window of the detector.

A fast remote control movement system (PLC Omron Sysmac C200H) for moving the whole apparatus and adjusting all the experimental parameters is now operative.

5.2.2 The drift-chamber area detector

Figure 8 shows the experimental apparatus schematically. Table VI lists the characteristics related to the performance of the detector.

144

TABLE VI
Performances of the diffraction apparatus and the drift-chamber

Diffraction Apparatus		
Diameter of pin-hole collimator (variable)	0.5	mm
Primary beam angular divergence: horizontal-vertical	76"-6"	arcsec
Cross section of the beam at specimen: horizontal×vertical	0.68×0.51	mm^2
Intensity on the sample (λ=1.54 Å, $\Delta\lambda/\lambda$=10^{-4}, I=30 mA		
single bunch)	2.4×10^7	phot/sec
Conical angle of parasitic scattering	495"	arcsec
Specimen-detector distance: max.-min.	500-40	mm
Angular range covered by the detector at max. and min. distance	2°-25°	deg
Angle range covered by the goniometer at max. and min. distance	25°-134°	deg
Max. and min. angular resolution on the detector plange: X coord.	50"-618"	arcsec
Max. and min. angular resolution on the detector plane: Y coord.	66"-825"	arcsec

Drift-Chamber		
Quantum efficiency at λ = 1.54 Å and using Ar (Xe) mixtures	20 (84)	%
Detecting area	17×20	mm^2
Spatial resolution on the detector plane: X(drift)×Y(delay)	120×160	μm^2
Pixel number	142×125	pixels
Maximum storage of the buffer memories	256×256	pixels
Maximum counting rate for each pixel	2.2×10^4	cps
Maximum count capacity of detector	1×10^6	cps
Maximum linear count of the whole system	7×10^5	cps

The detector has: (a) no wire grid to produce a uniform electric potential detecting area, and (b) a small charge proportional gas gap region (2.5 mm), separated from the "drift region", where the high density of ion discharge avalanches can be easily collected by a semi-cylindrical cathode.

The mechanism of temporal operation of the detector can be briefly described as follows: The X coordinate of the position of an impinging X-ray photon is detected by measuring the drift time $\Delta t = t_1-t_0$ of the electronic cloud, generated in the gas by the photon, which drifts in the detection plane at constant velocity up to the anode wire (t_0, is the "zero time" given by the time structure of the synchrotron radiation). To determine the Y coordinate, a continuous delay line (11 nsec/mm delay time) is placed at a distance of 2.5 mm from the anode to detect the position of the avalanche discharge along the wire. The use of high speed electronic circuits permits better resolution to be obtained for both coordinates. The detector is mounted on a goniometer.

Table VI lists the performances of the diffraction apparatus and drift-chamber.

5.3 The BX2-S Beam Line

At the BX2-S line, which shows an available spectral range identical to that of the BX1 line, three experimental stations have been connected in serial mode to conduct experiments on:

- fluorescence and absorption spectroscopy in the X-ray region with sample temperature control;
- time-resolved spectroscopy;
- standing waves.

Regarding the time-resolved spectroscopy,[19,20] a modular station has been connected to the BX2-S line. The apparatus is dedicated to biophysics where it is possible to realize X-ray absorption spectroscopy experiments, fluorescence experiments and X-ray reflection spectroscopy. In particular, the system has been set up so as to utilize the XANES and EXAFS angle- and time-resolved spectroscopy.

The detection system comprises five NaI:Tl multiplier phototubes connected to an amplifier which sends a set of signals to a multichannel CAMAC. A Macintosh Plus computer is used to control the experiments and data acquisition.

This setup allows the study of kinetic processes in the range 10 ms to 1 ms. The installation of an Nd-Yag laser in the experimental area will permit flash photolysis of proteins and the study of their metastable states will be carried out.

It is also foreseen that the measurement apparatus will be used for reflectivity measurements utilizing an appropriate sample holder operated by step motors and controlled by the computer to vary the angle of incidence.

The biological sample is placed so that the angle of the X-rays is less than one degree in order to perform experiments in the total reflection condition. The ionic channels of the membrane will be studied: in fact, analyses of the spectra obtained varying the X-ray energy in the neighbourhood of the K threshold of the ion provide information about the structural coordination of the ion itself inside the channel.

5.4 The Soft X-ray Beam Line for Lithography

The soft X-ray beam line, called BX2-L, utilizes the radiation produced by the Adone 6-equivalent full poles wiggler. Table VII reports its main parameters.

The BX2-L accepts 2 mrad of radiation in the horizontal plane, giving, without collimation, a horizontal beam size at the wafer of about 70 mm. Its main optical element is a gold-coated mirror which cuts off the hard X-rays produced by the wiggler. The shieldings and the building

TABLE VII

BX2-L beam line main parameters

Source	6-pole wiggler
	($B = 1.85$ T, $E_c = 2.7$ keV)
Horizontal angular acceptance	2 mrad
Beam line length	35 m
Distance source - first mirror	12.5 m
First mirror grazing angle	1.5°
Typical energy range	0.8 - 3.0 keV

TABLE VIII

Incident power (P_i) and power absorbed in 1-μm thick PMMA resist (P_a) in the 0.65 keV - 0.6 keV energy range for various configurations: 1 = source; 2 = 1 + 25 μm Be + one mirror refl.; 3 = 2 + 2 μm Si.

Configuration Number	P_i		P_a
	(mW/mA·mrad)	(mW/mA·cm²)	(mW/mA·mrad·μm)
1	111.0	-	-
2	10.1	1.38	-
3	7.3	1.02	0.60

geometry forced a reflection in the horizontal plane (s-polarization) and a grazing angle of 1.5°. This angle gives a cut-off energy of about 3 keV which is satisfactory for XRL requirements.

In this preliminary stage, the beam line was equipped with a 20 μm Kapton window and with the MAX-1 mask-wafer aligner supplied by Karl-Suss (Munchen, FRG).

Table VIII reports the total power, evaluated integrating the spectral power in the 0.65 keV - 6.0 keV energy range, the power outside this range being negligible. The mirror reflectivity has been calculated by using the scattering factors reported by Henke et al. and extrapolating the real part of the scattering factor up to 6 keV by means of the Kramers-Kronig integral. The mirror surface roughness has been assumed equal to 10 Å rms.

TABLE IX

Resist process

Spinning				
Resist	PMMA	FBM-12		HUNT WX-242
Rev.(RPM)	2200	500		4000
Time (s)	40	30		60
Temperature (°C)	22-24	22-24		22-24
Thickness (μm)				
Prebake (in air)				
Temperature (°C)	150	140		100
Time (min)	30	30		30
Exposure				
Dose (mA·min)	1500	120		200
Development				
Developer	MIBK/IPA	MIBK/IPA		LSI/DI
	1/1	11/25		1/1
Temperature (°C)	22	22		22
Time (s)	60	120		120
Rinse	IPA	IPA		DI water
Postbake (in air)				
Temperature (°C)	100	55		100
Time (min)	30	30		30

Table VIII also reports the values of the specific power (mW/mA.cm^2) and the power absorbed in a 1-μm thick poly-methyl-methacrylate (PMMA) X-ray resist.

The experimental value of the specific power obtained by means of calorimetric methods is in quite good agreement with the theoretical one[21,22].

Two kinds of masks were used during the last exposures.

The first kind, realized at the Fraunhofer Institut für Mikrostrukturtechnik (Berlin) consists of a 2-μm Si substrate supporting 0.8 - 1.0-μm thick gold patterns with smallest linewidth of 0.2 μm.

The second kind was realized at the Istituto di Elettronica dello Stato Solido (IESS) of CNR (Rome) by means of e-beam lithography and electroplating. It consists of a 4 μm BN substrate supporting 0.7-μm-thick gold patterns with dimensions down to 0.15 μm.

The resists used are the following:

PMMA (high resolution, low sensitivity);

FBM-120 (low resolution, high sensitivity) - Daikin Industries, Japan;

HUNT WX-242 (low resolution, high sensitivity) - Olin Hunt, USA.

The wafers used for the exposures were prepared by spinning the resists on a flat silicon substrate to reach the desired thickness of 0.7-10 μm and prebaking them.

Wafers and masks were aligned at a relative distance of 25 μm and 100 μm and put on the beam by means of the MAX-1 aligner, with an air path between the window and the mask ranging from 2 mm to 5 mm. After exposure, the resists were developed and postbaked.

Table IX reports the values used in the whole process[23].

Results

Figures 9 and 10 show some of the results obtained. The SEM pictures have been obtained after a metallization of 200 Å of gold. The deformation of the structure observed in Fig. 9 is probably due to effects related to the high voltage (30 V) used.

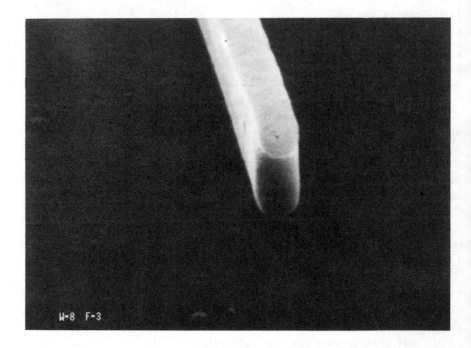

Fig.9 Replica of a 0.15-μm-wide structure on PMMA.

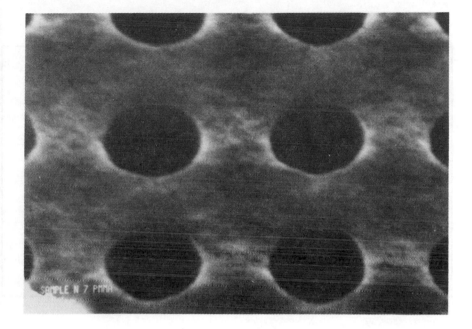

Fig.10 Replica of a periodic structure showing a resolution limit better than 0.2 μm.

Single structures of 0.15 μm were replicated on PMMA with quite a good aspect ratio and periodic structures with 0.2 μm linewidth were also obtained.

Future programmes will be devoted to the optimization of the processes and materials (resists and masks) and to the replica of more complex patterns.

6. FUTURE DEVELOPMENTS

6.1 The High Flux VUV Beam Line "CALF"

CALF is a beam line which will collect the radiation emitted by the bending magnet N.9 over a large angle (30 mrd). The useful spectral range is between 10 and 400 eV, with an average resolution power of $\Delta\lambda/\lambda \sim 5 \cdot 10^{-4}$. The optical design of this focused beam line has been obtained by ray-tracing calculations and consists of three elliptically-bent, shaped mirrors[24].

TABLE X

No. of poles	1 s.c. + 2 compensators
Magnetic full gap	6 cm
Compensator full gap	5 cm
Vertical beam stay-clear	3.2 cm
f.m.m./s.c. pole	777600 (at 6.1 T) Asp
f.m.m./compensator pole	11500 Asp
$\lambda_w/2$ (negative peak)	20 cm
Maximum field on orbit plane	6.1 T
Critical wavelength	1.38 Å
Photon flux at $\lambda = \lambda_c$ (phot/sec/mrad in $\Delta\lambda/\lambda = 0.1\%$)	2.4×10^{12}
Stored energy (s.c.)	184 KJ
Radiation emission angle	51 mrad
Total radiated power	≈1000 W
Iron weight	356 Kg

Much effort has been devoted to the construction of this new high-flux beam line in the region of high vacuum ultraviolet and, in particular, to the manufacture of mirrors of high optical quality, suited to the peculiar characteristics of synchrotron radiation. The grazing incidence geometry of this design needs complex optical systems, making use of long elliptical mirrors to refocus the source image. In addition, the short radiation wavelengths (in the range of ~25-1200 Å) require an error of the same magnitude on the optical parameters of the reflecting surfaces.

The CALF mirrors are obtained by evaporating highly reflecting metals (Au and Pt) on "Float Glass" blanks produced in an inert atmosphere on a melt tin bath, selected with industrial criteria and tested in our laboratory with interference methods.

Preliminary measurements on "Float Glass" flat samples showed a good roughness characteristic. The slope error of the mirror surface has been evaluated to be on the order of ten seconds of arc. Determination of the slope errors on the elliptic figure of our bent mirror (all the mirrors have been shaped in order to produce an elliptical curvature) is in progress, either using an interferometer, or by means of the study of optical abberations. To achieve this aim, a system capable of storing and processing images coming from a CCD camera has been set up.

6.2 The Superconducting Wiggler for Adone

The construction of a 6 Tesla, one-pole wiggler with NbTi superconducting windings, to be installed in a straight section of Adone, is in progress[25].

Taking into account the fundamental laws of synchrotron radiation emission as well as the machine requirements:

1) no beam deflection,
2) compensated field at any operation mode,
3) tolerances on the higher order field terms introduced the wiggler,

a transverse superconducting wiggler magnet has been chosen, creating a particular field pattern along the beam trajectory. The electron beam performs a single orbit bump in the orbit plane of the unperturbed storage ring. The wiggler parameters and the expected characteristics of the radiation are listed in Table X for $E = 1.5$ GeV and $I = 100$ mA.

REFERENCES

1. Jaegle, P. et al., Study of the Absorption of Ultrasoft X-ray by Bismuth and Lead Using the Orbit Radiation of the Frascati Synchrotron, 18, 21 (1967).

2. Balzarotti, A. et al., Role of the Density of Conduction States on the $L_{2,3}$ Spectrum of Aluminum, Phys.Rev. B 3, 12 (1974).

3. Balzarotti, A. et al., Far Ultraviolet Absorption Spectrum of the K^+ Ion in KCl, Solid State Communications 15, 1431 (1974).

4. Balzarotti, A. et al., Core Transition from the Al 2p Level in Amorphous and Crystalline Al_2O_3, Phys. Stat. Sol. 63, 77 (1974).

5. Barbini, R. et al., The Adone Wiggler Facility, Rivista Nuovo Cimento 4, 8 (1981).

6. Burattini, E. et al., Experimental Activity at the Adone Wiggler Facility, Nucl. Instrum. Methods 208, 91 (1983).

7. Balerna, A. et al., Dynamical Properties and Debye Temperature of Au Bulk and Clusters by Extended X-ray Absorption Fine Structure, Phys. Rev. B 34, 2293 (1986).

8. Belli, M. et al., Characteristics of Metal Sites in Nucleic Acids by High Resolution X-ray Spectroscopy, Physics in Environmental and Biomedical Research, World Scientific Publishing Co. (1986).

9. Chiaradia, P. et al., The Soft X-ray Beam Line of Adone, Vuoto 16, 83 (1986).

10. Evangelisti, F. et al., Photoemission Studies of Amorphous Silicon/Germanium Heterojunction, Mat. Res. Soc. Symp. Proc. 49, (1985).

11. Grassano, U.M. et al., Lifetime Measurements of Colour Centres by a Multifrequency Phase Fluorometer, Nuovo Cimento 7D, 379 (1986).

12. Colangeli, L. et al., Extinction Spectra of Amorphous Colour Submicron Grains in the UV-Visible Range, Astronomy and Astrophysics 168, 349 (1986).

13. Pizzoferrato, R. et al., Two-Photon Absorption Using Synchrotron Radiation: a Novel Technique, Europhys. Lett. 2, 571 (1986).

152

14. Bernieri, E. et al., Multielectron Transition Above the Kr K-edge, Phys. Rev. 35, 8 (1987).

15. Burattini, E., Synchrotron Radiation Application in Biophysics and Medicine, Physics in Environmental and Biomedical Research, World Scientific Publishing Co. (1986).

16. Burattini, E. et al., XANES Studies of Unoccupied Electronic States and Local Real Structures of some Antimony Chalcogenides, Nuovo Cimento 7D, 3 (1986).

17. Sciuti, S. et al., Trace Element Analysis with Synchrotron Induced X-ray Fluorescence at PWA Frascati; Synchrotron Radiation at Frascati: 1986 Users Meeting, Conf. Proc., Società Italiana di Fisica 5, (1987).

18. La Monaca, A. et al., Small Angle X-ray Diffraction of Collagen Fibrils using Three-Dimensional Imaging Gas Detector, Biophysics and Synchrotron Radiation, Springer Series in Biophysics, Springer-Verlag, Berlin-Heidelberg-New York (1987).

19. Bianconi, A. et al., Time and Angle Resolved EXAFS and XANES of Biological Systems on the Wiggler BX2-S Beam Line, Synchrotron Radiation at Frascati: 1986 Users Meeting, Conf. Proc., Società Italiana di Fisica [5], (1987).

20. Lagomarsino, S. et al., Surface Layers and Interface Studies by X-ray Standing Waves, Synchrotron Radiation at Frascati: 1986 Users Meeting, Conf. Proc., Società Italiana di Fisica 5, (1987).

21. Burattini, E. et al., Adone Wiggler Beam Lines Progress Report, Nucl. Instrum. Methods A246, 125 (1986).

22. Burattini, E. et al., The Adone Wiggler X-ray Beam Line, Rev. Sci. Instrum. 60(7), 2133 (1989).

23. Seligson, D., Photoresists and X-Radiation Universal Behavior, INTEL Technology Journal (1987).

24. Antonangeli, F. et al., High Flux VUV Beam Line at Adone Storage Ring, Synchrotron Radiation at Frascati: 1986 Users Meeting, Conf. Proc. Società Italiana di Fisica 5 (1987).

25. Aragona, A. et al., S.CO.W. Superconducting Wiggler for Adone, Synchrotron Radiation at Frascati: 1986 Users Meeting, Conf. Proc. Società Italiana di Fisica 5 (1981).

INSTRUMENTATION AND RESEARCH AT HASYLAB

V. Saile *

Hamburger Synchrotronstrahlungslabor HASYLAB at DESY
Notkestr. 85, D-2000 Hamburg 52
West Germany

ABSTRACT

At the Synchrotronstrahlungslabor HASYLAB, 32 experimental stations are operated for approximately 40 weeks per year. The DORIS ring, with electron energies of 3,7 GeV or 5,3 GeV, provides intense synchrotron radiation beams with photon energies up to 150 KeV for research in physics, chemistry, biology and medicine. Three wigglers and undulators emit superior intensities in the soft and hard X-ray range. In the second half of 1990, one quarter (75m) of the circunference of the DORIS ring will be reconstructed to provide seven 4m-long straight sections for additional insertion devices.

The instrumentation in the laboratory covers the whole range from visible light to hard X-rays. However, due to the spectral characteristics of the high energy ring, the majority of the beam lines is optimized for research with X-rays. The scientific program is very broad, ranging from basic research to applications in industry and medicine. Among the fields developing most rapidly are: time resolved spectroscopies with VUV and soft X-rays, surface diffraction of X-rays, protein crystallography, inelastic X-ray scattering, powder diffraction and small angle scattering.

* Present address   :   Louisiana State University
                        3990, West Lakeshore Drive
                        Baton Rouge, LA 70803
                        USA

SYNCHROTRON X-RAY LITHOGRAPHY. AN UPDATE.*

R. E. Acosta
IBM Research Division
P.O. Box 218
Yorktown Heights, NY 10598 USA

ABSTRACT

High volume production of submicron USLI devices demands high resolution lithographic techniques that are fast and economic. Synchrotron X-ray lithography is expected to meet these requirements. This paper gives a summary of the main differences between synchrotron X-ray, e-beam, and optical lithographies. The main components of an X-ray lithography system are enumerated and briefly described. Recent results in the application of X-ray lithography for the fabrication of devices are discussed. Some of the challenges that must be met for a successful transfer of the technology to manufacturing are discussed.

* The complete version is being published in Proceedings of the II Workshop Microlithography: High Integration in Microelectronics, World Scientific Publishers, Singapore (1990).

LITHOGRAPHIC MATERIALS FOR SYNCHROTRON RADIATION

J. BARGON

Institute of Physical Chemistry, University of Bonn, Wegelerstr. 12, D-5300 Bonn 1, West Germany

ABSTRACT

Highly sensitive X-ray resists have become available, which allow reproduction of the smallest features of currently available masks for X-ray lithography. This has become possible by using systems related to the classic dissolution-type photoresists but by splitting up the task of their photoactive compound between two components, a photoacid generator and an acid-sensitive dissolution inhibitor. This approach utilizes a catalytic conversion of a composite containing three components from an insoluble into a soluble form or vice versa, employing an aqueous base as the developer. In this mode, swelling of the resist is minimal but the sensitivity is high. It can be estimated that one absorbed photon generates 12 acid molecules, each one of which induces 500 catalytic cycles. X-ray lithography is especially powerful for producing structures with a high aspect ratio for replication processes in metal or for the mass production of micromechanic devices. Specialized resists for such applications have also been formulated.

1. Introduction

Since the ever increasing degree of miniturization of microelectronic circuitry puts stricter conditions on the smallest line dimensions that have to be manufactured consistently with lithographic techniques, the wavelength and, therefore, the type of the lithography has to be adjusted to the smallest required line dimension. In the time frame up to the early eighties it was generally believed that devices with line dimensions of 1 μm and less would have to be mass-produced using X-ray lithography. It has since become possible to fabricate devices containing structures and lines down to 0.5 μm using conventional g- or i-line UV-lithography. This suprising progress of optical lithography has pushed the onset of X-ray lithography into the sub-half-micron range, excluding some special applications for customized integrated circuits or those due to special boundary conditions of special manufacturers. Nevertheless, X-ray lithography has an attractive potential as an economic means for the mass-fabrication of integrated circuits, and if not yet now, then certainly in the future. The disadvantages of X-ray lithography are numerous. Among other problems it puts rather strict demands both on the X-ray source, the mask and the resists. Unlike the competing forms of lithography, it depends in a rather crucial way on masks, which have to be made using e-beam lithography. E-beam generated masks can be made for all types of lithography, but the technology of X-ray masks   not   simple or unique for this application. E-beam and ion-beam ltihgography can be used in a direct write mode, and masks for photo- and UV-lithography can in principle be obtained avoiding e-beam lithography, even though the latter is more attractive. Figure 1 shows the different types of competing lithographies in comparison together with their mask requirements.

By now the art of mask fabrication for X-ray lithography has been chiefly mastered, but it still represents a bottleneck. Therefore, it has taken a rather long time for X-ray lithography to be migrated from a research laboratory environment into a production line setting, where it is still at a stage, where it has to demonstrate its advantage and reliability in competition with modern UV-lithography.

On the other hand, X-ray lithography offers not only another alternative to UV-lithography, but it also has unique advantages for certain special applications, for example where a high aspect ratio is required. One such process, which puts this unique feature of X-ray lithography to use, is the LIGA-process [1], which produces a primary microstructure using lithography, which is subsequently replicated in metal many times via galvanoforming. Using the LIGA-process, microstructures with smallest characeristic dimensions in the micrometer range, structural accuracies of some tenths of a micrometer, and structural heights of several hundred micrometers have been manufactured successfully. For applications of this type, an additive mode rather than the conventional substractive mode of lithography is more advantageous. Figure 2 compares the steps required in the additive and the substractive mode of lithography. The advantage of the additive technique, whereby metal is deposited onto a suitable substrate is that once a primary microstructure is obtained, many replicas can be derived via a subsequent molding process. The LIGA-process has been developed at the Karlsruhe Nuclear Research Center in West Germany, using the synchrotron at the University of Bonn for exposing the samples. The synchrotron at Bonn is essentially a 2.5 GeV machine, operating at a maximum energy of 2.0 GeV, which corresponds to a characteristic wavelength of 0.534 nm.

CAPABILITIES OF VARIOUS TYPES OF LITHOGRAPHIES

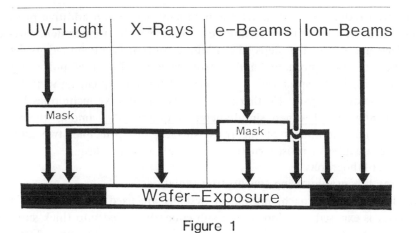

Figure 1

MODES OF LITHOGRAPHY

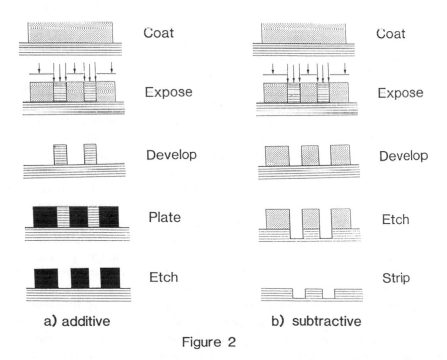

a) additive   b) subtractive

Figure 2

2. Synchrotron Radiation Lithography

Synchrotron radiation is attractive for both subtractive and additive processes in microstructure fabrication techniques. Whereas the former dominates the microelectronic processing steps, the additive concept is advantageous for the fabrication of micromechanic and sensor devices. For this purpose resist structures with high aspect ratios are essential for subsequent galvanoforming or plastic molding steps [1]. Furthermore, resists for additive techniques have to satisfy a number of other simultaneous requirements, among them high resolution and smoothness of the resist surface. In principle, two alternate approaches qualify for resist structures with high aspect ratios:
   a) optical lithography
   b) X-ray lithography using synchrotron radiation.
   In the optical approach, multilayer systems are used, whereby a thin top resist layer is exposed, developed, and subsequently copied into thick sublayers using an anisotropic oxygen plasma (i.e. reactive ion) etching steps. Details of this approach have been given elsewhere [2]. The synchrotron radiation approach, due to its more than thousandfold shorter wavelength, offers certain advantages but places special requirements on the resist system. Early attempts to explore the feasibility of X-ray lithography [3] succeeded to demonstrate the transfer of patterns by means of soft X-rays. The dominating lithographic materials in the early stages where essentially identical to previously identified e-beam resists [4], notably poly(methyl methacrylate) or closely related systems. However, in the course of time all key elements of lithography had to be adapted to the requirements of X-ray lithography, including the source, the masks and not at least the resists [5]. Along this line a compromise had to be established between the rapidly decreasing cross section of organic resist matter to X-rays of short wavelengths and their superior resolution capability due to lower diffraction effects. This as well as mask technology calls for an operating wavelength between 0.5 and 2.0 nm. A number of X-ray sources based upon different principles have become available [6], but all suffer from certain shortcomings, notably intensity of the X-ray radiation within the above window of the desirable wavelengths. As compact synchrotron storage rings become available [6], their superior brightness with an irradiance of about 100 mW/m^2 [7] is likely to improve the chances for X-ray lithography as a mass production tool in microelectronic technology. Due to the remarkable success of optical lithography, current submicron structures in the region 0.5 to 1 μm are still being manufactured optically, whereas, below 0.5 μm, X-ray lithography can be expected to replace the contemporary optical step- and repeat cameras as exposure tools. This onset of application at very high resolution puts rather extreme resolution requirements on any promising X-ray resist material.

Together with the notorious limitation in brightness of the available X-ray sources (including the currently available synchrotrons with very few exceptions), modern X-ray resists have to combine extreme resolution power with very high sensitivity at the same time.

3. The Interaction of Ionizing Radiation with Organic Matter

Both X-rays and e-beams represent different forms of ionizing radiation. When interacting with matter, they generate neutral species, ions and electrons. Due to their high energies they cause excitations of the inner non-valence electrons of the different atoms in the resist, more or less independently on the chemical bonding of these atoms. As such the primary absorption of X-rays in organic matter is more or less determined by the elemental composition with known and tabulated contributions of the individual chemical elements to the over all cross sections [8]. The primary electrons ejected from the inner shells give rise to cascades of secondary and tertiary electrons which spread overall extending volume while constantly loosing energy. The residual energy of the secondary or tertiary electrons is still sufficient to break chemical bonds like those occuring in organic resist molecules. Just like e-beams, X-rays and their subsequent cascades of secondary and tertiary electrons are well capable of breaking bonds, which are well above the equivalent energy of optical photons. This aspect provides for more flexibility of the chemistry operating in X-ray or e-beam resists in comparison to optical lithography.

4. X-Ray Resists

4.1. The Ideal Resist

A desirable X-ray resist should unite the following properties:

- A resolution of better than 0.1 μm
- A sensitivity of better than 100 mJ/cm^2
- A dissolution ratio of better than 10
- A contrast of better than 10.

In addition, due to a vast amount of knowledge and data gathered in the field of optical lithography using novolak-type resists containing diazo-naphthoquinones, a desirable resist should resemble the composition of such systems as closely as possible. As a bare minimum it should have a resistance to reactive ion etching conditions of a similar or better level than that of typical novolak-type resists, for example better than the quality of AZ1450.

4.2. Novolak-Systems

Unfortunately, the sensitivity of standard novolak-based resists is too low by a least an order of magnitude, if they are processed as is typical for optical lithography. It has been found, however, that if the development steps of the resist are optimized for X-ray exposure conditions, certain novolak-based systems give rather reasonable results, both with respect to resolution, sensitivity and of course, etch resistance to reactive ion plasma conditions [9,10]

4.3. Poly(methyl Metahcrylate)

A classic X-ray resist is poly(methyl methacrylate) (PMMA). It shows the highest resolution of all resists down to about 10 nm. However, it suffers from poor etching resistance and too low a sensitivity by about 2 orders of magnitude. PMMA belongs to the family of positive-tone resists, whereby the solubility of the polymer increases in the exposed areas due to chain scissions caused by the irradiation [2,11].

Radiation induced changes in polymers have been investigated long before the advent of X-ray lithography. Impirical rules have been formulated which correlate the polymer structure and the changes to be expected upon exposure to radiation. These concepts have since been expanded to allow for a prediction of the radiation sensitivities of polymers [12]. It has been found that typically:

a) polymers with quaternary carbon atoms in their backbone chain, i.e. so-called vinylidene polymers, undergo main chain scission, which causes a reduction of the average molecular weight and thus leads to an increased solubility in the exposed areas. Such systems act as positive resists.

b) Polymers with only a tertiary (and no quarternary) carbon atom in the backbone, i.e. so-called vinyl polymers, undergo crosslinking reactions, which lead to insolubility of the irradiated areas. Such systems act as negative resists.

Figure 3 and 4 illustrate these two types of polymers and their respective behavior upon irradiation. Figure 5 outlines the so-called "Miller Rule" of radiation sensitivity, which has been named after an early investigator of radiation induced changes in polymers.

Vinylidene polymers were first evaluated as potential e-beam resists by Haller and coworkers [13], who compared the e-beam induced degradation of poly(isobutylene), poly(α-methyl styrene) and poly(methyl metharylate). They found all of them to be positive resists with PMMA having the best properties.

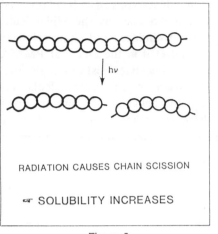

RADIATION CAUSES CHAIN SCISSION

☞ SOLUBILITY INCREASES

Figure 3

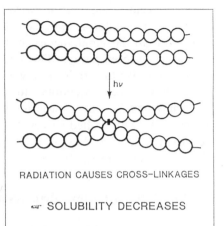

RADIATION CAUSES CROSS-LINKAGES

☞ SOLUBILITY DECREASES

Figure 4

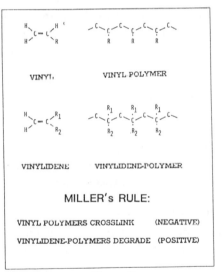

VINYL,   VINYL POLYMER

VINYLIDENE   VINYLIDENE-POLYMER

MILLER's RULE:

VINYL POLYMERS CROSSLINK   (NEGATIVE)

VINYLIDENE-POLYMERS DEGRADE   (POSITIVE)

Figure 5

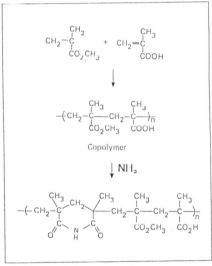

Copolymer

Figure 6

More recent evaluations of PMMA and vinylidene-type resists have revealed that the real situaiton is more complicated than expressed by the Miller Rule. This is due to the simultaneous formation of crosslinkages and chain scissions in a rather unspecific way. This difficulty is reflected in the fact that PMMA acts as a positive-tone resist at low doses, but as a negative resist at a high dose. There have been attempts to use quantum mechanical calculations (HF-approximation) as a basis for predicting the behavior of polymers upon exposure but with limited success [19]. Furthermore, it has been found that the tacticity, here of the PMMA, has a considerable influence on the sensitivity of the corresponding resists [20].

4.4. Modified Poly(methyl Methacrylate)

Efforts to improve the properties of PMMA, especially its adhesion to metal substrates, led to the evaluation of copolymers. During the investigation of methyl methacrylate / methacrylic acid copolymers it was accidentally observed that the sensitivity of these copolymers to e-beam exposure increased upon heating the systems prior to their exposure [14]. Heat treatment is known to result in the formation of anhydride structures [15], in this case in six-membered glutaric acid anhydride rings (GA).

The radiation induced decomposition of monomeric GA-type model structures had previously been investigated by Hiraoka [16]. When incorporated into a polymer backbone, however, the six-membered GA-type ring still yields the 1,4-diradical as an intermediate, but now the subsequent reactions differs remarkably from that of the low molecular weight model compound. In the polymer, cleavage occurs exclusively, resulting in a breakdown of the molecular weight and thus in an increase of the solubility, which explains the observed increase in sensitivity. The closely related - since isoelectronic - glutarimide system (GI) behaves essentially similar. It can be derived from PMMA or its copolymers with methacrylic acid or homopolymers thereof via conversion in the presence of ammonia at elevated temperature and pressure or via alternate routes [17]. The glutarimides derived from the methacrylic as well as the acrylic backbone polymers both show improved sensitivity to ionizing radiation [18]. The PMMA derivative, poly(dimethyl glutarimide) (PMGI) has since become a commercial resist, which is useful for UV-lithography as well as for e-beam or X-ray lithography. It has excellent planarizing properties (Figure 6).

4.5. Substituted Poly(methyl Metharcrlates)

Incorporation of substituents into conventional resist systems provides the opportunity to increase the interaction with ionizing radiation due to an increased cross-section for X-rays. Accordingly a variety of substituted monomers of the general type $CH_2 = C(CH_2X)COOCH_3$ as well as their polymers have been synthesized and evaluated [11]. For X = Cl, the homopolymer thereof has been found to be about three times as sensitive as PMMA. Related systems have been reported in the literature [6] (Table 1) [30].

4.6. Other Types of X-Ray Resists

Other than the above "classical" resists, namely the methacrylate family and the novolak/naphthoquinonediazide system, a significant number of alernate resists exist. Of the positive type, the photocatalytic systems are of particular interest, since they have potential for achieving high sensitivity while retaining resolution and plasma etch resistance. The other main catagories of resists, namely the crosslinking and the image reversal type, are both negative-tone resists [6].

5. Photocatalytic Systems

5.1. Photocatalytic Positive-Tone Systems

The basic concept of the conventional novolak/naphthoquinonediazide (DNQ) is that of dissolution inhibition. Accordingly the solubility of the novolak resin, which makes up about 75 % of the composition of a resist, is modified by the chemical state of the photoactive compound (PAC), here the DNQ, which is being converted from its dissolution inhibiting state to a carboxylic acid, which promotes the dissolution of the novolak matrix. This concept has been extremely successful in optical lithography, and products based on it account for almost all of the world market in photoresists.

Application of this concept to X-ray resists yields sensitivities around 1800 mJ/cm² due to the poor X-ray absorption coefficients of the individual components. If the task of photoactive compound is split up over two or more components, increased sensitivities can be achieved. One straightforward mode of splitting up the task is to improve the X-ray absorption of the resist by assigning this role to the novolak. This can be achieved, for example, by incorporating halogens into the aromatic units of the novolak. The results are mostly disappointing so far.

A far superior concept uses a dissolution inhibitor, which can be destroyed via acidic hydrolysis. If an acid generator is added, which yields an acid as a

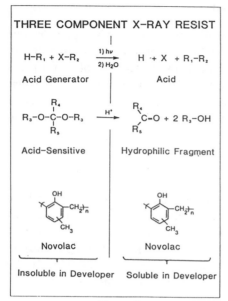

Figure 7

SYNCHROTRON LITHOGRAPHY

Halogen Containing Poly(acrylates)

Resist	Monomer	Sensitivity (μC/cm²)	T_g
Poly(methylmethacrylate) (PMMA)	$-CH_2-\overset{CH_3}{\underset{COOCH_3}{C}}-$	80	104° C
Poly(n-butylmethacrylate) P(n-BMA)	$-CH_2-\overset{CH_3}{\underset{COOC_4H_9}{C}}-$	0.5	19°C
Poly(hexafluorbutylmeth-acrylate) (FBM-110 (Daikin Kogyo))	$-CH_2-\overset{CH_3}{\underset{COOR}{C}}-$ R=-CH₂CF₂CHFCF₃	0.4	50°C
Poly(trichlorethylmeth-acrylate) (EBR-1(Toray Industries))	$-CH_2-\overset{CH_3}{\underset{COOCH_2CCl_3}{C}}-$	1.25	138°C
Poly(trifluorethylmeth-acrylate)	$-CH_2-\overset{CH_3}{\underset{COOCH_2CF_3}{C}}-$	4.5	---
Poly(methyl-α-chlor-acrylate) PMCA	$-CH_2-\overset{Cl}{\underset{COOCH_3}{C}}-$	46	130°C
Poly(trifluorethyl α-chloracrylate) (EBR-9(Toray Industries))	$-CH_2-\overset{Cl}{\underset{COOCH_2CF_3}{C}}-$	0.8 - 6.4	133°C

Table 1

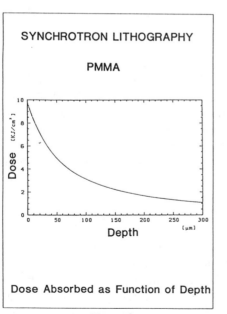

Figure 8

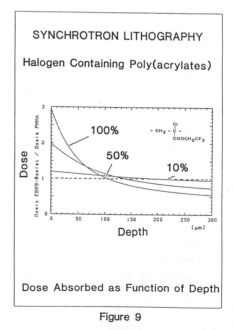

Figure 9

consequence of absorbed radiation, a lot of dissolution inhibitor can be destroyed catalytically by the photogenerated acid. This concept represents a chemical gain, which may increase the sensitivity of X-ray resists by two orders of magnitude. A variety of acid sensitive dissolution inhibitors have been identified, among them acetals, ketals, enol ethers etc.[6]. The acid required for the photocatalysis is derived from onium salts, ferrocene derivatives or halogen containing compounds[6]. These or similar systems have also been used or developed for the e-beam induced cure of resins. Exposure of these precursors typically yields strong Bronsted acids, but concepts yielding sulfonic acids from suitable precursors are also known[21]. Splitting up the role of the photoactive compound results in a three-component system (3CS), such as the polyaldehyde/novolak resists[22]. The experimental X-ray resists RAY-PF[23] and the negative RAY-PN[24] have been developed by HOECHST AG of Frankfurt, and have been evaluated for their suitability for synchrotron radiation. The positive resist RAY-PF consists of a novolak matrix, which assures good process compatibility, in particular development in aqueous base. The other two components are a Bronsted-acid generator and a hydrolysis sensitive though irradiation resistive dissolution inhibitor[25]. Since the acid acts only catalytically, a single molecule of acid may induce multiple hydrolysis steps, which can yield a chemical amplification of the sensitivity by orders of magnitude above that of ordinary novolak-type resists without photocatalytic enhancement. Figure 7 outlines the chemical transformations in a 3CS-type resist. The sensitivity of the RAY-PF resist has been evaluated at BESSY (755 MeV) to reach a D_0 value of 11 mJ/cm^2 or 17 mJ/cm^2 when exposing the resist with the softer X-rays from a laser focus source, using slightly different processing conditions. Assuming that a single absorption event will usually generate about 12 acid catalysts in RAY-PF in the average[26], and making certain assumptions about the size of the volume which is effected by the ensuing acidolysis[25], it can be calculated that approximately 6000 molecules of the dissolution inhibitor will become hydrolized. This converts to about 500 catalytic cycles per proton, based upon 12 acid molecules per absorbed photon. This crude calculation gives some estimate for the efficiency of the photocatalytic principle.

5.2. Photocatalytic Negative-Tone Systems

Negative-tone resists of the "classical type", i.e. those based on the crosslinking of the exposed areas, typically exhibit significantly higher sensitivities but at the price of a lower resolution than their classic positive counterparts. Accordingly, chloromethylated polystyrenes function at a useful dose of 1 μC/cm^2 as e-beam resists (20 keV electrons), combined with good thermal and plasma etching resistance. However, due to swelling of the cross-linked polymer in the liquid developer, the resolution of such systems is limited to about 0.7 μm lines & spaces.

An attractive alternative to such systems uses the well known novolaks or poly(hydroxstyrene) as a matrix, even in a negative-tone resist, and induces a three-dimensional crosslinking of the matrix via the combination of an acid generator and an acid-activated crosslinking agent. Suitable crosslinking agents may be melamines or benzylacohol derivatives; the acid generator can be identical to those used in the positive-tone 3CS resists as discussed above [25].

The optimized X-ray exposure dose for RAY-PN has been evaluated to be 50 mJ/cm^3 at BESSY, corresponding to an exposure time of 10 sec. at 200 mA, or for the COSY system 4.5 sec at 80 mA. The resolution of this system seems to be limited by the X-ray mask: The smallest dimensions of 0.2 μm on the mask could be faithfully reproduced with steep side walls over severe topography. In an e-beam exposure mode structures down to 150 nm were printed in 0.3 μm thick RAY-PN using 50 or 20 keV electrons [27].

Since in RAY-PN the crosslinking reaction becomes measurable only above 90 °C, baking times of 5 min at 105 °C are required. After a heat treatment at 140 °C, no thermal flow or rounding of the structures is observed up to 200 °C. Similarly, etch resistance is high even during the Cl-etch process [25].

5.3. Photocatalytic Demasking Schemes

Photochemical deprotection of polymeric systems has been used as a powerful concept of deep UV-resists [28]. This concept is based upon a photoactive acid precursor catalyzing a sequence of subsequent elimination reactions. In this way functional groups are set free to facilitate the subsequent development. Systems, which have found most attention thus far, are t-butoxycarbonyl (t-BOC) protected phenolic systems, in particular poly(p-hydroxy-styrene) [28]. Deprotection requires a subsequent heat treatment, which frees isobutene and ren7ers the matrix resin soluble in aqueous base developer. Using mixtures of organic solvents, for example a mixture of dichloromethane and hexane, this same system can be developed in a negative-tone mode with a sensitivity of 13 mJ/cm^2.

6. Resists for High Aspect Ratios

For applications, where a high aspect ratio is essential, such as for the LIGA process as outlined above, a rather homogeneous absorption of the synchrotron radiation in the thick resist layers is desirable. Two alternate approaches have been taken to achieve this goal.

One solution is based upon the optimization of the operating parameters of the synchrotron to a given resist [29]. This approach uses special cut-off filters and optimized wavelengths for the exposure of the resists, but is useful only where the operating conditions as well as the design of the beam line can be adjusted and customized for X-ray lithography. An alternate solution adjusts the X-ray resist to a given set of synchrotron parameters using heteroatoms as resist constituents in form of copolymers etc. For the synchrotron at the University of Bonn ($E_{max} = 2$ GeV, corresponding to $\lambda = 0.534$ nm) this problem has been treated in detail and tested with a number of custom-synthesized resist by Göttert and Hormes [30].

The approach is based upon the assumption that monochromatic X-ray radiation of the wavelength λ and a power P is absorbed as a function of depth z with the dose $D(z)$ after a time t:

$$D(z) = \dot{D}(z) \bullet t = \mu(\lambda)e^{-\mu(\lambda)\bullet z} \bullet t \bullet P/A$$

Whereby $\mu(\lambda) = $ the linear absorption coefficient of the resist and A the irradiated area. Figure 8 shows the deposited dose in the resist as a function of depth in kJ/cm^3 in PMMA using the parameters of the Bonn synchrotron. At a depth of 300 μm the deposited dose is about 1 kJ/cm^2, which corresponds to about one tenth of the deposited dose at the top [30]. As has been shown by Göttert and Hormes, atoms with high absorption coefficients can be used successfully to equlibrate the deposited dose on the top and in a depth of 300 μm to remain within narrower margins. Copolymers of the Pb-salt of (methacrylic acid) and methyl methacrylate with a Pb content of 3 % [31] reduce the ratio of the dose deposited at the top to that at a depth of 300 nm to 3:1 [30].

Another solution to this challenge is based upon using halogen containing copolymers of PMMA. One such candidate is the resist system EBR9 of Toray Industries, namely poly(trifluoroethyl-α-chloroacrylate) [32], whereas pure EBR9 yields a dose at the top which is three-times higher than that at a depth of 300 nm. Copolymers of methyl methacrylate and trifluoroethyl-α-chloroacrylate can be used to fine-tune the margins of the deposited dose at the top and at a depth of 300 nm (Figure 9).

7. Conclusions

This survey of current approaches to resists for synchrotron radiation reveals that X-ray lithography is in a position of yielding very narrow dimensions, essentially limited by the resolution of the structures on the mask and the exposure system in the range of one quarter micrometer. The improved resolution, reliability and economics of the competing UV-lithography has delayed the onset of synchrotron lithography well into the nineties of this century for the mass fabrication of microelectronic devices. For other applications, for example in micromechanics, synchrotron radiation and X-ray lithography offer significant advantages over any other competing technology. Modern resist systems taking advantage of photocatalysis have achieved high sensitivity combined with high resolution potential and thereby allowing a reasonable throughput of the devices in the synchrotron exposure facility.

Acknowledgement

This work has been funded in part by the Fonds der Chemischen Industrie, West Germany. The author thanks the X-ray resist team of HOECHST AG, Frankfurt, Dr. Maid and Dr. Hormes of the Physics Department of the University of Bonn and Dr. Vollenbroek, PHILIPS, Eindhoven for making the data of their evaluations available prior to their appearance in print.

References

1.   E.W. Becker, W. Ehrfeld, P. Hagmann, A. Masser and D. Münchmeyer, "Fabrication of Microstructures with High Aspect Ratios and Great Structural Heights by Synchrotron Radiation Lithography, Galvanoforming and Plastic Modeling, (LIGA Process)", Microelectronic Engineering 4 (1986), pp. 35 - 56.

2.   For a recent review see J. Bargon "Lithographic Materials", A. Craievich, G.G.B. DeSouza and V. Baranauskas, Eds., World Scientific, Singapore (1990).

3. a)   D.L. Spears and H.I. Smith, Solid State Technology, Vol. 15, (1972), p. 21.
   b)   D.L. Spears and H.I. Smith, Electronic Letters, Vol. 8, (1972), p. 102.

4.   I. Haller, M. Hatzakis and R. Srinivasan, IBM J.Res.Dev. 12, (1968), 251.

5. a)   A. Heuberger, Proc. SPIE, Vol 771, (1987), p. 1.
   b)   A. Heuberger, J.Vac.Sci.Technol., Vol. B6 (1988), p. 107.
   c)   A. Heuberger, Microelectronic Eng., Vol. 7, (1988).

6.   J. Lingnau, R. Dammel, J. Theis, Solid State Technol., Vol. 32 (1989), 105 - 112.

7.   J.S. Pearlman, J.C. Riordan, Proc. SPIE, Vol. 537, (1985), p. 102.

8.   D. Seligson, L. Pan, P. King and P. Pianetta, Nuclear Instr. Meth., Vol. A266 (1988), p. 612.

9.   S. Pongratz, H. Betz, A. Heuberger, "Application of Novolak Resist Systems in X-Ray Mask Fabrication", Proc. Kodak Microelectronics Seminar, San Diego 1983, pp. 143-147.

10.   H.-L. Huber, H. Betz, A. Heuberger, S. Pongratz, "Application of Diazo-Type Resists in Synchrotron Lithography", in: A. Heuberger, H. Beneking, ME '84, Berlin, Academic Press 1985.

11.   J. Bargon in "Methods and Materials in Microelectronic Technology", J. Bargon, Ed., Plenum Press, New York (1984), pp. 181-242.

169

12.	D. O'Sullivan, P.B. Price, K. Kinoshita, C.G. Willson, J.Electrochem.Soc.129, (1982), 811-813.
13.	I. Haller, M. Hatzakis and R. Srinivasan, IBM J.Res.Dev.12, 251 (1968).
14.	R. Feder, I. Haller, M. Hatzakis, L.T. Romankiw and E.A. Spiller, IBM Research Center, Yorktown Heights, New York (1974), private communication.
15.	K. Kevan and W.F. Libby, Advances Photochem. 2 183, (1964).
16.	H. Hiraoka, J.Am.Chem.Soc.95, 1664, (1973).
17. a)	J. Bargon, E. Gipstein and H. Hiraoka, U.S. Patent 3,964,908, (1976).
	b)	H. Hiraoka, E. Gipstein, J. Bargon and L.W. Welsh,Jr., J.Appl.Polym.Sci. 22, 3397, (1978).
18.	J. Bargon, E. Gipstein and H. Hiraoka, IBM Techn.Disc.Bull. 18, 2622, (1976).
19.	M. Tsuda, Materials Sci.Rep., Vol. 2, (1987), p. 185.
20.	R. Pethrick, Macromolecules 86, Conference on Functional Polymers and Biopolymers, Oxford, UK Sept. 15-19, (1986).
21. a)	F.A. Vollenbroek, W.P.M. Nijssen, C.M.J. Mutsaers, M.J.H.J. Geomini, M.E. Reuhman and R.J. Visser, "The Chemistry of g-Line Photoresist Processes", Polym.Eng.Sci. 29, 928, (1989).
	b)	F.A. Vollenbroek, C.M.J. Mutsaers and W.P.M. Nijssen, "The Chemistry of i-line Photoresist Processes", Polym.Mat. Sci.Eng. 61, 283, (1989).
22.	H. Ito, M. Ueda, R. Schwalm, J.Vac.Sci.Technol., Vol. B6, p. 2259, (1988).
23. a)	K.F. Dössel, H.L. Huber and H. Oertel, Microelectronic Eng. 5, 97, (1986).
	b)	R. Dammel, K.F. Dössel, J. Lingnau, J. Theis, H.L. Huber and H. Oertel, Microelectronic Eng.6, 503, (1987).
	c)	J. Lingnau, R. Dammel and J. Theis, Proc. 8th, Int.Conf. Photopolym., Ellenville 1988.
	d)	F. Bijkerk, G.E. van Dorssen, M.J. van der Wiel, R. Dammel and J. Lingnau, Microelectronic Eng. 9, 121, (1989).
	e)	F. Bijkerk, E. Louis, G.E. van Dorssen, M.J. van der Wiel, Proc. SPIE 1089, 274, (1989).
24.	R. Dammel, K.F. Dössel, J. Lingnau, J. Theis, H.L. Huber, H. Oertel and J. Trube, Microelectronic Eng. 9, 575, (1989).
25.	J. Lingnau, R. Dammel, C.R. Lindley, G. Pawlowski, U. Scheunemann and J. Theis, to be published.
26.	G. Buhr, R. Dammel and C.R. Lindley, Proc. ACS Div., PMSE 61, 269, (1989).
27.	S. Pongratz, R. Demmeler, C. Ehrlich, K. Kohlmann, K. Reimer, R. Dammel, W. Hessemer, J. Lingnau, U. Scheunemann and J. Theis, Proc. SPIE 1089, 303, (1989).
28. a)	J.M.J. Frechet, T.G. Tessier, C.G. Willson and H. Ito, Macromolecules, Vol. 18, p. 317, (1985).
	b)	H. Ito, C.G. Willson and J.M.J. Frechet, EP 0.102.450.
	c)	J.M.J. Frechet, et.al., Polymer Bulletin, Vol. 20, p.427,(1988).
	d)	J.M.J. Frechet, F.M Houlihan, F. Bouchard, B. Kryezka and C.G. Willson, J.Chem.Soc., Chem.Commun., p.1514, (1985).
	e)	F.M. Houlihan, F. Bouchard, J.M.J. Frechet and C.G. Willson, Macromolecules, Vol. 19, p. 13, (1986).
	f)	J.M.J. Frechet, et. al., Polymer.J., Vol. 19, p.31, (1987).
29.	B. Maid, PhD-Thesis, University of Bonn (1989), ISSN 0172-89xx
30.	J. Göttert, Masters Thesis, University of Bonn (1987), ISSN 0172-8741.
31.	D.J. Webb and M. Hatzakis, J.Vac.Sci.Techn. 16, (1979), pp. 2008-2013.
32.	T. Tada, J.Electrochem.Soc. 130 (1983), 912-917.

MICROFABRICATION TECHNOLOGIES APPLIED TO THE FABRICATION OF SOFT X-RAY OPTICAL ELEMENTS FOR SYNCHROTRON RADIATION

C. Khan Malek

Laboratoire de Microstructures et de Microélectronique, 196 Av. H. Ravera, 92 220 Bagneux, France.

1. INTRODUCTION

The availability of bright sources such as dedicated synchrotron, storage rings, and laser generated plasmas along with the need of diagnosing and exploiting their potential, has renewed interest in developing optical elements working in the X-ray range. In reflective optics, the development of layered synthetic microstructures (LSM) based on advances in thin film deposition technology has led to a breakthrough in the X-ray domain[1, 2] It has permitted the fabrication of versatile optical components with a high reflection coefficient and broad spectral capability, large collection angle, stability to high flux and the possibility to work at non grazing incidence. Along with the control of one dimension layering, a growing interest has arisen in tailoring in-the-plane microstructures with the micron or submicron features applying technologies up until recently, exclusively used in the semiconductor industry. The use of microfabrication technologies in X-ray optics has been an active topic of review in the recent years,[3, 4, 5] and improved diffractive optics as well as new optical devices have been designed and manufactured.

An outline of various microfabrication techniques and processes that are relevant to X-ray optics is presented here. Applications to some selected examples are also discussed. Emphasis is placed on both high resolution diffractive components composed of periodic microstructures such as gratings and zone plates and three dimensional reflective diffracting structures. The performances of these components is directly related to the minimum achievable feature size.

Similarities with needs commonly encountered in micro-electronics fabrication are stressed. In general the structure to be fabricated is less complex, requiring a simpler process without multilevel alignments. However, some fabrication sequences are more critical given the need of extremely high positional accuracy of the patterns. The circular geometry for a zone plate can also make fabrication more difficult.

Possible applications of soft X-ray optical components in the field of X-ray lithography have also been envisioned.

2. MICROFABRICATION TECHNOLOGY

2.1. Microfabrication Processes

The manufacture of high resolution optical components involves several stages; first the generation of a high resolution pattern, second its transfer to the substrate.[6, 7, 8, 9, 10] It requires:

-- a lithographic tool capable of writing with very high resolution.[11] Electron beam lithography is the most developed and versatile technique for high pattern generation presently available, but X-ray, holographic and ion beam lithographies can also be used for some applications.

-- a recording medium with very high resolution capability. Polymer resists are the most extensively used.

-- a suitable (additive or substractive) transfer process that permits one to transfer the features of the structure from the resist to the substrate without loss of resolution.

Specific processes are often dictated by the materials and geometry of the structure to be fabricated. When the feature sizes are decreased (below 100 nm), some problems become more acute (effect of the substrate and geometry on the pattern quality, etc.) and some additional problems can occur (loss of interlayer adhesion, etc.).

2.1.1. Transfer processes. A wide range of techniques is available for pattern transfer. Among the additive processes, the lift-off process is commonly used in microfabrication. It consists of evaporating a material on the structures which have been delineated in the resist by some lithographic technique. It requires the formation of undercut resist profiles, so that the unwanted evaporated material over the resist can easily be removed by simply dissolving the underlying resist. The lift-off is often used to deposit a metallic intermediate mask to increase the steepness of the walls during an etching process or to form thin metallic structures.

The plating process uses a resist (simple or multilayer scheme) stencil as a mould, placing metal only where there are openings in the stencil. The resolution and wall profile depend on the stencil quality and anisotropic pattern transfer with high aspect ratio has proved succesful (30-50 nm linewidths[12, 13, 14]). However, only few materials (Au, Ni, Ag, Cu, etc.) can be deposited by this technique. Thickness uniformity can be difficult to obtain when plating simultaneously large and very small areas. In addition, defect control is also more difficult than with a dry substractive method that takes place in vacuum. However, electroplating permits the fabrication of microstructures with a higher resolution and aspect ratio than with present dry etching techniques.

In a substractive process, the material to be structured is applied first to the substrate. Then a resist layer (simple or multilayer scheme) is applied and patterned. Vacuum evaporation, sputtering, and C.V.D. are readily available for the deposition of low–defect films. Material can then be removed from unwanted areas by etching through the opened areas. While wet chemical anisotropic etching of silicon is used in the fabrication of thin membranes that support some diffractive elements working in transmission, in high resolution usually only dry etching methods are used because of their ease of control, their cleanliness and their versatility. In particular reactive ion etching (R.I.E.), which combines both chemical etching (formation of a volatile compound) and physical sputtering, is widely used. It permits both selective and directional etching that can result in very steep–walled structures. Simple mechanical sputtering (ion beam etching) can be used if the aspect ratio is small but it leads to tapered profiles due to redeposition and faceting. The precise control of etching parameters during the transfer process, in order to avoid linewidth alteration of the patterns, such as side-etching in R.I.E., is critical for dry methods.[15]

A high aspect ratio (maximum thickness over minimum feature size up to 5 or 10 in some applications) is needed for some applications. For example, fabrication of transmitting optical elements for shorter wavelengths necessitates thick absorbing metal layers for the opaque areas. Multilayer resist schemes have been developed in order to separate the imaging and masking functions of the resist material. The exposure is carried out in a thin top layer of resist separated from the substrate by a thick layer material (usually a polymer). This increases the process latitude with regards to the use of a single resist layer and enhances the resolution limits of the lithographic process.

2.1.2. Stress Consideration. In all high–resolution applications, the finer the pattern features and the higher the aspect ratio of the microstructures, the more important the influence of stress in the structured layer becomes. This stress needs to be controlled to avoid distorsions in the pattern structure, especially in self-supporting transmitting optical devices like Fresnel zone plates and diffraction gratings. The X-ray absorption coefficients of gold, tungsten, and tantalum over a large wavelength range are very similar and make all three metals suitable as absorbing materials in transmitting diffractive optics based on spatial intensity modulation. However, stress in refractory metals like W or Ta can be very high if deposition conditions are not very finely controlled. Ductile and low melting point metals such as gold have much lower stress values. However, gold cannot be structured by R.I.E. due to its chemical stability, and its mechanical properties are inferior to those of tantalum and tungsten.

2.2. Lithographic Tools

The various types of lithography that can achieve submicronic pattern capability can be divided into several groups:
-- those that use pattern transfer with parallel exposure through a mask (optical and X-ray lithographies, electron and ion projection printing).
-- those that permit direct pattern generation by a serial process (focused electron or ion beam writing, laser beam writing, X-ray microprobe, scanning tunneling microscopy)
-- holographic techniques that do not use a mask, yet permit parallel exposure.
A direct writing technique is slow but offers more flexibility by permitting the specifications of the optical devices to be easily changed by computer program modifications. It is used in pattern delineation of the mask for other lithographies.
The advantages of two lithographic techniques can also be combined to reduce some process constraints, enhance process latitude, and performances of the devices. For example, one can use electron beam lithography to define the master mask and use X-ray lithography to make a replica with a better contrast, or spatial division techniques to make finer period structures than that of the parent mask.

The need of smaller features has led to the extension of high-resolution lithography technology, nanolithography which brings additional problems and new concepts.[16]

2.2.1. Electron beam lithography. The scanning electron beam method is by far the most widely used and highest-resolution method for direct write and mask making. Electron beam lithography is normally carried out at accelerating voltages between 10 and 50 kV with vector scan systems using Gaussian electron beam. The minimum diameter of the finely focused electron beam varies from some number of nanometers to some tenth of nanometers. S.E.M,, T.E.M. or S.T.E.M. can deliver smaller probe size but were not designed as lithographic tools, so they offer less flexibility than standard pattern generators. They have severe limitations in field size, in alignment capability, in defining complex patterns, and the exposure times are longer. Their mechanical and electrical stabilities are also critical. In most applications, the attainable resolution is not limited by the minimum size of the focused electron beam. Resolution is limited mainly by the proximity effects created by the forward-scattering of the primary electrons in the resist and especially their backscattering from the substrate. This can result in partial exposure of the resist up to several microns from the point of impact. Corrections for these effects can be applied. The smaller the features to be patterned, the more stringent the correction requirements. The use of a multilayer system with a thin recording resist layer on top permits the limitation of forward scattering effects. The thick spacer layer attenuates exposure by backscattered electrons from the substrate. The use of high energy beams results in a decrease of the electron beam size and a reduction of electron scattering, but at the expense of increased difficulty in deflecting the beam and lower resist sensitivity. Patterning on thin substrates or membranes, when possible, also permits to minimize backscattering from the substrate and to improve the contrast. Metal nanostructures with dimensions smaller than 10 nm were patterned with an accelerating voltage of 350 KV in 50 nm thick positive-tone polymethylmetacrylate (PMMA) electron–sensitive resist.[17] Instead of patterning polymer resists, electron beams can also be used to polymerize residual hydrocarbons present in the vacuum chamber and build up carbon features with extremely high resolution capability (5 nm metal lines obtained by that technique).[18] Negative contamination resist has been used to fabricate optical diffractive components.[19] However, both PMMA and contamination resist exhibit a very low sensitivity. The sensitivity of conventional high resolution resists is limited and new schemes based on chemical amplification with a catalyst have been developed. For very high resolution applications, inorganic materials and Langmuir-Blodgett films have also aroused interest. Direct electron beam etching techniques without a development step are also under investigation (in-situ vaporization of NaCl, LiF, etc., by the electron beam), but the exposure time is much longer than with conventional processes. Hence, the drift of the writing system is more important.

Some applications in the fabrication of diffracting optical elements have more demanding requirements than can be offered with a standard electron beam exposure system, for example those requiring a high degree of positional accuracy. In the case of zone plates composed of alternately transparent and opaque rings of decreasing width, it is necessary that the pattern features be placed within a fraction of the thinnest zone in order to preserve spatial phase relationship between all the zones of the plate.

The smooth scanning of an electron beam on a circle, an ellipse or an arbitrary geometry is also difficult to obtain in a conventional cartesian coordinate system where the electron beam can only be deflected along two orthogonal directions. Curved lines are then drawn stepwise by overlapping small elemental rectangle or parallelogram shaped structures . Programs have been developed to improve pattern quality and writing speed for those applications,[20, 21] in particular systems with polar coordinates where circular ring segments are used as primitive shape.[22] The fabrication of special relief structures such as sawtooth profile can necessitate a graduation of the dose that might also require special software developments on the electron beam writing system.[23]

Electron beam demagnifying projection[24] has also been used, but the resolution achieved is much lower.

2.2.2. Holographic techniques. Holographic lithography is the preferred technique for defining large area periodic structures with a short exposure time. It is used in the pattern delineation of regularly spaced gratings or Fresnel zone plates. The generation of a periodic structure on a resist-coated sample is made by utilizing the interference pattern between two coherent laser beams. The period of the grating can be varied by changing the angle between the two incident beams but its minimum width is limited by the wavelength of the source. The reflection of the incident beam on the substrate interferes with the incoming beam and creates standing waves orthogonal to the substrate. With thick photoresists, the in-depth modulation results in variation of exposure throughout the resist layer, which manifests itself in ragged lines after development. The use of a multilayer resist scheme permits the exposure of a thin top resist layer which is then followed by the transfer of the pattern to the bottom resist. Grating patterns with a spatial period below 100 nm have been fabricated with this technique.[25] To obtain patterns with a shorter spatial period than normally permitted in the free space while still using U.V. coherent sources, optical techniques have been developed in order to artificially lower the effective wavelength. These include the use of prisms and index matching fluids.[26] The use of non–coherent deep U.V.sources is also developed with various achromatic holographic set-ups.[27,28]

A variant of holographic lithography, spatial period division, uses a mask with a periodic pattern in transmission. It has been developed in the U.V. and X -ray range[29, 30]. The diffraction field from a parent mask of a given spatial period is used to expose higher spatial frequency multiples. It is important to emphasize that it is a replication technique, so that the first mask needs to be generated by some other type of lithography. Its implementation with deep U.V. and X-ray synchrotron radiation would permit one to expose sub-100 nm period gratings and other periodic or quasiperiodic structures. Various schemes to do this have been proposed.[31, 32] However, several problems, among which the lack of a large depth of field, need to be solved.

2.2.3. X-ray lithography.

X-ray lithography is a proximity print scheme by transmission based on a one–to–one shadow technique. It is used as a second step to copy master masks bearing the microstructure defined by another lithographic technique.

As alignment techniques are not needed, soft contact lithography (no gap between mask and resist–coated substrate, at the expense of mask or substrate damage though) or close proximity[33] schemes can be used, which permits the minimization of diffraction problems and increases the resolution. The ultimate resolution of the X-ray exposure process also depends on the energy range of the photoelectrons generated in the resist. A shorter wavelength results in a higher photoelectron energy. Contact X-ray nanolithography has demonstrated minimum 17.5 nm lines and spaces[34], and 10 nm linewidth.[35]

X-ray lithography is known to produce very high aspect ratio profiles because of its large depth of field, its abscence of X-ray scattering and low absorption of x-rays in the resist. The use of X-ray lithography with the replication of master masks as a second step in the fabrication of optical devices permits the variation of overall parameters (thickness, profile, material, etc.) over a much wider range. The process can also be simplified by using a single layer resist.

2.2.4. Ion beam lithography. Another direct writing technique that has undergone much development and is becoming more wide spread because of its high potential is focussed ion beam lithography (FIBL). It allows direct maskless engraving into the substrate and the patterning on curved substrates because of its larger depth of field . It benefits from a much higher resist sensitivity due to the larger cross section between heavier particules and the resist. In addition the background exposure is reduced, which results in negligible proximity effects.

However, due to the larger probe size presently available with focussed ion beams F.I.B.L. has not yet achieved resolutions less than 50 nm.

2.2.5. Photolithography. Conventional photoreduction techniques[36] can be used to produce low-resolution patterns but its limited resolution capability,due to diffraction effects at the mask, restricts its application to coarse structures in the 0.5 - 1 µm range, though the use of excimer laser has pushed the limits further down.[37]

2.3. Non Lithographic Techniques

Several techniques have been developed in order to reduce the linewidth of a patterned microstructure that rely on shadowing techniques and edge techniques.[38, 39] The shadow of an edge leaves a horizontal gap whose width is determined by the thickness of the step and the angle of evaporation. X-ray masks with linewidth below 10 nm have been made by sidewall evaporation[35] with this technique without necessitating high-resolution lithography means. Shadowing techniques were also used to reduce the pattern size in transmission gratings [40] and Fresnel zone plates.[41]

3. EXAMPLES OF MICROFABRICATION PROCESSES APPLIED TO THE MANUFACTURE OF OPTICAL DEVICES

3.1. Transmission Diffraction Devices

A periodic microstructure consisting of periodically alternating materials spatially modulates an X-ray beam with an efficiency that depends on the adequacy of both the spatial periodicity and the material nature and thickness, to the wavelength considered for the experiment. Most transmitting diffractive devices are based on amplitude modulation that depends on the difference in the absorption coefficients (real part of the refractive index) between both the opaque solid features and the transparent or empty ones composing the optical component. Two broad types of transmitting diffractive devices exist :

-- gratings[42, 43, 44] that consist of a distribution of opaque bars and disperse an incident beam into a number of output beams (hence their use as order sorters in monochromator schemes, filters and analyzers in X-ray optics[45]). The dispersion of the orders and the efficiency of the device depend on the spatial period, the thickness of the absorber material and the correct spacing.

-- Fresnel zone plates[46, 47, 48, 14] that have a non-uniform distribution of transparent and opaque zones whose width and separation decrease with increasing distance from the center. Those devices are generally used to focus the incident X-ray beam into a spot (circular or elliptic Fresnel zone plate) or into a line (linear Fresnel zone plate). Circular zone plates are the heart of the optics in X-ray microscopy. Image resolution and contrast are ultimately limited by the width of the smallest zone and the accuracy of the zone placement. Zone plates can also be used as a dispersive element of a monochromator, like a grating.

A number of important parameters relevant to the microfabrication of a zone plate or a grating stand out: The bar/opaque zone-aperture ratio, the bar/opaque zone thickness, the bar/opaque zone thickness profile. The width of the outermost zone of the plate or the periodicity of the grating depends directly on the lithographic tool. It is decisive in the choice of a given process as far as the choice and thickness of the opaque material and the pattern transfer process are concerned. The ability to produce a structure that is thick enough to be fully opaque can be restricted by practical fabrication limitations for high aspect ratio microstructures. Manufacturing inaccuracies and geometrical distorsions (correct spacing, width of line or zone, accuracy of shape, smoothness of the pattern, edge quality, etc.) lead to a reduction in the efficiency of these devices and affect their imaging properties. In particular, placement of the patterns in a zone plate must be accurate to a fraction of the narrowest zone if aberrations are not to limit resolution. The minimum linewith and the total number of lines or zones of the device might favour a particular lithographic technique. The support structure holding together the diffractive system also must be carefully considered. It may itself involve some additional lithographic steps, as in the case of free-standing structures with solid and empty features only supported by struts, rings or bars. A thin light material film (membrane) can also support the device at the expense of a loss of intensity through the transparent zones and thus a reduction in contrast. To minimize distorsion, the pattern structure and the membrane should be made of a high Young's modulus material. Apodized zone plates used as objective lenses in a scanning X-ray microscope require additional thickness in the central zone to block the undiffracted radiation. Single exposure, double development / double plating technique has been used for that purpose.[14]

Circular zone plates are extensively used in X-ray microscopy with wavelengths ranging from 1 to 10 nm. These wavelengths are best suited for high resolution imaging of biological material. For example, with an imaging set-up similar to the one developed by the Gottingen group,[49] two types of zone plates are required. One condenser zone plate collects as much synchrotron radiation as possible and focuses it in the object plane. This plate has a large diameter, therefore a large number of zones (up to several tens of thousands), for which holographic lithography is well adapted to define the pattern structure. The enlarged image of the object is obtained with a second high-resolution zone plate (microzone plate) that requires the narrowest outermost zone width possible to increase the resolution of the plate. Much fewer zones (several hundreds) are needed in order to have sufficient intensity, reducing the area that needs to be patterned. This makes less critical the problems of both pattern distortion during the lithographic step (especially if electron beam lithography is used), and of mechanical stability of the final structure. The smallest zone width which can be fabricated by electron electron beam lithography is on the order of 40-50 nm due to the proximity effect by the scattered electrons. However, in partial transmittion zone plates,[50] where only part of the transparent zones is transparent, the distance between the lines is larger and the proximity effect is reduced. Higher spatial resolution can therefore be achieved, at the expense of lower efficiency.
The production of higher resolution zone plates by spatial-frequency multiplication[51] or demagnification[52] is also being studied.

Both a significant increase in efficiency and contrast (reduction of background light due to the undiffracted zeroth order) can be achieved by using phase-shifting devices[53, 54, 55] based on the difference of the imaginary part of the refractive index between neighbouring layers. All phase-shifting devices are also amplitude modulators because all materials absorb in the X-ray range. However, the nature and thickness of the material can be optimized to have the maximum phase shift and yet the minimum absorption in the opaque layers.

Further improvements in performance can be obtained by appropriately blazing the diffracting microstructure at the expense of optical modeling and fabrication complexity, especially in precision thickness and profile control.

The contrast that can be achieved is an extremely important parameter since the radiation dose required to form the image depends inversely on the contrast. In particular, shorter exposure times are needed to reduce the irradiation dose for live biological samples.

Development of optical elements for X-rays of higher energy, of interest to the plasma diagnostics community, require smaller features and very large aspect ratios (ten or more) to avoid large transmissions through the absorbing zones, resulting in a significant loss of contrast. Those devices cannot be obtained by conventional microfabrication technologies. New techniques are under study such as the sputter-slice technique where alternating layers of transparent and opaque material are sputtered onto a wire core, which is subsequently sliced.[56, 57] Large aspect ratios are readily obtainable with thicker slices. Both amplitude and phase zone plates of sufficient contrast can be manufactured.

Another interest that the synchrotron community shares with that of plasma diagnostics concerns the possibility of tomography and three dimensional imaging . The use of Fresnel zone plates as coded apertures permits low resolution three dimensional imaging of microplasmas[58] With optical elements having a smaller depth of field, tomography of samples is envisioned.

The control and modulation of X-ray beams using Bragg-Fresnel optics (see next paragraph),which is emerging as "X-ray electronics,[59]", with potential applications in space communication, has some common problems (therefore, perhaps common solutions) with the branch of electronics more especially devoted to optical communications and optical information processing (optoelectronics). For example, various kinds of optical elements such as microlenses and microgratings[60, 61, 62] are needed in the infrared range . Electron beam pattern generators for curved geometries have been developed for such purpose.[23, 63, 64] Techniques such as X-ray lithography[65, 66] are also used.

Many critical problems addressed in mask fabrication technology for X-ray lithography,[67] and the methods (materials and processes) used to solve them are also similar to those encountered in X-ray transmission optics. X-ray lithography uses a thin membrane transparent to X-rays that supports an absorbing pattern. Issues such as high-resolution pattern definition, placement accuracy of the absorbing features, and low pattern distortion are also encountered . Good mechanical properties and low stress in the absorbing and support materials are necessary to insure the dimensional stability. High radiation durability is also necessary for optical elements used under thermal loads such as experienced with synchrotron radiation from undulator devices or intense plasmas. Metrology and repair of the masks are of paramount importance in X-ray lithography. It is possible that some of the tools developed in semiconductor environment will be applied to microoptics.

3.2. Reflective Optics

3.2.1. Bragg-Fresnel optics.
New types of three dimensional optical elements are developed based on the Bragg-Fresnel optics.[68, 69, 70, 59] The combination of both the volume Bragg diffraction and the in-plane Fresnel optics results in selective properties in space and energy. In particular, new focusing elements, such as three dimensional zone plates, have been manufactured, exhibiting better diffraction efficiency and resolution, and a wider spectral range with a larger aperture. Silicon crystals and multilayers[71, 72, 73, 74, 75, 76, 77] are structured and used in reflection for the 0.4-2 nm and 2.0-40 nm regions, respectively. Another definite advantage of using multilayer mirror-based structures is their larger resistance to thermal loads and mechanical deformations. The volume diffraction of x-ray radiation also permits one to modulate and steer the X-ray beams by external means (electrical field, ultrasounds, etc.) both in amplitude or phase. This opens up a very wide scope of applications, in particular in optical communications and in microelectronics with direct writing or diagnosing with X-rays.

3.3. X-ray lithography.

Alternative lithographic systems to the conventional X-ray lithography by transmission are being sought. The need of thin films and the one to one replication mode which necessitates accurate pattern formation make both the mask technology and handling critical. X-ray lithography by reflection[78, 79, 80, 81] offers some advantages over a proximity print scheme by transmission, especially if the possibility of demagnification is used. The patterns are written on a thick   hard substrate. In this case the difference in reflectivity between the patterns and the substrate is used to replicate the structures. Several methods have been proposed to make the pattern plates, either by using the difference of critical angle of total reflection between the pattern material[82] and the substrate material, or by engraving multilayer mirrors to lower the reflectivity in the patterned areas.[81] The focussing system needs to permit the imaging of a field that is large and free of aberrations.

Another approach, derived from the advances in scanning X-ray microscopy, is the possibility of direct writing with X-ray probes focused by Fresnel zone plates.[16] In particular, this would permit the use of the high potential of X-rays, especially the high aspect ratio and high resolution capability, while having the flexibility of a direct write method.

4. CONCLUSION

The most commonly used techniques to manufacture optical components working in the X-ray range have been reviewed, with selected examples discussed. It is clear that progress in this field depends heavily on advances in materials science and microfabrication technology, driven by the highly competitive semiconductor industry. However, along with the necessity of interdisciplinary research and technology transfer, its specific needs necessitate further new developments in microfabrication and conception of new devices.

Advances in X-ray micro-optics have led to the development or renewal of a broad range of applications in various fields of science (biology, materials science (surface and interface), X-ray optics, plasma physics, astrophysics, micro-electronics, etc.) and techniques (microanalysis (EXAFS, photoemission, fluorescence, etc.), X-ray microscopy, X-ray imaging (holography, tomography, etc.), interferometry, spectroscopy, photonics, X-ray instrumentation, X-ray lithography, metrology, etc.). The activities in microfabrication technology applied to optical elements are expected to increase in the coming years for both technology and science applications.

5. REFERENCES

1Dhez, D., "Soft X-Ray Optics and Technology," SPIE 773, 308 (1986).
2Underwood, J. H and Atwood , D.T., "The Renaissance of X-ray Optics", Physics Today April, 44 (1984)
3.Ceglio , N.M, "The Impact of Microfabrication Technology on X-ray Optics" Proc. Am. Phys. Soc. Top. Conf. on Low Energy X-ray Diagnostics, Monterey, 210 (Aug. 1980). Ceglio , N.M.,"Recent advances in X-ray Optics" X-ray Microscopy, G. Schmahl and D. Rudolph Eds. Springer Series in Optical Science 43, 97 (1984). Ceglio, N. M., "Revolution in X-ray optics"J. X-Ray Science and Technology 1, 7(1989).
4Smith, H.I., Anderson, E.H., Hawryluk, A.M , and Schattenburg, M.L., "Planar Techniques for Fabricating X-ray diffraction Gratings and Zone Plates " in X-ray Microscopy, G. Schmahl and D. Rudolph Eds. , Springer Series in Optical Science 43, 51 (1984).
5 Michette, A. G., "Optical systems for Soft X-ray" Plenum Press, N.Y. : p.147 : Design and Manufacture of X-ray diffraction gratings ; Manufacture of Zone Plates : p 217 (1986).
6Mackie, S. and Beaumont, S. P., "Materials and Processes for Nanometer Lithography," Solid State Technology Aug., 117 (1985).
7Hatzakis, M., "Materials and Processes for Microstructure Fabrication," I.B.M. J. Res. Develop., 32 (4), 441 (July 1988)
8Walaurmont, M., "Status of Microstructure fabrication," S.P.I.E. 316, 109 (1981).
9Howard, R. E.and Prober, D. E., "Nanometer Scale fAbrication Techniques, VLSI Electronics Microstructure Science," Einspruch, N. G., Ed. 5, 146 (1981).
10Flanders, D. C., "Nanometer structure and device fabrication," Microcircuit Engineering 2, 1-3, 82 (1984).
11Smith, H. I., "A review of submicron lithography," Superlattices and Microstructures, 2, 2, 129 (1986).
12 Kratschmer, E., Erko, A., Petrashov, V. T., and Beneking, H., "Device fabrication by nanolithography and electroplating for magnetic flux quantization measurements," Appl. Phys. Lett. 44(10), 1011 (1984).
13)Anderson, E. H., Kern, D. P., and Smith, H. I., "Fabrication by Tri-Level Electron Beam Lithography of X-Ray Masks with 50 nm Linewidths, and Replication by X-Ray Nanolithography," Microcircuit Engineering 6, 541 (1987).
14Kern, D., Coane, P., Acosta, R., Chang, T. H. P., Feder, R., Houzego, P., Molzen, W., Powers, J., Speth, A., and Viswanathan, R., "Electron Beam Fabrication and Characterization of Fresnel Zone Plates for Soft X-Ray Microscopy," SPIE 447, 204 (1984). Vladimirsky, Y., Kern, Chang, T. H. P., Atwood, D., Ade, H., Kirz, J. McNulty, I., Rarback, H., and Shu, D., High-resolution Fresnel zone plates for soft x rays, J. Vac. Sci. Technol. B6(6), 311 (1988). Vladimirsky, Y., Kern, D. P., Meyer-Isle, W., Greinke, B., Guttmann, P., Rishton, S.A., and Atwood, D., "Soft X-ray

184

lenses with outer zone width for nanostructure imaging," Microcircuit Engineering 9, 87 (1989). .

15Pilz, W., Hubner, H., Heinrich, F., Hoffmann, P., and Franosch, M., Microcircuit Enginneering 9, 491 (1989).

16Chang, T. H. P., Kern, D. P., Kratschmer, E., Lee, K. Y., Luhn, H. E., McCord, M. A., Rishton, S. A., and Vladimirsky, Y., "Nanostructure technology," IBM J. Res. Develop. 32, 4, 462 (1988)

17Broers, A. N.and Timbs, A. E., "Nanolithography at 350 KV in a TEM," Microcircuit Engineering 9, 187 (1989).

18Broers, A. N., "Electron Beam Fabrication of 80 Å Metal Structures," Appl. Phys. Lett. 29, 596 (1976).

19Buckley, C. J., Browne, M. T., and Charalambous, P., "Contamination Lithography for the Fabrication of Zone Plate X-Ray Lenses," SPIE 447, 213 (1985).

20Aristov, V., Babin, S. V., Davydov, A. V., Erko, A. I., Svintsov, A. A., and Redkin, S. V., "Precise lithography for component integral optics of nanometer range," Microcircuit Engineering 6, 129 (1987).

21 Klein, U.and Gotz, F., "Definition of geometries with complicated, curved boundaries for electron beam pattern generation," Microelectronic Engineering 9, 495 (1989).

22Kern, D. P., Coane, P.J., Houzego, P.J., and T.H.P.Chang, "Practical Aspects in Microfabrication in the 100 nm Regime," Solid State Technology Feb., 217 (1984).

23Shiono, T., Setsune, K., Yamazaki, O., and Wasa, K., "Computer-controlled electron-beam writing system for thin film micro-optics," J. Vac. Sci. Technol. B5(1), 33 (1987).

24Koops, H. W. P. and Grob, J., "Submicron Lithography by Demagnifying Electron-Beam Projection," X-ray Microscopy, G. Schmahl and D. Rudolph Eds. Springer Series in Optical Science 43, 119 (1984).

25Anderson, E.H., Horwitz, C.M., and Smith, H.I., "Holographic Lithography with Thick Photoresist," Appl. Phys. Lett. 43(9), 874.(1983).

26Shank, C.V. and Schmidt, R.V., "Optical Technique for Producing 0.1 μm periodic surface structures," J. Appl. Phys. Lett. 23(3), 154 (1973).

27Anderson, E. K., Komatsu, K,and Smith, H.I., "Achromatic holographic lithography in the deep ultraviolet,"J. Vac. Sci. Technol. B6(1), 216 (1988).

28Yen, A., Ghanbari, R. A., Anderson, E. H., and Smith, H. I., "Fabrication of 100 nm-period gratings using achromatic holographic lithography," to appear in Proc. Microcircuit Engineering , Cambrige, Sept. 1989

29Flanders, D.C., Hawryluk, A.M., and Smith, H.I., "Spatial period division - A new technique for exposing submicrometer-linewidth periodic and quasiperiodic patterns," J. Vac. Sci. Technol. 16(6),1949 (1979).

30Hawryluk, A. M., Smith, H. I., Osgood, R. M., and Ehrlich, D. J., "Deep-ultraviolet spatial-period division using an excimer laser," Opt. Lett. 7(9), 402 (1982).

31Hawryluk, A.M., Smith, H.I., and Ehrlich, D. J.,"Deep-U.V. spatial -frequency doubling by combining multilayer mirrors with diffraction gratings," J. Vac. Sci. Technol. B1(4),1200 (1983)

32Csonka, P.L., "Holographic X-ray Gratings Generated with Synchrotron Radiation," J. Appl. Phys. 52(4), 2692 (1981).

33 Schattenburg, M.L., Tanaka, I., and Smith, H.I. , "Microgap X-ray Nanolithography," Microcircuit Eng. 6, 273 (1987).

34Flanders, D. C., "Replication of 175-Å lines and spaces in polymethylmethacrylate using x-ray lithography," Appl. Phys. Lett. 36, 93 (1980).

35Flanders, D.C.,"X-ray lithography at = 100Å linewidths using x-ray masks fabricated by shadowing techniques," Vac. Sci. Technol. 16(6), 1615 (1979).

36Tatsumi, K., Saheki, T., and Nukui, K., "High-Performance Micro-Fresnel Lens Fabricated by UV Lihography," Appl. Opt. 23(11), 1742 (1984).

37Kodate, K., Kamiyama, T., Okada, Y., and Takenaka, H., "Focusing Characteristics of High-Efficiency Fresnel Zone Plate Fabricated By Deep Ultraviolet Lithography," Jap. J. Appl. Phys. 25(2), 223 (1986).

38 Flanders, D.C. and White, A.E., "Applications of = 100 Å linewidth structures fabricated by shadowing techniques," J. Vac. Sci. Technol.19(4), 892 (1981).

39Flanders, D. C. and Efremov, N. N., "Generation of 50 nm period gratings using edge defined techniques," J. Vac. Sci. Technol. B1(4), 1105 (1983).

40Michette, A. G., Fill., Taguchi, T., and Kuhne, M., "High-resolution transmission gratings for use in the spectroscopy of laser-produced plasmas," to appear in Proc. Int. Congress on Opt. Science and Engineering, Paris, France (April 1989).

41Buckley, C. J., , Browne, Burge, R. E., Charalambous, P., Ogawa, K., and Takeyoshi, T., "Zone Plates for Scanning X-Ray Microscopy: Contamination Writing and Efficiency Enhancement," X-Ray Microscopy II, Springer Verlag, Sayre, D, Howells, M, Kirz, J, and Rarback, H. Eds. 56, 88 (1988).

42Hawryluk, A. M., Ceglio, N. M., Price, R. H., Melngailis, J., and Smith, H. I., "Gold transmission gratings with submicrometer periods and thicknesses >0.5 μm," J. Vac. Sci. Technol. 19(4), 897 (1981)

43Dr. J. Heidenhain GmbH, Germany.

44Vladimirsky, Y., Kallne, E., and Spiller, E., "Fabrication of free-standing x-ray transmission gratings and zone plates," SPIE 448, 25 (1984).

45Kallne, E., Tatchyn, R. O., Csonska, P. L., and Lindau, I., "Apllications of transmission X-ray optics," Nucl. Instr. Meth. Phys. Res. A246, 327 (1986).

46 Shaver, D.C., Flanders, D.C., Ceglio, N.M., and Smith, H. I. , "X-Ray Zone Plates Fabricated using electron-beam and X-ray lithography,"J. Vac. Sci. Technol. 16(6), 1626 (1979).

47Schmahl, G., Rudolph, D., Guttmann, P., and Christ, O., "Zone Plates for X-Ray Microscopy", X-ray Microscopy II, Springer Verlag, Sayre, D, Howells, M, Kirz, J , and Rarback, H. Eds. 56, 63 (1988). Bogli, V., Unger, P., Beneking, H., Greinke, B., Guttmann, P., Niemann, B., Rudolph, D., and Schmahl, G., "Microzone Plate Fabrication by 100 keV Electron Beam Lithography," X-ray Microscopy II, Springer Verlag, Sayre, D, Howells, M, Kirz, J , and Rarback, H. Eds. 56, 80 (1988).

48Sekimoto, M., Ozawa, A., Okhubo, T.,Yoshihara, H., Kakuchi, M., and Tamamura, T., "X-Ray Zone Plate with Tantalum film for an X-Ray Microscope," X-ray Microscopy II, Springer Verlag, Sayre, D, Howells, M, Kirz, J, and Rarback, H. Eds. 56, 178 (1988).

49Rudolph, D., Niemann, B., Schmahl, and Christ, O., "The Gottingen X-Ray Microscope, and X-Ray Microscopy Experiments at the BESSY Storage Ring," in X-ray Microscopy, G. Schmahl and D. Rudolph Eds. , Springer Series in Optical Science 43, 192 (1984)

50Aritome, H. and Namba, S., "Fabrication of x-ray optical elements by electron beam lithography," SPIE 773, 55 (1986).

51Yun, W. B. and Howels, M. R., "Experimental Demonstration of Producing high Resolution Zone Plate by Spatial Frequency Multiplication," X-ray Microscopy II, Springer Verlag, Sayre, D, Howells, M, Kirz, J, Rarback, H. Eds. 56, 182 (1988).

52Burge, R. E., Browne, M. T., and Charalambous, P., "An X-Ray Projection Method Using Zone Plates for Mask Preparation with Sub-Micron Size," Microelectronic Engineering 6, 227 (1989).

53Kirz, J., "Phase Zone Plates for X-rays and the Extreme U.V.,"J. Opt. Soc. Am. 64, 3, 301 (1974)

54Ceglio, N.M., "X-ray Phase Lens Design and Fabrication," J. Vac. Sci. Technol.

186

B1(4), 1285 (1983).

55Hilkenbach, R., Thieme,J., Guttmann, P., and Niemann, B, "Phase Zone Plates for the Gottingen X-ray Microscopes," X-ray Microscopy II, Springer Verlag, Sayre, D, Howells, M, Kirz, J, Rarback, H. Eds. 56, 95 (1988).

56Bionta, R.M., Jankowski, A.F., and Makowiecki, D.M., "Sputtered Sliced linear zone plate for the 8 KeV X-ray," X-Ray Microscopy II, Springer Verlag, Sayre, D, Howells, M, Kirz, J and Rarback, H. Eds. 56, 142 (1988).

57Saitoh, K., Inagawa, K., Kohra, K., Hayashi, C., Iida, A., and Kato, N., "Characterization of sliced multilayer zone plates for hard x rays," Rev. Sci. Instrum. 60 (7), 1519 (1989).

58Ceglio, N. M., Stone, G. F., and Hawryluk, A. M., "Microstructures for high-energy x-ray and particle imaging applications," J. Vac. Sci. Technol. 19(4), 886 (1981).

59Erko, A. I., "Synthesized Bragg-Fresnel Multilayer Optics," to appear in J. X-Ray Science and Technology

60Fujita, T., Nishihara, H., and Koyama, J., "Fabrication of micro lenses using electron-beam lithography," Opt. Lett. 6 (12), 613 (1981). Fujita, T., Nishihara, H., Koyama, "Blazed gratings and Fresnel lenses fabricated by electron-beam lithography," Opt. Lett. 7 (12), 578 (1982).

61Shiono, T., Setsune, K., Yamazaki, O., and Wasa, K., "Rectangular-Apertured Micro-Fresnel Lens Arrays Fabricated by Electron-Beam Lithography," Appl. Opt. 26, 587 (1987).

62Shiono, T., Setsune, K., Yamazaki, O., and Wasa, K., "Rectangular-apertured micro-Fresnel lens arrays fabricated by electron-beam lithography," Appl. Opt. 26(3), 587 (1987).

63Campbell, N. J.and Nixon, W. C., "Electron beam lithography for integrated optical elements,", Microcircuit Engineering 83, 75 (1983).

64Ohki, H., Nakazawa, H., Kosaka, Y., Sato, H., Asari, T., and Isobe, M., "Fabrication of fine and smooth curved features by e-beam lithography system," Microelectronic Engineering 6, 207 (1987).

65Nishida, T., Nakao, M., Tamamura, T., Ozawa, A., Saito, Y., Nishimura, K., and Yoshihara, H., "Synchrotron Radiation Lithography for DFB Laser Grating," Jap. J. Appl. Phys. 28 (11), 2333 (1989).

66Kodate, K., Okada, Y., and Kamiya, T., "A Blazed Grating Fabricated by Synchrotron Radiation Lithography," Jap. J. Appl. Phys. 25 (10), L822 (1986).

67Shimkunas, A.R., "Advances in X-ray Mask Technology," Solid State Technol. Sept., 192 (1984).

68Aristov,V.V., Erko, A.I., and Martynov,V.V., "Principles of Bragg-Fresnel multilayer optics," Revue Phys. Appl. 23, 1623 (1988).

69Aristov, V.V., "Bragg-Fresnel Optics : Principles and Prospects of Applications," X-Ray Microscopy II, Springer Verlag, Sayre, D, Howells, M, Kirz, J, and Rarback, H. Eds. 56, 108 (1988).

70Barbee, T. W. Jr., "Combined microstructure x-ray optics," Rev. Sci. Instrum. 60 (7), 1588 (1989).

71Aristov, V. V. et al. "Focussing properties of shaped multilayer x-ray mirrors," JETP Lett. 44 (4), 265 (1986).

72 Aristov, V.V., Erko, A.I., Panchencko, L.A , Martynov, V.V., Redkin, S.V., and Sazanova, G.D., "Zone Plates for the Nanometer Wavelenghth Range,"X-Ray Microscopy II, Springer Verlag, Sayre, D, Howells, M, Kirz, J, and Rarback, H. Eds. 56, 138 (1988)

73Aristov, V. V., Basov, Y. A., and Snigirev, A. A., "Synchrotron radiation focusing by Bragg-Fresnel lens," Rev. Sci. Instrum., 60 (7), 1517 (1989).

74Utsumi, Y., Takahashi, J., and Urisu, T., "Soft x-ray W/Be multilayer and its

application to a diffraction grating," Rev. Sci. Instrum. 60 (7), 2024 (1989).
75Rife, J. C., Hunter, W. R., Barbee, T. W.Jr., and Cruddace, R. G., "Multilayer-coated blazed grating performance in the soft x-ray region," Appl. Opt. 28(15), 2984
(1989). Barbee, T. W. Jr., Rife, J. C., and Pianetta, P., "Multilayer Diffraction Gratings: Application to Synchrotron Radiation Instrumentation," SPIE 1160, 636 (1989).
76Berrouane, H., Andre, J. M., Khan Malek, C., Fouchet, S., Ladan, F. R., Rivoira, and R. Barchewitz, R., "Fabrication and test of soft X-ray multilayer diffraction gratings," To appear SPIE 1160 (1989).
77Ross, T. S., Perkins, R. T., and Knight, L. V., "A Liftoff Process for Multilayer Gratings," SPIE 1160, 655 (1989).
78Hawryluk, A.M.and Seppala,L. G., "Soft x-ray projection lithography using an x-ray reduction camera," J. Vac. Sci. Technol. B6(6), 2162(1988)
79Hoh, K.and Tanino, H., "Feasibility Study on the Extreme UV/Soft X-Ray Projection-type Lithography," Bulletin Electrotechnical Lab. 49 (12), 983 (1985).
80Matsumura, H., "Theoretical Consideration on New Type X-Ray Lithography," Extended Abst. 18th Conf. Solid State Devices and Materials, Tokyo, 17 (1986).
81Cerrina, F., "X-ray Imaging with Synchrotron Radiation," J. Imaging Science 30, 2, 80 (1986).
82Matsumura, H.and Tanaka, T., "A New X-Ray Lithography Technique Using Total Reflection of X-Rays from a Pattern Plate," Jap. J. Appl. Phys.,26 (3), 487 (1987) .

APPLICATIONS OF FREE-ELECTRON LASERS

Abraham C.-L. Chian

Institute for Space Research - INPE

P.O. Box 515, São José dos Campos-SP 12201, Brazil

ABSTRACT

Free-electron lasers are tunable sources of coherent radiation from mm to UV wavelengths. Potential applications of free-electron lasers in magnetic and inertial confinement fusion, particle accelerators, energy transmission in space, and cosmic radiation are discussed. Saturation processes such as wavebreaking, particle trapping, and pump depletion that may determine the efficiency of free-electron lasers are reviewed.

1. INTRODUCTION

Free-electron lasers (FEL) are tunable sources of high-power coherent radiation, from millimeter to ultraviolet wavelengths, resulting from the interaction of a relativistic electron beam with a transverse periodic magnetic wiggler or an electromagnetic wave. The operation of free-electron lasers is based on the stimulated scattering process. The interesting feature of the interaction of electromagnetic wave with a relativistic reflector was first noted by Einstein[1]. The stimulated scattering of photons by an electron ensemble was predicted by Kapitza and Dirac[2]. The first analytical analysis of radiation amplification from an electron beam propagating through a magnetic wiggler was made by Motz[3].

The first experiment on stimulated emission with an electron beam-wiggler configuration was performed by Phillips[4]. His device, called "Ubitron", generated kilowatts of microwave radiation by using a weakly relativistic electron beam of 150 keV.

The first relativistic stimulated-scattering experiment was carried out at Stanford-USA in 1976 by Elias et al.[5] by utilizing a low-current electron beam in a R.F. linear accelerator($I=70$ mA, $V=24$ MV) to obtain 7% amplification of a CO_2 laser at 10.6 μm with a helical magnetic field of 2.4 KG and period of 3.2 cm. In 1977, the first FEL in the oscillator mode was achieved by Deacon et al.[6] at Stanford, obtaining a peak power of 7 KW at 3.4 μm by using a more intense and higher energy electron beam($I=2.6$ A, $V=43$ MeV).

Since the successful operation of the first FEL at Stanford, a large number of FEL experiments have been carried out in numerous laboratories throughout the world using a variety of electron beams produced by RF linacs, storage rings, microtrons, pulse-line-generated beams, electrostatic accelerators, and induction linacs[7-14].

The first FEL using storage ring, which is usually attached to a synchrotron-radiation project, was operated at Orsay-France by Billardon et al.[15]. The storage ring operated at energies of 160-244 MeV and currents of 16-100 mA with a lifetime of 60-90 min. The FEL oscillator produced radiation at a visible wavelength $\lambda \approx 6500$ Å. Recently, a storage ring FEL at Novosibirsk-U.S.S.R. achieved[14] lasing over the wavelength range $\lambda \approx 1000 - 5000$ Å.

In this paper, some relevant aspects of FEL research are briefly reviewed. In Section 2, the basic concepts of free-electron lasers are discussed. In Section 3, some nonlinear mechanisms that can lead to saturation of free-electron lasers are considered. In Section 4, some potential applications of free-electron lasers are mentioned. In Section 5, a conclusion is given.

2. BASIC CONCEPTS OF FREE-ELECTRON LASERS

Free-electron lasers can operate in three distinct regimes depending upon the nature of the electron-beam source[7-14]. In the Raman regime, the pump wavelength in the electron beam frame is much greater than the Debye wavelength λ_D, where $\lambda_D = (\varepsilon_o K T_e / n_o e^2)^{1/2}$; in this regime, the interaction is dominated by collective space-charge effects and wave-

wave processes. In the low-gain Compton regime, the pump wavelength in the electron beam frame is comparable to or smaller than the Debye wavelength; in this regime, the scattering is primarily off single particles and the interaction is dominated by kinetic wave-particle processes. In the high-gain Compton regime, both features of Raman and low-gain Compton regimes are present.

Consider the backscattering of an electromagnetic wave from a relativistic electron beam. By the theory of special relativity, the frequency of the scattered electromagnetic wave ω_s is related to the frequency of the incident electromagnetic wave ω_o by the double Doppler shift formula[11].

$$\omega_s \simeq 4\gamma_b^2\omega_o \qquad , \qquad (1)$$

where $\gamma_b = (1-v_b^2/c^2)^{-1/2}$ and v_b= electron beam speed. Moreover, the energy of the scattered wave W_s is related to the energy of the incident wave W_o by the Manley-Rowe relation, $W_s/W_o = \omega_s/\omega_o$, thus

$$W_s \simeq 4\gamma_b^2 W_o \qquad . \qquad (2)$$

Equations (1) and (2) show that both frequency up-conversion and energy amplification take place when an electromagnetic wave is backscattered from a relativistic electron beam. This double Doppler effect is a fundamental feature of FEL. In the static wiggler case $(\omega_o=0)$, (1) is replaced by a formula in terms of the wavelengths

$$\lambda_s \simeq \lambda_o /2\gamma_b^2 \qquad . \qquad (3)$$

Equations (1) and (3) show that the frequency of the scattered radiation is tunable by varying the electron beam energy (γ_b) or the wiggler frequency/period (ω_o/λ_o).

At the point of injection of FEL, the electrons are randomly phased and radiate incoherently, producing spontaneous bremsstrahlung radiation. In the interaction region of FEL, the ponderomotive force resulting from the beating of the wiggler and radiation fields bunches the electrons and produces coherent radiation. The ponderomotive force is the averaged force due to the radiation pressure of a spatially varying electromagnetic field. For example, in the beating field of two traveling waves $\vec{E}=\vec{E}_1 \exp i(\vec{k}_1 . \vec{r} - \omega_1 t) + \vec{E}_2 \exp i(\vec{k}_2 . \vec{r} - \omega_2 t)$, with $|\omega_1 - \omega_2| \ll \omega_{1,2}$, the force averaged over the periods of the partial oscillations acting on an electron is[16].

$$\vec{F}_p = - \frac{e^2}{2m_e \omega_1 \omega_2} \vec{\nabla} <\vec{E}_1 . \vec{E}_2^*> \qquad , \qquad (4)$$

with the associated ponderomotive potential

$$\phi_p = \frac{e^2 E_1 E_2^*}{2m_e \omega_1 \omega_2} e^{i (\vec{k}.\vec{r} - \omega t)} \qquad , \qquad (5)$$

where $\omega = \omega_1 - \omega_2$ and $\vec{k} = \vec{k}_1 - \vec{k}_2$. The ponderomotive force drives a longitudinal ponderomotive wave which causes the axial bunching of beam electrons in the beam direction by decelerating some and accelerating others depending on their initial phase.

When FEL operates in a regime where the effects of electron space-charge are important, the amplification of radiation occurs if ω and $\vec{k}$ of the ponderomotive potential wave satisfy the dispersion relation of beam space-charge waves. Through this resonant interaction of three waves the kinetic energy of electron beam is fed into the wave fields, leading to the growth of radiation. The linear dispersion relations of space-charge waves in a relativistic electron beam is given by $\omega - v_b k = \pm \omega_p/\gamma_b^{3/2}$, which can be obtained from a Lorentz transformation of the frequency of Langmuir oscillations in a stationary plasma[17]. It follows that the wave energy density for beam space-charge waves is proportional to $\omega/(\omega-v_b k)^3$ [18,19]. Hence, for the negative-energy(or slow) mode

$$\omega - v_b k = \mp \; \omega_p/\gamma_b^{3/2} \qquad , \qquad (6)$$

where the minus(plus) signs refer to $\omega > 0 (\omega < 0)$, and for the positive-energy(or fast) mode

$$\omega - v_b k = \pm \; \omega_p/\gamma_b^{3/2} \qquad , \qquad (7)$$

where plus (minus) refer to $\omega > 0$ ($\omega < 0$). In a conventional FEL, the interaction is usually attributed to the coupling between the positive-energy electromagnetic wave and the negative-energy space-charge wave. Note, however, that the positive-energy space-charge wave traveling in the counter direction to the electron beam can also give rise to down-conversion FEL instabilities [19, 20].

3. SATURATION MECHANISMS OF FREE-ELECTRON LASERS

The efficiency of a free-electron laser is defined as the ratio of the electromagnetic radiation energy generated to the sum of the wiggler energy and electron beam energy. The FEL efficiency depends on the nonlinear saturation mechanisms. Three saturation processes will be considered:(i) wavebreaking, (ii) particle trapping, and (iii) pump depletion.

3.1. Wavebreaking

The breaking of space-charge waves[19] in a relativistic electron beam can saturate the FEL instability operating in the Raman regime. As the space-charge wave reaches large amplitudes, higher harmonics of the fundamental wave oscillation are generated which leads to the nonlinear steepening of the wave. The steepening of space-charge wave proceeds until the wave attains a critical amplitude beyond which wavebreaking occurs. The expression for the maximum electric field of space-charge waves in a relativistic electron beam is given by[19]

$$E_{max} = \sqrt{2} \, (m\omega_p c/e) \, [\gamma_{ph}(1-\beta_{ph}\beta_b)-1/\gamma_b]^{1/2} \quad , \tag{8}$$

where $\beta_{ph} = v_{ph}/c$, $\beta_b = v_b/c$, $\gamma_{ph} = (1 - \beta_{ph}^2)^{-1/2}$ and v_{ph} = wave phase velocity. Equation (8), valid for both negative-energy and positive-energy space-charge waves, determines the critical wave amplitude above which wavebreaking takes place. It indicates that wavebreaking imposes severe limitation on FELs that employ space-charge waves, either negative-energy or positive-energy modes, with phase velocity close to the electron-beam velocity since in that case the normalized maximum wave amplitude $eE_{max}/m\omega_p c \ll 1$. On the other hand, wavebreaking presents little(or no) restriction for FELs that employ positive-energy space-charge waves, either parallel or antiparallel propagating, with phase speed near(or greater than) the speed of light, since in that case extremely large wave amplitudes, such as $eE_{max}/m\omega_p c \gg 1$, are attainable.

3.2. Particle Trapping

The trapping of electrons[11] in the ponderomotive potential produced by the beating of wiggler and scattered fields can be a saturation mechanism for FEL operating in either Compton or Raman regime. If the amplitude of the ponderomotive wave is sufficiently large, a substantial fraction of beam electrons can become trapped in the wave potential well. In the reference frame moving with the wave phase velocity, the condition for the onset of particle trapping is given by[19]

$$|e\phi_{max}| \geq (\gamma-1)mc^2 \qquad , \qquad (9)$$

namely, when the maximum electrostatic potential energy of the ponderomotive wave exceeds the kinetic energy of beam particles. When this occurs, electrons become trapped and continuously gain energy from the wave, thus limiting the wave growth.

3.3. Pump Depletion

The pump depletion[21,22] can be a saturation mechanism for FEL, operating in either Compton or Raman regime, using an electromagnetic wiggler. In this type of FEL, the instability process takes place partly at the expense of the electromagnetic pump energy. Thus, both electron beam and electromagnetic wiggler provide energy for the growth of FEL radiation. In practice, there is a threshold condition for the FEL instability due to either dissipative processes in the system or a frequency mismatch in the wave coupling. Hence, the lasing process is terminated when the pump power is depleted to a level below the threshold required for sustaining the FEL instability.

4. APPLICATIONS OF FREE-ELECTRON LASERS

The tunability, high power, and high efficiency of free-electron lasers make them suitable for many exciting potential applications. Among a great number[10, 11] of applications of FEL, we shall discuss specifically:(i) the magnetic and inertial confinement fusion , (ii) particle accelerators, (iii) energy transmission in space, and (iv) cosmic radiation.

4.1. Magnetic and Inertial Confinement Fusion

Two of the major problems for achieving thermonuclear power reactors, using the magnetic confinement scheme such as tokamaks, are plasma heating and plasma confinement. FEL can be used for radio-frequency plasma heating or current-drive in plasma through the electron-cyclotron resonance[23], whereby FEL electromagnetic energy is transformed to plasma energy or plasma momentum.

For the success of inertial confinement fusion, a high-power laser with short wavelength is required. FEL can become the required driver for the inertial confinement scheme.

4.2. Particle Accelerators

As high-energy physics experiments are performed at higher and higher energies, exceedingly large particle accelerators are required. Smaller particle accelerators may be achieved through collective particle acceleration mechanisms using high-power radiation sources. For example, FEL can be employed in the plasma beatwave accelerators[24], in which the beating of two laser fields produces a large-amplitude ponderomotive wave which trap and accelerate charged particles to high energies.

4.3. Energy Transmission in Space

FEL can be used in space for transmiting power from a space station to another space station and for beaming power from space to Earth and vice-versa. The use of FEL for energy transmission in space has the advantage of reducing the vehicle mass. Moreover, since FEL operates in vacuum, most of the problems inherent in moving and recycling gases in gas and chemical lasers are absent. For a solar-powered FEL, the overall efficiency depends on the conversion efficiency of solar energy to electrical energy and the conversion efficiency of electrical energy to laser energy. Studies indicate that suitable choices of accelerators for space-based FEL are electrostatic accelerators and storage rings.

4.4. Cosmic Radiation

Some of the interesting features of FEL can also be found in naturally occurring radiation processes in cosmic plasmas[26]. The role of FEL wiggler is played by large-amplitude electrostatic or electromagnetic waves in cosmic plasmas. These large-amplitude plasma waves lead to strong coupling of high-phase velocity waves with low-phase velocity beat waves, resulting in transfer of electron-beam energy to radiation energy. The concepts of FEL have been applied to explain the generation mechanisms of AKR-Auroral Kilometric Radiation[27,28], and may be relevant for the study of other cosmic radiation phenomena such as pulsar radiation[29] and solar radiation[30].

5. CONCLUSION

Free-electron lasers hold the promise of making available coherent, high power, high efficiency, tunable sources of radiation over a wavelength range from millimeter to ultraviolet. More research on nonlinear processes such as saturation mechanisms is required in order to improve the efficiency of FEL. As shown in this paper, FEL has potential applications in a variety of scientific and technological fields. In addition, FEL research can provide basis for a better understanding of many interesting naturally occurring cosmic radiation phenomena in the universe.

REFERENCES

1. Einstein, A., Ann. Phys. (Leipzig) 17, 891 (1905).
2. Kapitza, P.L., and Dirac, P.A.M., Proc. Cambridge Philos. Sec. 29, 297 (1933)
3. Motz, H., J. Appl. Phys. 22, 527 (1951)
4. Phillips, R.N., IRE Trans. Electron Devices 7, 231 (1960)
5. Elias, L.R., Fairbank, W.M., Madey, J.M.J., Schwettman, H.A., and Smith, T.I., Phys. Rev. Lett. 36, 717 (1976).
6. Deacon, D.A.G., Elias, L.R., Madey, J.M.J., Ramian, G.J., Schwettman, H.A., and Smith, T.L., Phys. Rev. Lett. 38, 892. (1977).
7. Sprangle, P., Smith, R.A., and Granatstein, V.L., in "Infrared and Submillimeter Waves" (K.J. Button, ed.), Vol. 1, p. 279, Academic Press, New York (1979)
8. Marshall, T.C., Schlesinger, S.P., and McDermott, D.B., in "Advances in Electronics and Electron Physics", Vol. 53, p.47, Academic Press, New York (1980).
9. Corrêa, R.A., "Theory of Free-Electron Lasers", M. Sc. thesis, INPE, São José dos Campos-Brazil (1983).
10. Sprangle, P., and Coffey, T., Phys. Today 37, 44 (1984).
11. Marshall, T.C., "Free-Electron Lasers", McMillan, New york (1985).
12. Serbêto, A.P.B., "Hamiltonian Analysis and Simulation of Free-Electron Lasers", Ph.D. thesis, INPE, São José dos Campos-Brazil (1988).
13. Roberson, C.W., and Sprangle, P., Phys. Fluids B1 , 3 (1989).
14. Granatstein, V.L., Fliflet, A.W., Levush, B., and Antonsen, T.M., Comments Plasma Phys. Controlled Fusion 12, 217 (1989).
15. Billardon, M., Elleaume, P., Ortega, J.M., Bazin, C., Bergher, M., Velghe, M., Petroff, Y., Deacon, D.A.G., Robinson, K.E., and Madey, J.M.J., Phys. Rev. Lett. 51, 1652 (1983).
16. Litvak, A.G., and Trahktengerts, V.Yu., Sov. Phys. JETP 33, 921 (1971).
17. Chian, A.C.-L, Plasma Phys. 21, 509 (1979).

18. Hasegawa, A., "Plasma Instabilities and Nonlinear Effects", Springer-Verlag, New York (1975).

19. Chian, A.C.-L. (1989), Phys. Rev. A39, 2561 (1989).

20. Steinberg, B., Gover, A., and Ruschin, S., Phys. Rev. A33, 421 (1986).

21. Chian, A.C.-L., and Serbêto, A.P.B., in Proc. IV Japan-Brazil Symposium on Science and Technology, Vol. III, p. 223 (1984).

22. Lin, A.T., and Dawson, J.M., Phys. Fluids, 23, 1224 (1980).

23. Chian, A.C.-L., in Proc. IV Japan-Brazil Symposium on Science and Technology, Vol. III, p. 339 (1984).

24. Tajima, T., and Dawson, J.M., Phys. Rev. Lett. 43, 267 (1979).

25. Segall, S.B., Hiddleston, H.R., and Catella, G.C., in "Free-Electron Generators of Coherent Radiation" (S.F. Jacobs et al., ed.), Vol. 9, p. 1013, Addison-Wesley, Reading (1982).

26. Chian, A.C.-L., and Lee, L.C., Space Science Rev., in press (1990).

27. Palmadesso, P., Coffey, T.P., Ossakow, S.L., and Papadopoulos, K., J. Geophys. Res. 81, 1762 (1976).

28. Grabbe, C.L., Papadopoulos, K., and Palmadesso, P.J., J. Geophys. Res. 85, 3337 (1980).

29. Chian, A.C.-L., and Kennel, C.F., Astrophys. and Space Sc. 97, 9 (1983).

30. Chian, A.C.-L., and Alves, M.V., Astrophys. J. 330, L77 (1988).

Contributed Papers

EXCITATION AND IONIZATION OF TiCl₄ AROUND THE Ti 3p EDGE

G.G.B. de Souza, R.J. Martins, A.C.A. Souza and C.A. Lucas

Instituto de Quimica, Universidade Federal do Rio de Janeiro Cidade Universitaria, Rio de Janeiro, 21910, RJ , BRAZIL

P. Morin, P. Lablanquie and I. Nenner

LURE, Laboratoire mixte CNRS, MEN, C.E.A., Bat. 209 D, Univ.

Paris Sud, 91405 Orsay Cedex, France and C.E.A.- IRDI/DESICP

Département d'Etude des Lasers et de la Physico-Chimie,

Saclay-91191, Gif-sur Yvette Cedex, France

The excitation and ionization processes of the $TiCl_4$ molecule around the Ti 3p edge (43.6 eV) have been studied by electron energy-loss, photoelectron and photoionization techniques. A pseudo photoabsorption spectrum, measured with 1 keV incident electrons, agrees with previously published data and shows, in addition, two new bands centered at 12.2 and 15 eV. Photoelectron and fragmentation spectra have also been measured as a function of the photon energy, in the range of 30 to 70 eV, using synchrotron radiation. The observed results demonstrate that the 3p-3d excitation decays through autoionization resonating and Auger processes.

I Introduction:

The $TiCl_4$ molecule can be considered as a prototype for the study of the electronic and bonding properties in transition metal compounds, due to its very high symmetry and to its closed-shell structure. As a consequence, its electronic structure has been the focus of several experimental and theoretical papers[1-9]. These studies have been, nonetheless, either dedicated to the excitation and ionization of valence shell electrons or to the ionization of deep core-level electrons[10-13]. In the present work the photoabsorption spectrum of $TiCl_4$ has been extended to 70 eV using electron impact excitation. Photoelectron spectra have been determined up to 50 eV binding energy, using synchrotron radiation as ionization source. These new measurements encompass the 3p excitation and ionization region to which our atention is addressed. The fragmentation processes following 3p excitation and ionization have also been observed as a function of the photon energy.

II Experimental:

The electron energy-loss measurements were done using a spectrometer which has been described before[14]. It consists basically of a rotatable electron gun, a neutral-gas beam, and a Möllenstedt velocity analyzer. The pseudo photoabsorption spectrum has been obtained at a scattering angle of 1.0 degree, with an energy resolution of approximately 0.6 eV. The incident electron energy was 1 keV, and the data has been corrected for background contributions and for the field sweeping mode of the analyzer. The apparatus employed in the photoelectron and mass spectrometry measurements has also been described elsewhere[15] . Briefly, the UV synchrotron radiation emitted from the ACO (Anneau de Collisions d'Orsay) storage ring is focused on the entrance slit of a toroidal grating monochromator, providing a high photon flux (e.g. 6 X 10^{11} photons/A. s. 100 mA) in the 20 - 140 eV energy range. The monochromatic beam is refocused at the center of the interaction chamber where it crosses at right angles an effusive jet of gas. We have used two different experimental set-ups :

i) an angle-resolved photoelectron spectrometer which allows to measure photoelectron spectra at fixed photon wavelength at magic angle. The overall resolution (analyzer plus monochromator) was about 1 eV.

ii) A TOF mass spectrometer operated in the conventional and coincidence mode (PIPICO). The TOF spectra are obtained by extracting the ions in the source with a pulsed field (400 V/cm at 50 kHz); the free field time equals 1 microsecond. The sample was prepared from $TiCl_4$ commercially available, previously submmited to a low-pressure distillation. Due to its reactivity towards water, the sample was processed under nitrogen atmosphere.

III Results and Discussion

TiCl$_4$ has 90 electrons and belongs to the Td symmetry group, with a known Ti-Cl band length of 2.185 A. Its electronic configuration in the ground state is[9] :

$$(Ti\ 1s)^2\ (Cl\ 1s)^8 (Ti\ 2s)^2\ (Ti\ 2p)^6\ (Cl\ 2s)^8\ (Cl\ 2p)^{24}$$

CORE

$$(6a_1)^2(6t_2)^6(7a_1)^2(7t_2)^6 \qquad (8t_2)^6(8a_1)^2(2e)^4(9t_2)^6(2t_1)^6$$

INNER-VALENCE   VALENCE

$$(3e)^0(10t_2)^0(9a_1)^0\ ,^1A_1$$

UNOCCUPIED

The parentage of the occupied orbitals is presented in table I[2,9] . The HOMO $2t_1$, as well as the $9t_2$ and $8a_1$ orbitals are mostly chlorine p in character; the bonding orbitals are the $2e$ (d_π-p_π) and the $8t_2$ (d_σ-p_σ). The $7a_1$ and $7t_2$ orbitals are predominantely Cl 3s and the $6a_1$ and $6t_2$ orbitals are Ti 3s and Ti 2p, respectively[9].

TABLE I : Parentage of valence orbitals[9].

Parentage	
$6a_1$	Ti 1s
$6t_2$	Ti 2p
$7a_1$	Cl 3s
$7t_2$	Cl 3s
$8t_2$	dσ-pσ (bonding)
$8a_1$	Cl lone pair, small% Ti
$2e$	dπ-pπ (bonding)
$9t_2$	mainly Cl p, partially Ti 3p - 3d
$2t_1$ HOMO	pure Cl lone pair, (non-bonding)
$3e$ LUMO	Ti 3d
$10t_2$	Ti 3d

204

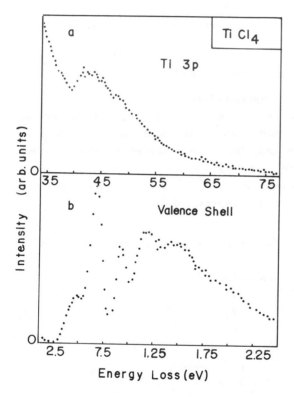

The valence-shell excitation spectrum obtained by the pseudo-photon technique can be seen in fig. 1b Figure 1a shows the 3p-3d excitation in the 40 to 60 eV energy range. The energies and assignments for the observed bands are presented in table II.

Our valence-shell result shows a good agreement with previous data in the energy range of 4 to 10 eV and in addition shows two other bands, centered at 12.2 and 15 eV. There is a general agreement in the literature concerning the assignment of the two lowest energy bands in the photoabsorption spectrum of $TiCL_4$ as $2t_1 \rightarrow 3e$ and $2t_1 \rightarrow 10t_2$. The 9.3 and 10.0 eV bands are assigned to transitions from the $9t_2$ and $8t_2$ orbitals to the same final state, namely, $9a_1$.

Figure 1: Valence-shell (1b) and Ti 3p (1a) excitation spectra of $TiCl_4$ as determined by electron energy-loss technique.

TABLE II: Energies and Assignment for the Photoabsorption Bands.

Experimental Energy (eV)		Assignment
Ref. 9	This Work	
4.4	4.4	$2t_1 \rightarrow 3e$
5.4	5.4	$2t_1 \rightarrow 10t_2$
7.1		$8t_2 \rightarrow 3e$
		$8a_1 \rightarrow 3e$
	7.0	
7.4		$8t_2 \rightarrow 10t_2$
		$8t_2 \rightarrow 9a_1$
9.4		$9t_2 \rightarrow 9a_1$
10.0	9.8	$8t_2 \rightarrow 9a_1$
	12.2	
	15.0	
	43.0	Ti (3p) $\rightarrow$ Ti (3d)

The band observed at 7.0 eV in our spectrum has been shown to be composed of two bands located at 6.9 and 7.3 eV. In the higher resolution spectrum obtained by Iverson and Russell[5] they have been assigned to transitions from the bonding orbital $8t_2$ to the 3e and $10t_2$ orbitals. The bands observed above the first ionization potential (11.8 eV) have not been reported before. The assignment of these bands remains an open question, although one could speculate, on energetical grounds, that the band at 12.2 eV is associated with transitions from 2e, $8a_1$ or $8t_2$ orbitals to the unoccupied states 3e, $10t_2$ or $9a_1^o$. The band at 15 eV is most probably related to transitions from the $7a_1$ and $7t_2$ (chlorine 3s) orbitals. The large band centered at 43 eV (fig. 1b) is associated to electronic transitions having the $6t_2$ (Ti 3p) orbital as initial state and the 3e and $10t_2$ orbitals (Ti 3d) as final states. In fact, as shown by Mayer[16] et al, atomic Titanium also presents a number of lines around 40 eV in its photoabsorption spectrum, due to the multiplet structure of Ti $3p^6 3d^2 - 3p^5 3d^3$ transitions.

Figure 2 shows photoelectron spectra measured at 38 and 40 eV photon energies, respectively below and on the broad resonance associated to the Ti 3p-3d transitions. Four bands are observed below 15 eV binding energy, in agreement with previous results, and their binding energies and assignment are presented in Table III. Above 15 eV a continuous satellite structure demonstrates the importance of correlation processes in this energy-range. A dramatic change in the intensity ratio of the bands can be seen as one moves from 38 to 40 eV. In particular the $2e^{-1}$ band (13.3 eV binding energy) becomes more than three times more intense than the $2t_1^{-1}$ band ; the intensity of the satellite region is also enhanced with respect to the binding energy range below 15 eV . The former behaviour clearly shows the $2e^{-1}$ orbital to have a Ti 3p character, while the $2t_1^{-1}$, as expected, has a pure Cl p character and consequently its intensity is not expected to resonate significantly.

TABLE III - Binding Energies (eV)

Green et al[2]	This Work	Assignment[9]
11.8	11.8	$2t_1^{-1}$
12.66	12.7	$9t_2^{-1}$
13.3	13.3	$2e^{-1}$
13.88	13.8	$8a_1^{-1}$ and $8t_2^{-1}$
16.4 - 19	continuous satelite structure standing from 1s to 3d.	
	44.4	Ti $3p^{-1}$

The satellite enhancement can probably be explained by Resonating Auger processes, in which the excited Ti 3p electron remains as a spectator while the core-hole excited molecule relaxs by ejecting another electron. This behaviour is very often observed in molecular inner-shell excitation, as exemplified by our recent work on SiF_4[17,18]. An additional and complementary view on the excitation and relaxation processes of this molecule can be obtained from the data shown in figure 3, in which the intensity of the ionic fragments observed in the mass spectrum of $TiCl_4$ are plotted as a function of the photon energy.

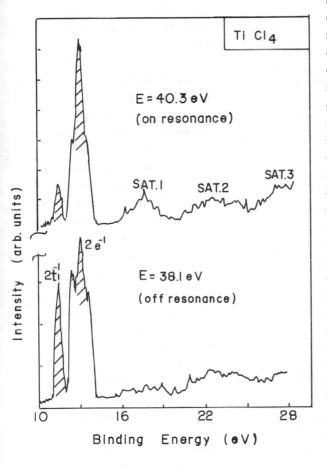

Ti Cl$_4$

E = 40.3 eV
(on resonance)

SAT.1   SAT.2   SAT.3

2 e^{-1}

2 t$_1^{-1}$

E = 38.1 eV
(off resonance)

Intensity (arb. units)

Binding Energy (eV)

Figure 2: Photoelectron Spectra of TiCl$_4$ Measured on and off resonance.

208

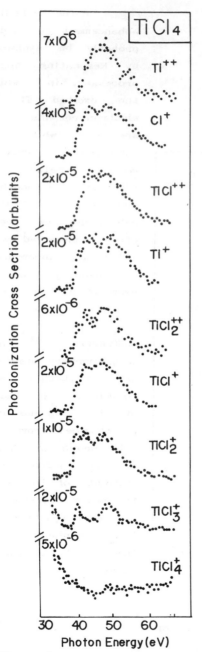

$TiCl_4$

Ti^{++}

Cl^+

$TiCl^{++}$

Ti^+

$TiCl_2^{++}$

$TiCl^+$

$TiCl_2^+$

$TiCl_3^+$

$TiCl_4^+$

Photoionization Cross Section (arb.units)

Photon Energy (eV)

Except for the parent ion, $TiCL_4^+$, which is formed mainly through direct ionization, the intensity of all other ions is shown to reproduce the photoabsorption spectra. This is a clear experimental evidence of the presence of resonating ionizations schemes such as autoionization and resonating Auger or double (multiple) Auger processes.

IV Acknowledgments.

We thank the staff of the Laboratoire pour l'Utilisation du Rayonnement Electromagnetique for their operation of the ACO storage ring and for general facilities. Financial assistance from CNPq and FINEP (Brazil) is also acknowledged.

<u>Figure 3</u>:

Intensity of ionic fragments in the mass spectra of $TiCl_4$ as a funtion of photon energy.

V References.

(1) Becker, C.A.L.; Ballhausen, C.J. and Trabjerg, I., *Theoret. Chim. Açta* (Berl.), 13, 355 (1969).

(2) Green, J.C.; Green, M.L.H.; Joachim, P.J.; Orchard, A.F.; Turner, D.W. *Phil., Trans. Roy. Soc. London*, A268, 111 (1970)

(3) Cox, P.A.; Evans, S.; Hammett, A. and Orchard, A.F., *Chem. Phys. Lett.*, 67, 527 (1979).

(4) Parameswaran, T. and Ellis, D.E., *J. Chem. Phys.*, 58, 2088 (1973).

(5) Iverson, A.A. and Russell, B.R., *Spectra Acta*, 29A, 715 (1973).

(6) Hillier, I.H. and Kendrick, J., *Inorg. Chem.*, 15, 520 (1976).

(7) Surana, S.S.L. and Müller, A., *Chem. Phys. Lett.*, 67, 527 (1979).

(8) Onopko, D.E. and Titov, S.A., *Opt. Spectrosc.* (USSR), 51, 715 (1981).

(9) Foti, A.E.; Smith, V.H. and Whitehead, M.A., *Mol. Phys.*, 45, 385 (1982).

(10) Wallbank, G.; Main, I.G. and Johnson, C.E., *J. Elect. Spectrosc. and Rel. Phenom.*, 5, 259 (1974).

(11) Tse, J., *Chem .Phys. Lett.*, 77, 373 (1981).

(12) Davis, L.C., *J. Appl. Phys.*, 59, R25 (1986).

(13) Mousty-Desbuquoit, C.; Riga, J. and Verbist, J.J., *J. Chem. Phys.*, 26, 1212 (1987).

(14) de Souza, G.G.B. and Souza, A.C.A., *J. Phys.* E, 18, 1037 (1985).

(15) Lablanquie, P.; Nenner, I.; Millié, P.; Morin, P.; Eland, J.H.D.; Hubin-Franskin, M.J. and Delwiche, J., *J. Chem. Phys.*, 82, 2951 (1985).

(16) Meyer, M.; Prescher, Th.; von Raven, E.; Richter, M.; Schmidt, E.; Sontag, B. and Wetzel, H. -E., *Z. Phys. D – Atoms, molecules and Clusters*, 2, 347 (1986).

(17) de Souza, G.G.B.; Morin, P. and Nenner, I., *J. Chem. Phys.*, 90, 7071 (1989).

(18) Lablanquie, P.; Souza, A.C.A.; de Souza, G.G.B.; Morin, P.; Nenner, I., *J. Chem. Phys.*, 90, 7078 (1989).

HIGH RESOLUTION POWDER DIFFRACTION USING SYNCHROTRON RADIATION: APPLICATION TO THE STRUCTURAL INVESTIGATION OF n-ALKANES AND THEIR HOMOLOGUES MIXTURES.

A. R. Gerson[1], K. J. Roberts[1,2], J. N. Sherwood[1], R. J. Cernik[2], P. Pattison[2], A. N. Fitch[2,3]

(1) Department of Pure and Applied Chemistry,
   Strathclyde University, Glasgow G1-1XL, Scotland.

(2) S.E.R.C. Daresbury Laboratory,
   Warrington WA4-4AD, England.

(3) Department of Chemistry, University of Keele,
   Staffs, England.

ABSTRACT

A new high-resolution powder diffractometer has been constructed for operation on station 8.3 of the Daresbury synchrotron radiation source. This new instrument which is based on the Hart-Parrish[1] design incorporates a channel-cut mononchromator, a two circle diffractometer and a long (35.6 cm) diffracted beam collimator. The use of a long beam collimator in conjunction with the low angular dispersion of the synchrotron radiation beam removes the need to consider the reciprocal relationship between angular resolution and diffracted beam intensity inherent in the more common Bragg-Brentano focussing geometry. This configuration also eradicates diffraction pattern errors resulting from sample misalignment. The application of this facility to studies of the structure of long chain hydrocarbons is demonstrated in examples of four recent case studies; 1) the ab-initio indexing of the unit cell of triclinic n-eicosane ($C_{20}H_{42}$), 2) the phase identification of recrystallised mixtures of n-eicosane and n-docosane ($C_{22}H_{46}$), 3) the measurement of the long lattice constant of n-triatriacontane ($C_{33}H_{68}$) and 4) the structural refinement by the Rietveld method of n-octodecane ($C_{18}H_{38}$).

1. INTRODUCTION

The definition of the structure of long–chain hydrocarbons is of current technological importance in relation to the understanding of their crystallisation and co–crystallisation as waxes from hydrocarbon mixtures such as diesel and home–heating fuels.

Previous studies[2] have shown that homologous n–alkanes with an even number of carbon atoms in the range $C_{18}H_{38}$ to $C_{22}H_{46}$ crystallise in a triclinic lattice of space group $P\bar{1}$ with 1 molecule to the unit cell. In contrast those n–alkanes with an odd number of carbons in the range $C_{19}H_{40}$ (n–nonadecane) to $C_{27}H_{56}$ (n–heptacosane)[2] yield orthorhombic structures with 4 molecules to the unit cell.

In the study[3] of co–crystalliation of homologous mixtures, $C_{20}H_{42}$ and $C_{22}H_{46}$ were shown to crystallise from the melt to yield orthorhombic unit cells which closely resemble those of alkanes containing an odd number of carbons. In these structures the a and b axes remain approximately constant in length throughout the solid solution and the c–axis length increases proportionally to the percentage of $C_{22}H_{46}$.

There is a need to extend these investigations of the relationship between wax structure and homologue content. Structural studies using single crystal X–ray diffraction are restricted due to the lack of availability of well–defined single crystals which for these waxy and hence ductile materials are difficult to prepare and maintain. Structural analysis using conventional powder diffraction is difficult due to the large unit cells of low symmetry expected[4] for these materials. In principle these difficulties can be overcome by using the synchrotron powder diffraction technique.

In this paper we describe a new facility for high resolution diffraction studies that has been developed on station 8.3 of the Daresbury synchrotron radiation source (SRS) and present four examples from our current research programme into wax crystallisation. These examples demonstrate the applicability of this technique to structural studies of complex materials, structures and mixtures.

2. Instrumental Facilities for High Resolution Powder Diffraction on the Daresbury SRS.

Synchrotrons provide a tunable (0.7-2.5Å), low divergence, intense photon beam ideal for crystallographic studies.

Conventional powder diffraction analysis using Bragg/Brentano geometry is prone to peak displacement and deformation due to sample misalignment or beam focussing errors. These can be overcome[5] by using long diffracted-beam collimators. The use of synchrotron radiation[6,7] sources enables excellent angular resolution to be achieved. Diffractometers designed specifically for use with synchrotron radiation have been developed by Hart, Parrish and co-workers[1,8,9,10]. These designs have been used as the basis for the development of the high resolution diffractometer on station 8.3 of the Daresbury SRS.

The powder diffractometer shown in Figure 1 comprises:

(a) a Si (111) monochromator which operates in the wavelength range 0.7 – 2.5 Å

(b) horizontal and vertical entrance slits which define the incident beam cross-section,

(c) a flat-plate sample stage which can rotate the specimen about an axis orthogonal to the diffractometer axes,

(d) diffracted-beam collimators fabricated from sets of parallel stainless steel foils. The collimators are housed in a vacuum vessel to reduce air scatter and are attached to the 2θ arm of the diffractometer. Two sets are used:

(i) the first set consists of foils 0.21 mm apart and 35.6 cm long which provide a receiving beam divergence of 0.069˚. These define the angular resolution in 2θ and enable a incident beam of large cross-section to be used with no loss of angular resolution.

(ii) The second set is orientated at 90˚ with respect to the first set and reduces the axial divergence which results in peak assymetry at low angles of 2θ.

(e) an Ar/Xe proportional detector mounted after the collimator and at the end of the 2θ arm.

The sample and detector arms are attached to two completely decoupled Franke rotary tables mounted with their axes parallel to the plane of the synchrotron orbit. Due to the lack of need for beam focussing, θ and 2θ can be varied independently allowing scans with a fixed sample angle or θ/2θ geometry. Angular positioning of the detector and sample is defined by rotary encoders with a resolution of 0.1 mdeg and 1 mdeg respectively.

The performance of the instrument was defined from a diffraction pattern recorded for a Si NBS640b standard up to 120° 2θ. In this data the positions of all observable peaks obtained were compared with the theoretically defined peak positions. The maximum deviation observed for any one peak was 1.0 mdeg. It was found that the diffracted beam peak shape could be described by a pseudo-Voight function. Figure 2 shows the comparison of the Si (111) peak with a symmetric pseudo-Voight function. The mixing parameter for this particular function was 0.3 giving a peak half width of 0.046°. The very small deviations between the observed and calculated peak positions over a wide range of 2θ demonstrate the lack of systematic alignment errors in this apparatus. The extremely symmetrical peak shape confirms that peak assymetry is effectively removed by the second set of foils.

Figure 1a: The high resolution powder diffraction facility on Station 8.3 of the Daresbury SRS.

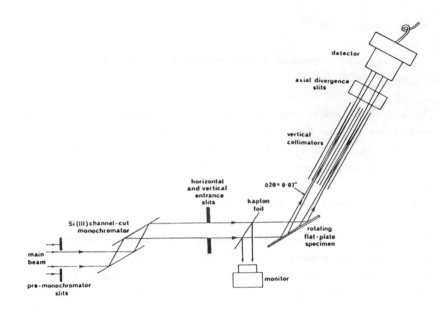

Figure 1b: Schemetic representation showing instrument details.

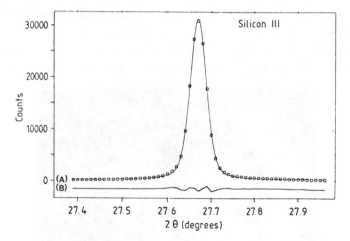

Figure 2: Si 111 diffraction peak recorded using the high resolution powder facility. The full curve (A) shows how well the theoretical symmetrical pseudo–Voight function correlates with the experimetnal data points. (B) shows the difference between the two peak functions.

The performance of the instrument was defined from a diffraction pattern recorded for a Si NBS640b standard up to 120° 2θ. In this data the positions of all observable peaks obtained were compared with the theoretically defined peak positions. The maximum deviation observed for any one peak was 1.0 mdeg. It was found that the diffracted beam peak shape could be described by a pseudo-Voight function. Figure 2 shows the comparison of the Si (111) peak with a symmetric pseudo-Voight function. The mixing parameter for this particular function was 0.3 giving a peak half width of 0.046°. The very small deviations between the observed and calculated peak positions over a wide range of 2θ demonstrate the lack of systematic alignment errors in this apparatus. The extremely symmetrical peak shape confirms that peak assymetry is effectively removed by the second set of foils.

3. Application to Structural Investigations of n-alkanes

3.1 Materials

Samples were prepared by recrystallisation twice from n-dodecane ($C_{12}H_{26}$) or by recrystallisation from the melt. For recrystallisation from solution the solvent was removed by placing the sample between absorbent paper and applying pressure for one week. The low vapour pressure of $C_{12}H_{26}$ and low melting points of the solid n-alkanes under examination, eg n-octodecane ($C_{18}H_{32}$) melts at 301.3K, preclude the removal of solvent by evaporation techniques. The samples were ground at room temperature to give a particle size of approximately 0.05 μm.

3.2 Data Collection

The diffraction patterns were recorded using θ/2θ geometry with 2θ ranging from 2 to 95° in step sizes of 10 mdeg. The data collection time at each step was 2 seconds. The wavelengths and zeropoints were calibrated by peak position measurements of the first 5 peaks observed for a Si standard.

3.3 Pattern Indexing and Unit Cell Determination

Ab–initio indexing of triclinic crystal systems has in the past been extremely difficult. The low degree of symmetry in the crystal system produces highly complicated powder diffraction patterns with little relationship between peak positions. In the present study the high pattern definition produced by the synchrotron powder technique has enabled us to determine in a routine manner the unit cells of several n–alkane homologues[2].

In past literature a number of different lattice systems have been used to define the unit cells of triclinic alkanes[2]. The lack of definition of these lattices in the literature has made correlation between results difficult. The most useful convention is to align the c axis with the long molecular axis of the alkane chains but unfortunately this can only be done with certainty where the structure of the alkane is known. In this paper where the structure of several samples is unknown we adopt the convention of defining β to be as close as possible to 90°.

The indexing of the diffraction pattern and determination of lattice parameters were carried out using a computer program written by J. W. Visser[11] and based on a suggestion by Wolff[12]. This program was specifically designed for indexing powder diffraction patterns from low symmetry crystal systems. Lattice parameters were calculated by identifying intersecting zones from which an origin can be determined and a reciprocal lattice defined. This program, unlike a previous program by Ito[13], then seeks to reduce this reciprocal lattice by crystal symmetry considerations. The degree of fit of the observed peak positions to the peak positions defined by the calculated lattice parameters is defined by a figure of merit and by the number of peaks indexed out of the first 20 observed. A peak is considered indexed if the discrepancy between the observed and calculated postions is less than 0.03°. The figure of merit is defined as:

$$\frac{\sum_{i=1}^{n} (Q_{i\ obs} - Q_{i\ calc})/n}{\sum_{i=1}^{n} (Q'_{i\ obs} - Q'_{i\ calc})/n}$$

where Q is the square of the distance from a point in the reciprocal lattice to the origin. Q_{obs} and Q_{calc} are the observed and calculated values for the crystal system. Q'_{obs} and Q'_{calc} are the same values but for an arbitrary system with the same sized reciprocal lattice. n is the number of peaks. It is suggested that if a proposed lattice results in the indexing of fewer than 18 out of the first 20 peaks or produces a figure of merit of less than 4, then it should not be considered as realistic. In the case of diffraction patterns for samples containing more than one phase the former constraint is not valid.

The program input consists of between 20 and 40 peak positions, the wavelength and zeropoint. Up to four possible sets of lattice parameters are output along with a listing for each of the peaks indexed and the figure of merit. Further refinement of lattice parameters is possible by inputting them as test lattices with the data.

Lattice parameters have been calculated for the low symmetry crystal systems of n–eicosane ($C_{20}H_{20}$) and n–docosane ($C_{22}H_{46}$). Samples were prepared by crystallisation from the melt and solution. The lattice parameters obtained for these two types of samples did not show any signifigant difference. The diffraction patterns obtained for the samples recrystallised from solution are shown in Figure 3. The lattice parameters that were obtained for $C_{20}H_{42}$ were

$$a=4.285\text{Å} \quad b=4.821\text{Å} \quad c=25.529\text{Å} \quad \alpha=91.015° \quad \beta=93.557° \quad \gamma=107.408°.$$

The figure of merit for this lattice was 170.3 with all of the first 20 peaks being indexed. These lattice parameters agree well with previous measurements[14]. The lattice parameters determined for $C_{22}H_{46}$ were

$$a=4.288\text{Å} \quad b=4.829\text{Å} \quad c=27.927\text{Å} \quad \alpha=91.591° \quad \beta=92.395° \quad \gamma=107.825°$$

with figure of merit of 286.4 and all of the first 20 peaks indexed. No previous measurements have been carried out on $C_{22}H_{46}$ but these parameters agree well with theoretical predictions[4]. The lattice parameters for $C_{18}H_{38}$, $C_{20}H_{42}$ and $C_{22}H_{46}$ follow a distinct pattern; all parameters staying constant except the c–parameter which increases proportionally with alkane chain length. It is reasonable therefore to assume that the structures of these three solids are very similar.

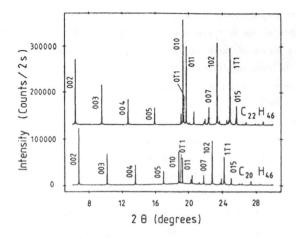

Figure 3: Synchrotron powder diffraction patterns of the triclinic alkanes $C_{20}H_{42}$ and $C_{22}H_{46}$.

3.4 Measurement of Long Lattice Constants

Using conventional powder diffraction geometry it is not a trivial task to detect the diffracted beam at low 2θ angles and the determination of long unit cells can present difficulties. The low divergence of the synchrotron beam coupled with the improved collimation of the 8.3 instrument has allowed us to determine such unit cells with no significant difficulty. One example is n–triatriacontane ($C_{33}H_{68}$) for which the synchrotron powder diffraction pattern is given in Figure 4. The lattice parameters of $C_{33}H_{68}$ as determined from the diffraction pattern are

$$a=4.955\text{Å} \quad b=7.457\text{Å} \quad c=87.716\text{Å} \quad \alpha=\beta=\gamma=90.00°.$$

The unit cell volume was calculated to be 3241.28 $Å^3$. The figure of merit for this lattice was 27.7 and all of the first 20 peaks observed were indexed. These lattice parameters are in good agreement with those predicted by Nyburg and Potwrowski[4]; of

$$a=4.970\text{Å} \quad b=7.478\text{Å} \quad c=87.78\text{Å} \quad \alpha=\beta=\gamma=90.00°.$$

It was observed that the (0 0 2l+1) peaks were systematically absent so that the first peak observed was (0 0 2) with a d spacing of 43.858Å. This peak occured at 2.182˚.

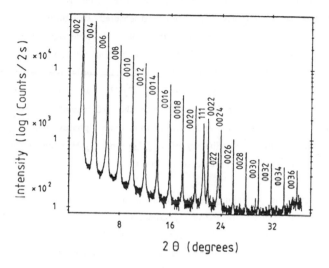

Figure 4: A diffraction pattern of an alkane with a large unit cell: $C_{33}H_{68}$.

3.5 Phase Identification in Homologous Mixtures of $C_{20}H_{42}$ and $C_{22}H_{46}$

The unit cell parameters obtained for mixtures of $C_{20}H_{42}$ and $C_{22}H_{46}$ crystallised from the melt (Table 1) confirm the observations of Luth et al[3]. The a and b parameters remain constant for the entire series of mixtures whereas the c lattice parameter varies proportionally with the percentage of $C_{22}H_{46}$ present. The orthorhombic unit cells observed in these mixtures are very similar to those observed for alkanes containing an odd number of carbons. It is very likely therefore that their structures are very similar and that they both contain 4 molecules per unit cell.

A different behaviour was observed when the same mixtures were crystallised from n–dodecane solutions. The data are summarised in Table 2 and show that a rather complex phase behaviour occurs in n–alkane mixtures crytallised from solution. At low fractions (<= 5%) of the longer ($C_{22}H_{46}$) homologue, phase separation takes place and the triclinic (z=1) and orthorhombic (z=4) phases are observed. After this and up to 40% $C_{22}H_{46}$ only the orthorhombic phase is observed. Between 45–70% $C_{22}H_{46}$ phase separation occurs again, this time resulting in a mixture of orthorhombic (z=4) and triclinic (z=2) phase. The latter is pseudo–monoclinic in nature and closely resembles the recently discovered structures for $C_{24}H_{50}$ and $C_{26}H_{54}$[2]. Additionally in this range a third phase is observed for some of these homologoue mixtures. Due to the low fraction present we have not been able to characterise the unit cell. Between 70–90% $C_{22}H_{46}$ only the pseudo–monoclinic (triclinic z=2) phase is observed but at 95% $C_{22}H_{46}$ we get phase separation to give the $C_{22}H_{46}$ triclinic (z=1) structure plus the orthorhombic phase. We expect that both the orthorhombic and pseudo–monoclinic phases will be disordered structures with a random distribution of $C_{20}H_{42}$ and $C_{22}H_{46}$ molecules across the crystal sites resulting in an increase in molecular volume.

Diffraction patterns containing such multiple phases resulting from these low symmetry crystal systems are extremely complex and to index these patterns good quality high resolution data are needed. An indication of the complexity of the patterns produced is shown in Figure 5a which shows a central section of a set of peaks from the 40% $C_{20}H_{42}$: 60% $C_{22}H_{46}$ mixture crystallised from solution. The number of phases present is clearly indicted by the 3 sets of (0 0 1) peaks present in Figure 5a.

As noted above the number of peaks indexed out of the first 20 observed is not a valid criteria for judging the accuracy of the lattices predicted from patterns of mixed phases. Consequently this figure is not quoted. The figure of merit for all lattice parameters was above 4. Judgement must be exercised when indexing mixed phase systems as it difficult to achieve high orders of merit if only a few peaks of a certain phase are observed.

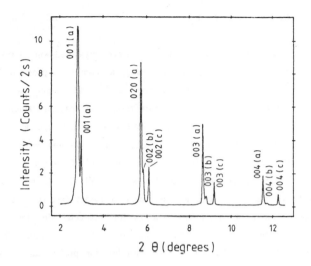

Figure 5a: Synchrotron radiation diffraction patterns between 2° and 12° 2θ of the mixed crystals formed by recrystallising a 40%, 60% mixture of n-alkanes $C_{20}H_{42}$ and $C_{22}H_{46}$ respectively, from solution.

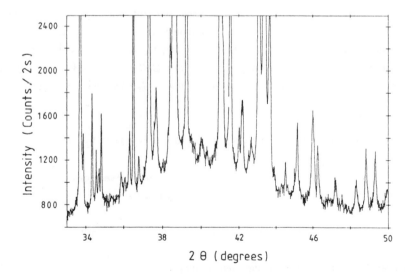

Figure 5b: Synchrotron radiation diffraction pattern of the same sample as shown in Figure 5a between 35° and 50° 2θ.

3.6 Structural Refinement of $C_{18}H_{38}$.

Structural refinement from the diffraction pattern measured on station 8.3 was carried out for n-octadecane ($C_{18}H_{38}$) using a computer program written by Murray et al[15] based on the Rietveld method [16]. All atomic parameters were refined as were the zero-point, lattice parameters, peak shape parameters based on a pseudo-Voight peak shape, anisotropic temperature factors and a x^3 polynomial for the background. A number of 'soft' chemical constraints were included. All C–C bonds were constrained to be the same length, H–C bonds were constrained to 1.073 Å, H–C–H angles to be tetrahedral and all C–C–C bond angles were constrained to be the same. The anisotropic temperature factors were held to be the same for all atoms in an attempt to allow for molecular vibrations which could be high due to the proximity of the temperature of observation (295K) to the melting point (301.3K) of the sample. A correction for preferential orientation in the (0 0 1) plane was included but no correction for peak assymetry was included. A preferred orientation correction was felt to be necessary due to the extremely plate-like habit and morphology of n-alkane crystals.

The powder diffraction pattern generated from the determined structure and the observed pattern is shown in Figure 6. The standard fitting parameters[16] were R_{wp}=18.47, R_i=9.87 for a R_{ex} of 6.02. Although Rwp is relatively high it is felt that the structure is reliable. The C–C bond lengths vary from 1.49Å at the end of the carbon chain to 1.53Å at the middle. The C–C–C bond angle is on average 114.02°. The molecular structure is shown in Figure 7a. The vibrational parameters were:

$$b_{11}=0.157 \quad b_{22}=0.104 \quad b_{33}=0.001 \quad b_{12}=0.112 \quad b_{13}=0.002 \quad b_{23}=0.003$$

A single crystal structural determination has previously been carried out[17] for $C_{18}H_{38}$. The lattice parameters used in this analysis were[18]:

$$a=4.285\text{Å} \quad b=4.820\text{Å} \quad c=23.070\text{Å} \quad \alpha=91.10° \quad \beta=92.07° \quad \gamma=107.30°$$

compared with those found in the present study of

$$a=4.292\text{Å} \quad b=4.825\text{Å} \quad c=23.065\text{Å} \quad \alpha=91.15° \quad \beta=91.98° \quad \gamma=107.46°.$$

These data are in very good agreement as are the C–C bond lengths and C–C–C bond angles. The packing of the molecules within the unit cells (Figure 6b) differ. The theoretical diffraction pattern generated by the previously obtained structure[17] is not consistent with our observed pattern. Whilst it is possible that this could be due to polymorphism resulting from different methods of preparation it could also be due to an incorrect definition of the unit cell[17] with respect to the fractional coordinates of the constituent atoms.

The successful determination of low symmetry crystals system using the Rietveld refinment technique is perhaps the ultimate bench–mark for the quality of our synchrotron powder data. The fact that a realistic structure can be obtained ab–initio for such a compound especially one having a low symmetry triclinic lattice indicates that the diffractometer on which the pattern was obtained has very high resolution and extremely low systematic errors.

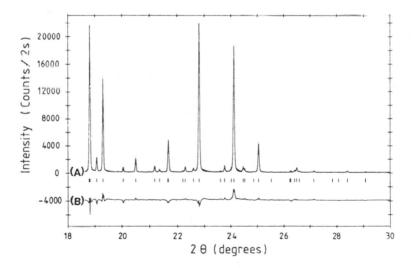

Figure 6a: Showing (A) the self–consistency between the basic experimental data and the pattern generated by use of the resulting fractional atom coordinates. Curve (B) gives the difference curve between the two patterns.

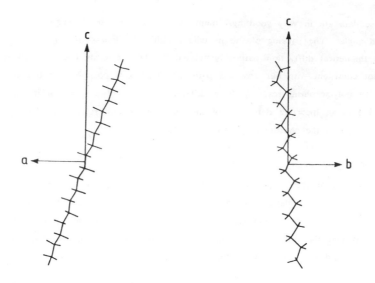

Figure 6b: The Rietveld refined molecular structure of $C_{18}H_{38}$.

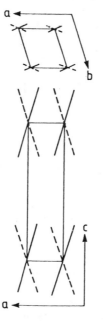

Figure 6c: The molecular packing observed (————) compared with that proposed by Nyburg and Luth[17] (– – – –).

4. Conclusions

This paper demonstrates that high quality data can be obtained using parallel-beam high resolution synchrotron radiation powder diffraction. The new facility of station 8.3 of the Daresbury SRS enables high quality data to be obtained from complicated systems such as n-alkanes which do not easily yield samples for conventional analysis. The data demonstrate diffraction peak resolution sufficient to allow unit cell indexing of triclinic unit cells, resolution of long lattice constants, indentification of phases in complex homologous mixtures and refinement of atomic parameters by the Reitveld method.

Acknowledgements

This work has been carried out as part of an SERC Co-operative research programme in collaboration with Exxon Chemicals. AG, KJR, JNS thank both bodies for their financial assistance. We also gratefully acknowledge the assistance of the Director of the Daresbury SRS and his staff for the provision of facilities and equipment.

REFERENCES

1) Hart, M. and Parrish, W., J. Mater. Res. In Press (1989)

2) Gerson, A. R., Roberts, K. J. and Sherwood, J. N., Submitted to Acta Cryst. (1989)

3) Luth, H., Nyburg, S. C., Robinson, P. M. and Scott, H. G., Mol. Cryst. Liq. Cryst. 27, 337 (1974)

4) Nyburg, S. C. and Potworowski, J. A., Acta. Cryst. B29, 347 (1973)

5) Wilson, A. J. C., Mathematical Theory of X-Ray Powder Diffractometry, Philyis, Eindhoven (1963)

6) Cox, D. E., Hasting, J. B., Thomlinson, W. and Prewitt, C. T., Nucl. Instrum. Methods. 208, 573 (1983)

7) Hastings, J. B., Thomlinson, W. and Cox, D. E., J. Appl. Cryst. 17, 85 (1984)

8) Parrish, W., Hart, M. and Huang, T. C., J. Appl. Cryst. Growth. 19, 92 (1986)

9) Hart, M., and Parrish., W., Materials Science Forum, 9, 39 (1986)

10) Lim, G., Parrish, W., Ortiz, C., Bellotto, M. and Hart, M., J. Mater. Res., 2, 471 (1987)

11) Visser, J. W., J. Appl. Chem., 2, 89 (1969)

12) Wolff, P. M. De., J. Appl. Cryst., 1, 108 (1968)

13) Ito, T., Nature Lond., 164, 755 (1948)

14) Crissman, J. M., Passaglia, E., Eby, R. K. and Colson J. P. J. Appl. Cryst. 3, 194 (1970)

15) Murray, A. D. and Fitch, A. N., "MPROF – A program for Multipattern Rietveld Refinement of Crystal Structures from X-Ray and Neutron Powder Data", To be published.

16) Rietveld H. M., J. Appl. Cryst., 2, 65 (1969)

17) Nyburg, S. C. and Luth, H., Acta Cryst. B28, 2992 (1972)

18) Muller, A. E. and Lonsdale, K., J. Chem,. Phys. 21, 2229 (1953)

Table 1. Unit Cell Parameters of Mixtures of $C_{20}H_{42}$
and $C_{22}H_{46}$ Crystallised from the Melt

$\%C_{20}$:* $\%C_{22}$	a(Å)	b(Å)	c(Å)	$\alpha(°)$	$\beta(°)$	$\gamma(°)$	Volume /Cell Å^3	Molecules /Cell
100:0	4.282	4.818	25.515	91.011	93.553	107.393	501.0	1
91: 9[3]	5.025	7.626	55.460	90.000	90.000	90.000	2125.3	4
80:20	5.024	7.648	56.335	90.000	90.000	90.000	2174.9	4
72:28[3]	5.025	7.657	57.460	90.000	90.000	90.000	2210.9	4
50:50	5.027	7.650	57.819	90.000	90.000	90.000	2223.4	4
42:58[3]	5.023	7.646	58.630	90.000	90.000	90.000	2251.7	4
27:73[3]	5.030	7.622	58.760	90.000	90.000	90.000	2252.8	4
0:100	4.289	4.823	27.903	91.433	92.477	107.903	548.4	1

* Concentration in the ratio (mole:mole).

Table 2. Cell Parameters of Mixtures of $C_{20}H_{42}$ and
$C_{22}H_{46}$ Crystallised from Solution

%C$_{20}$:*/%C$_{22}$	a(Å)	b(Å)	c(Å)	α(°)	β(°)	γ(°)	Volume/Cell Å^3	Molecules/Cell
100:0	4.282	4.818	25.515	91.011	93.553	107.393	501.0	1
95: 5	4.289	4.828	25.541	91.303	93.493	107.435	503.3	1
	5.022	7.688	57.011	90.000	90.000	90.000	2145.7	4
90:10	5.046	7.668	57.467	90.000	90.000	90.000	2201.2	4
75:25	5.046	7.668	57.467	90.000	90.000	90.000	2223.0	4
60:40	5.023	7.617	58.631	90.000	90.000	90.000	2243.6	4
55:45	4.983	7.539	59.179	90.000	90.000	90.000	2223.1	4
	4.637	6.974	28.032	84.135	93.188	97.516	893.2	2
			(d spacing 29.33)					
50:50	5.003	7.522	59.619	90.000	90.000	90.000	2243.5	4
	4.632	7.016	28.123	84.687	93.078	97.456	901.6	2
40:60	5.017	7.517	59.196	90.000	90.000	90.000	2232.5	4
	4.638	6.959	28.018	84.754	93.167	97.454	892.0	2
			(d spacing 29.21)					
30:70	4.980	7.505	59.213	90.000	90.000	90.000	2212.9	4
	4.639	7.002	28.009	84.547	93.132	97.232	897.7	2
			(d spacing 29.20)					
25:75	4.636	7.064	28.026	84.707	93.164	97.231	906.0	2
10:90	4.634	7.038	28.039	84.272	93.165	97.231	901.8	2
5 :95	4.959	7.503	58.599	90.000	90.000	90.000	2180.0	4
	4.292	4.829	27.916	91.662	92.237	107.180	549.8	1
0:100	4.289	4.823	27.903	91.433	92.477	107.903	548.4	1

* Original concentration in the ratio (mole:mole).

Table 3. Fractional Atomic Coordinates for n–Octodecane

	Fractional Coordinates		
	a	b	c
C1	−0.759	−0.175	0.440
C2	−0.710	−0.275	0.384
C3	−0.568	−0.051	0.341
C4	−0.408	−0.197	0.286
C5	−0.362	−0.004	0.238
C6	−0.354	−0.165	0.182
C7	−0.190	0.028	0.133
C8	−0.172	−0.131	0.076
C9	−0.001	0.074	0.030
H11	−0.622	0.045	0.456
H12	−0.992	−0.143	0.434
H13	−0.836	−0.301	0.482
H21	−0.535	−0.392	0.390
H22	−0.928	−0.425	0.365
H31	−0.735	0.068	0.330
H32	−0.336	0.092	0.356
H41	−0.425	−0.385	0.289
H42	−0.761	−0.262	0.271
H51	−0.118	0.095	0.255
H52	−0.467	0.175	0.229
H61	−0.216	−0.314	0.189
H62	−0.599	−0.283	0.167
II71	−0.333	0.171	0.125
H72	0.052	0.152	0.148
H81	−0.027	−0.274	0.085
H82	−0.413	−0.257	0.061
H91	0.104	0.001	0.112
H92	0.243	0.198	0.044

CRYSTALLISATION FROM THE LIQUID PHASE: RECENT *IN–SITU* DIFFRACTION EXPERIMENTS USING SYNCHROTRON RADIATION AT THE DARESBURY SRS

D. Cunningham[1], R. J. Davey[1,2], S.E. Doyle[1], A. R. Gerson[1], D. Hausermann[3], M. E. Herron[4], K. J. Roberts[1,5], J. Robinson[6], J. N. Sherwood[1], T. Shripathi[1] and F. C. Walsh[4,7]

[1]Department of Pure and Applied Chemistry
    University of Strathclyde, Glasgow G1 1XL, UK.

[2]ICI Chemicals and Polymers, Runcorn
    Cheshire WA7 4QE, UK

[3]Department of Crystallography,
    Birkbeck College, London WC1E 7HX, UK

[4]Department of Chemistry, University of Southampton,
    Southampton SO9 5NH, UK.

[5]SERC Daresbury Laboratory, Warrington WA4 4AD, UK.

[6]Department of Physics, University of Warwick,
    Coventry CV4 7AL, UK

[7]Department of Chemistry, Portsmouth Polytechnic,
    Portsmouth, PO1 2DT, UK

Abstract

An overview is given of recent experiments utilising the synchrotron radiation source at Daresbury Laboratory, UK. The techniques and experiments described all involve the use of X–ray diffraction for the study of the crystallisation of solids *in–situ*. Such experiments provide for the first time, a means of characterising the structural aspects of crystallisation phenomena at the atomic level.

1 INTRODUCTION

Many chemical processes are dependent at some stage upon crystal/fluid interactions, and it is obvious that an understanding of the role of the structure of the solid/liquid interface on crystallisation could have a significant impact on the optimisation and control of such processes. Analysis of crystal structure typically involves removal of the sample from the growth environment, leading to the loss of vital information concerning the nucleation or growth process, and to possible phase transformation and decomposition where the material is unstable outside of its growth environment. Despite the enormous potential benefits of the *in–situ* monitoring of crystallisation processes by X-ray methods, to date little work has been carried out in the field. Synchrotron X-ray sources offer many advantages for such *in–situ* experiments; synchrotron X-radiation is extremely intense and penetrating, the continuous wavelength spectrum offers the possibility of element specific experiments such as absorption spectroscopy and anomalous dispersion measurements, and the low divergence and sensitivity of X-rays to lattice strain and particle size make synchrotron radiation an ideal tool for the real-time study of *in–situ* crystallisation processes. In this paper we describe some recent *in–situ* studies of crystallisation, using the Synchrotron Radiation Source (SRS) at Daresbury Laboratory in the UK. The experiments involve the formation of $PbO_2/PbSO_4$ films on Pt electrodes, precipitation of long chain hydrocarbon waxes from solution and the growth and dissolution of the (100) surface of $NH_4H_2PO_4$.

2 X-RAY METHODS FOR *IN–SITU* CRYSTALLISATION STUDIES

The experiments described in this section outline three different approaches to the investigation of crystallisation phenomena *in–situ*. These approaches are to some extent dictated by the type of information required in each case, and in the present work involve the use of powder diffraction using a curved position sensitive detector, energy dispersive diffraction and high resolution triple axis diffraction in non-dispersive mode.

Generally in crystallisation experiments three features are of interest; firstly the kinetics of the process ie. the formation and development of nuclei and the detection of the initial stages of crystallisation, secondly the 'gross' crystallographic character of the material eg. structure, crystallite size, orientation etc, and lastly the 'high resolution' characterisation of surface specific phenomena such as lattice relaxation, impurity adsorption and surface strain. In each case it is possible to take advantage of a different aspect of the synchrotron X-ray source and different methods of detection of the scattered radiation, in order to optimise the experimental arrangement to the type of information being sought. In the first case for example, we are interested in the early stage of the crystallisation process and hence in acquiring data as quickly as possible. The requirement for high resolution is not so stringent, provided that we can identify characteristic peaks in the diffraction spectrum associated with the crystallisation of the material. In the second case we have need of moderate resolution combined with rapid data aquisition. In contrast, crystal growth on ordered single crystal faces involves subtle structural changes, such as those associated with boundary layer diffusion, surface adsorption and desolvation. Until now optical microscopy using phase contrast techniques has been the only means available for the *in–situ* study of such crystal surfaces, and this technique has provided useful information relating growth kinetics to surface morphology (steps, growth hillocks etc) on a scale of at best 5nm. However it provides no information on the local atomic structure at the growth interface. Indeed, the structural features of the crystal/solution interface are, at present, totally unknown. High resolution X-ray diffraction can provide a structural probe for the crystal/solution interface[1,2], analogous to the facilities available for characterising the vacuum/crystal interface (eg LEED, RHEED, ESCA).

Recent developments in curved position sensitive detectors provide a possible means of combining rapid data acquisition with relatively high resolution[3]. These gas filled proportional chambers operate with monochromatic radiation and offer relatively high count rate capabilities (around 2×10^5 cps), combined with good spatial resolution of the order of 0.02°. They thus offer a feasible alternative to solid state devices in real–time studies.

One of the disadvantages of such detectors is that for experiments involving surface or near surface studies, the extent of peak broadening, determined by the incident beam size, becomes prohibitive at relatively low incidence angles, typically around 1°. However, with data collection times of the order of a few minutes for unfocused radiation from a bending magnet, and significantly shorter (typically a few seconds) from focused wiggler radiation, the use of position sensitive detectors offers considerable potential for real−time studies. Figure 1 shows the experimental set−up for the *in−situ* electrochemistry studies, on station 7.4 at the SRS, and illustrates the use of the curved PSD for detection of scattering from electrode surfaces under potential control[4].

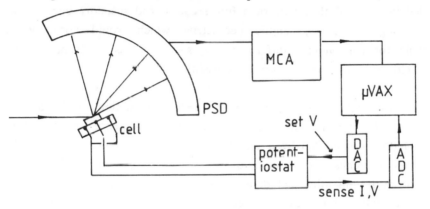

Figure 1: Schematic of experimental arrangement and data acquisition
for *in−situ* electrochemical studies on station 7.4 at the SRS

For energy dispersive X−ray diffraction (EDXRD) use is made of the continuous wavelength spectrum available from the synchrotron source in combination with an energy sensitive detector, typically a hyper−pure Ge or Si(Li) solid state device. Such devices have count rate capabilities of around 5x10⁴ cps, and a resolution of about 170eV at 6keV, or about 0.1Å. This makes them well suited to *in−situ* experiments requiring time resolution of the order of between 10 and 100 seconds.

The basis of energy dispersive diffraction derives from the alternative formulation of Bragg's law in terms of energy,

$$E \ (keV) = hc/\lambda = hc/2d \ \sin \theta = 6.2/d \ \sin \theta \qquad\qquad (1)$$

Each set of lattice planes satisfies Bragg's law for a discrete energy, and because all wavelengths are present in the incident beam a diffraction spectrum as a function of energy can be recorded at a fixed detector angle θ. Since the wiggler line at the SRS produces useful X–rays over an energy range between 5 and 60keV, the detector angle θ is chosen so that a significant fraction of the spectrum falls between these energies. The main advantages of the energy dispersive technique are twofold; firstly since no angular scanning is required the diffraction, spectrum can be recorded in times of the order of a few seconds, and secondly because the detector angle is fixed, sample geometries which would normally be unsuitable for conventional diffractometry, such as cells or furnaces with limited exit apertures, can be used successfully.

The experimental arrangement for EDXRD on station 9.7[5] at the Daresbury SRS is shown in figure 2. The axial divergence and therefore the resolution is contolled by a set of Soller slits placed prior to the solid state detector. These are composed of 25 metal foils 50 cm long each separated by 0.1mm. Slits and detector are both mounted on a 2θ rotation arm. Horizontal and vertical slits reduce the incident beam size to within the counting limits of the solid state detector.

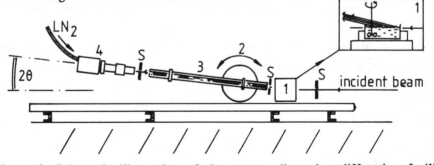

Figure 2: Schematic illustration of the energy dispersive diffraction facility on station 9.7 of the Daresbury SRS: 1) sample area, 2) rotary arm, 3) Soller slit, 4) detector, S – slits.

The crystallisation cell is shown in the inset to figure 2, and consists of a

6 cm diameter chamber surrounded by a temperature controlled water jacket. An inner Kapton wall allows the level of the solution to be raised above the surrounding glass to minimise scatter and absorption of the beam. The solution is stirred by a mechanical stirrer offset from the beam path, the incident beam passing horizontally through the Kapton wall to minimise absorption due to solution.

A detailed structural characterisation of interfacial processes requires the high resolution provided by single crystal diffraction in low dispersion triple–axis (monochromator/sample/analyser) mode. The +/+ setting of monochromator and analyser defines an illuminated region for which Bragg's law may be satisfied. The addition of the sample and the resulting +/–/+ set–up gives a rocking curve which is the intrinsic reflection width broadened slightly by any mismatch between monochromator and sample lattice spacings. This configuration enables very slight changes in crystal structure associated with crystallisation processes to be detected. The experimental set–up is shown in figure 3 with the resolution of the optical elements illustrated in the inset Du Mond diagram.[6]

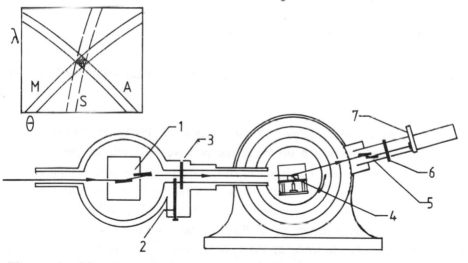

Figure 3: (a) The triple–axis geometry used on Station 9.4 of the Daresbury SRS: 1) monochromator, 2) beam stop, 3) slits, 4) cell, 5) analyser, 6) detector slit, 7) detector, (b) Du Mond representation of +/–/+ optics: M – monochromator, S – specimen, A – analyser

A crystal growth cell[7] for use with the triple–axis diffractometer is shown in figure 4. An associated temperature control system has been constructed and this system has been used for the present structural investigation of the growth interface.

Figure 4: *In–situ* crystal growth cell used in triple axis studies

3 EXPERIMENTAL RESULTS AND DISCUSSION

3.1 Crystallisation on Electrode Surfaces Under Conditions of Potential Control

The reversible electrochemical transformation of PbO_2 to $PbSO_4$ is the fundamental process which occurs at the positive electrode of the lead/acid battery. The reactions involved in this transformation are complex and, despite many studies, the structural changes taking place are still not well understood. In recent experiments[8,9] it has been possible to observe, *in–situ*, the transformation of α–PbO_2 (space group Pbcn) to β–PbO_2 (P42/mn) on a Pt electrode in 1M H_2SO_4. We have further been able to demonstrate that the phase transformation is pH dependent, as is the structure of the resulting surface layer. Figure 5 shows that diffraction patterns taken from these films over a large (ca. 60) number of oxidation/reduction cycles reveal a slow transformation from the initial 1 μm film of α–PbO_2 to an almost completely transformed film of β–PbO_2.

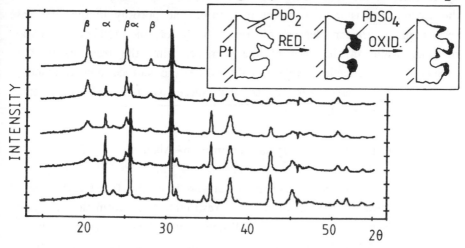

Figure 5: Transformation of α–PbO_2 to β–PbO_2 with increasing number of potential cycles of the electrode for the 'porous' electrode (see inset).

When the electrode surface is prepared at a different pH the α–PbO_2 film transforms to the β phase almost entirely within the first few cycles, as illustrated in figure 6.

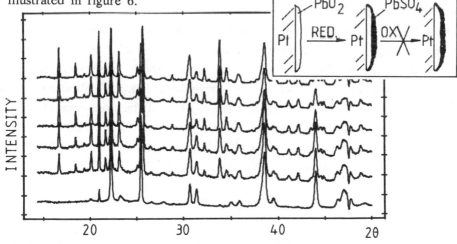

Figure 6 : transformation of β–PbO_2 to $PbSO_4$, for the 'non–porous' electrode, (see inset)

As will be described more fully elsewhere,[8] the effect can be rationalised by considering the first PbO_2 film as a porous, conducting electrode, while the second film is more compact in nature. The porosity in the first case results in a greater degree of reversibility of the reduction/oxidation reaction, while in the case of the compact film, the transformation to $PbSO_4$ in the reduction cycle rapidly makes the surface non−conducting, inhibiting the reverse reaction, so that successive potential cycles show little change in the phase composition.

3.2 EDXRD Studies of the Crystallisation of n−Alkanes

The crystallisation of long chain hydrocarbons is of significant technological interest in view of the importance of restricting wax formation in diesel and home heating fuels. The crystallisation of waxes is complex due to their mixed homologous content, and *in−situ* studies could provide important structural information on the crystallising material. Correlated with kinetic data this would provide a better insight into the mechanisms involved in the crystallisation process.

The technique of energy dispersive powder diffraction is ideal for real−time analysis of wax crystallisation, since relatively low angle (and hence long d−spacing) data can be collected in seconds. This is of benefit when dealing with waxes which often have extremely long unit cells. Detection using a PSD is not trivial under these conditions, so the approach used in section 3.1 is not convenient. Figure 7 illustrates the dependence of peak position on detector angle, and the occurence of large peaks at low diffraction angles due to the low order $00l$ reflections. The patterns shown are from eicosane ($C_{20}H_{42}$) which is triclinic ($P\bar{1}$) with lattice parameters a=4.285, b=4.820, c=25.529, α=93.56, β=93.56, γ=107.41.[10]

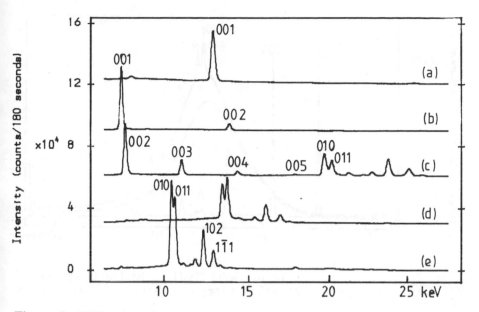

Figure 7: Diffraction Patterns of solid $C_{20}H_{42}$ at varying detector angles. (a) 1˚, (b) 2˚, (c) 4˚, (d) 6˚, (e) 8˚.

Figure 8 shows EDXRD patterns of solid $C_{20}H_{42}$, together with *in–situ* patterns of undersaturated and crystallised samples of 50% $C_{20}H_{42}$ in $C_{12}H_{26}$ (dodecane). All spectra were recorded for 10 minutes with a detector angle of 3.05˚. Well resolved, identifiable peaks are observed in the diffraction patterns of samples containing crystalline material. By comparing the spectra it is apparent that all the (00l) peaks are absent when solvent is present. From the spectra obtained from the pure and crystallised samples of $C_{20}H_{42}$ it is possible to confirm that the structure of this material is the same in the solution environment and that no phase change occurs on the removal of $C_{20}H_{42}$ from its growth environment. It is thus possible to investigate crystallisation of homologous mixtures of long chain hydrocarbons where it is known[11,12] that the growth environment influences structure. From this work it is possible to see the applicability of this method for *in–situ* structural confirmation and its potential for studies of crystallisation.

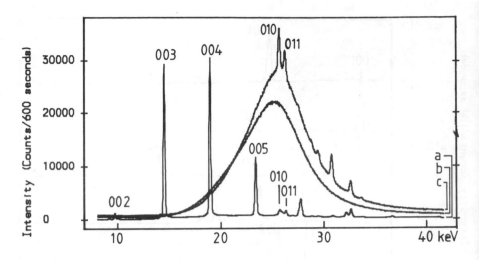

Figure 8: Diffraction patterns of (a) Solid $C_{20}H_{42}$, (b) Liquid solution of 50% $C_{20}H_{42}$ in $C_{12}H_{26}$, (c) 50% $C_{20}H_{42}$ crystallised in $C_{12}H_{26}$. $2\theta = 3.05°$.

3.3 Crystal Growth on the (100) Surface of $NH_4H_2PO_4$

High resolution X-ray diffraction has been used to study crystal growth on the (100) surface of ammonium dihydrogen phosphate ($NH_4H_2PO_4$ or ADP), in aqueous solution. Large, typically 20x20x5mm, high quality single crystals of ADP were mounted in the cell and aligned for diffraction from the (200) lattice plane at a Bragg angle of 4.72° and wavelength of 0.618Å. X-ray rocking curves of the crystal were recorded under a variety of surface conditions; in air, under a covering of n-hexane and under a saturated aqueous solution of ADP. In air, the rocking curves measured for the ADP crystals were found to be extremely sharp with a half width of slightly less than 4" arc. Allowing for the slight dispersion in triple axis mode, this compares favourably with a theoretically predicted value of 2.5". When covered with an insoluble solvent, in this case n-hexane, there was no noticable variation in the diffraction profile, but on replacing the n–hexane with a saturated solution of ADP the *in–situ* reflection curve broadened asymmetrically to a width of 14". On dissolution of the crystal, induced by a step increase in the growth cell temperature, the reflection width increased again, showing the process to be reversible. Rapid recording of the rocking curve as dissolution proceeded showed this process to occur within several minutes and to reach eqilibrium within 1 hour. Figure 9 shows data taken during the subsequent regrowth of the crystal surface, initiated through cooling the cell, and the results in general mirror the principal observations of the dissolution experiment[7].

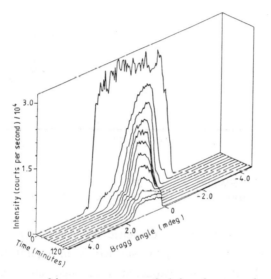

Figure 9: X–ray rocking curves recorded *in–situ* as a function of time during re–growth on the (100) face of ADP.

The growth process at this interface was also investigated through the evaporation of solvent from saturated solution. When the change in curve width is plotted as a function of time, (figure 10), it is found that there are four main regions. Point A relates to the rocking curve width in air. On addition of a thin layer of solution the value increases rapidly to 9.7" (point B). This is then followed by a more gradual increase to 14.9". The rocking curve width remains constant at this value until point D whereupon there is a substantial decrease to 6", consistent with the loss of solvent until a point is reached where the system cannot continue to support an interfacial layer; the final value of 6" arc is related to the formation of an imperfect solid surface layer caused by rapid crystal growth.

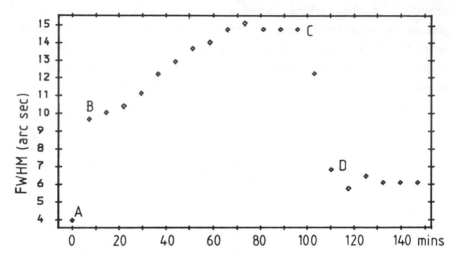

Figure 10: Plot of the FWHM of the 200 reflection during crystal growth induced by solvent evaporation at the crystal/solution interface.

From these experiments there is evidence of an interfacial layer, of substantial thickness, when the crystal surface is in equilibrium with the saturated solution. It might be expected that such an interface would consist of weakly bonded layers. Additionally these layers would be highly labile and at the outset of crystallisation or dissolution thermal fluctuations would destroy the interfacial ordering and hence the diffraction conditions for this region. This supposition is supported by the study of the dynamic change in reflection curve shape and width. The transformation is rapid; in both cases involving temperature change the rocking curves reduce to half their initial width in under three minutes. After this initial reduction in width there follows a longer period as the interface returns to an equilibrium state – possibly involving an ordered interfacial structure. The structure for the interfacial layer remains speculative but it will undoubtedly involve varying degrees of surface relaxation and solvation, as well as the formation of a preorientated layer of NH_4^+ and $H_2PO_4^-$ ions. Within this region the intermolecular forces will be weaker and this would be reflected in an increase in disorder and hence mosaic spread.

4 CONCLUSIONS

The feasibility of utilising synchrotron X-ray diffraction for the real-time *in-situ* crystallisation has been demonstrated. The ability to obtain X-ray data from the crystal surface/liquid boundary, under both equilibrium and non-equilibrium conditions, illustrates the potential of these techniques for the determination of the interrelationship between structure and kinetics at interfaces.

Acknowledgements

The SERC is gratefully acknowledged for financial support of the research described here as well as for providing experimental facilities at the Daresbury SRS. The high resolution studies were carried out as part of a co-operative research programme in collaboration with Dr. R. J. Oldman at ICI Chemicals and Polymers Group. We also gratefully acknowledge EXXON Chemicals for their generous and continuing support of wax crystallisation research at Strathclyde.

References

[1] Ryan, T. W., Ph.D. Thesis, University of Edinburgh, 1986
[2] Fewster P. F., J. Appl. Cryst. 22 64 (1989)
[3] Pons, F., Megtert, S., Pivin, J. C., Perquinot, M., Mairey, D., and Roques-Carmes, C., J. Appl. Cryst. 21 197 (1988)
[4] Barlow, N., Brennan, C., Doyle, S. E., Greaves, G. N., Miller, M., Nahlé, A. H., Roberts, K. J., Robinson, J., Sherwood, J. N. and Walsh, F. C., Rev. Sci. Instrum. 60 2386 (1989)

244

[5] Clark, S. M., Nucl. Instrum. Meth., <u>A276</u> 387 (1989)

[6] Du Mond, J. W. M., Phys. Rev., <u>52</u> 871 (1937)

[7] Cunningham, D., Davey, R. J., Roberts, K. J. and Shripathi, T.
J. Cryst. Growth, <u>99</u> 1065 (1990)

[8] Doyle, S. E., Herron, M. E., Roberts, K. J., Robinson, J. and
Walsh, F. C., Appl. Surf. Sci., in preparation

[9] Doyle, S. E., Herron, M. E., Greaves, G. N., Roberts, K. J.,
Robinson, J. and Walsh, F. C., Il Nuovo Cimento, 1990, in press

[10] Gerson, A. R., Roberts, K. J. and Sherwood, J. N.
submitted to Acta. Cryst. B

[11] Gerson, A. R., Hausermann, D., Roberts, K. J., and
Sherwood, J. N., J. Cryst. Growth, <u>99</u> 145 (1990)

[12] Gerson, A. R., Roberts, K. J., Sherwood, J. N., Cernik, R.,
Fitch, A. N. and Pattison, P., these proceedings

THIN CRYSTAL MONOCHROMATORS FOR SYNCHROTRON
RADIATION AT BRAGG ANGLE NEAR π/2

S.Caticha-Ellis and Ariel Caticha
Instituto de Fisica "Gleb Wataghin"
Universidade Estadual de Campinas
CP 6165,Campinas,S.P.,13081,Brasil

ABSTRACT

A well-known problem which affects monochromators for synchrotron radiation is that the crystal lattice is impaired by the intense incident radiation. In this paper we demonstrate that this problem can be avoided using a thin crystal reflecting at Bragg angle close to π/2 as a monochromator; most of the incoming radiation is just transmitted through the crystal without heating or destroying it, while radiation of the appropriate wavelength is diffracted back with a very high efficiency.

The suggestion made by one of us[1], that back-reflected beams, to which S.R. sources are transparent, can be reintroduced into the storage ring insertion and used on the back side to perform back scattering experiments, has recently been studied[2] with a view to developing possible arrangements to be introduced at SSRL for SPEAR and PEP, as this would provide a new, relatively cheap, clean and very unique facility for back-scattering experiments.

In this paper we demonstrate that there are definite advantages in using a thin crystal as the back-reflecting monochromator[3] First, the lattice monochromator degradation problem would be greatly diminished, and second, the synchrotron radiation of the "wrong" wavelengths would be transmitted with little losses. This radiation can still be used on a beam line behind the thin crystal π/2 monochromator where the whole SR spectrum except for a very thin slice will be completely available.
In other words a new monochromatic beam line will be created at a very low additional cost.

INTRODUCTION

The reflected and transmitted intensities diffracted by thin crystals at Bragg angles near Π/2 have recently been calculated[3] as a function of the angle of incidence, of the energy of the incident photons, and of the thickness. Both reflected and transmitted beams display several interesting features. Typical profiles are shown in Fig.1, calculated for the (333) reflection from a crystal of copper 10 μm thick taken with CuKβ radiation , a new matching pair at the easily accessible temperature of about 58°C [3, 4].

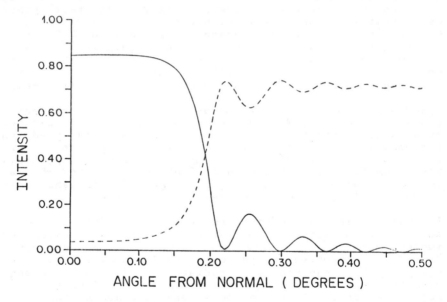

Fig.1. (333) reflection (solid line) and transmission (dashed line) coefficients for a copper crystal 10 μm thick and Cu Kβ radiation as a function of the angle of incidence measured from the normal to the planes at constant temperature of 57°C.

Pendellösung fringes are clearly seen on both profiles at separations of the order of several minutes of arc rather than seconds as is common for Bragg angles far from Π/2.

The transmitted beam has a relatively large angular central region where the crystal is practically non-transparent for the appropriate wavelength, and where the reflected beam is very intense. Accordingly, we have suggested [3,4] the use of thin crystals diffracting at nearly Π/2, as monochromators for synchrotron radiation. Thin crystals have been used in the past as monochromators for synchrotron radiation for Bragg angles not close to Π/2[5]. Their use is, however, subject to strict requirements of mechanical stability of the thin crystal device, and of crystalline and surface perfection. The large angular width of the reflected beam in this regime suggests that crystal perfection is far less important here, so that the preparation of the thin crystal should be much simpler than when it is to be used at common Bragg angles for then the diffracted peaks are angularly very narrow . The influence of bulk and surface defects, found for instance by Renninger[6] are then not to be feared here. Thus, thin

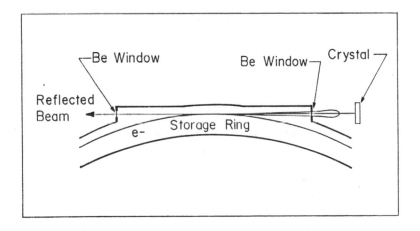

Fig.2. Conceptual design of a back-reflection beam line. After Reference 2.

crystals for this purpose can be obtained by different methods such as thinning down a thicker wafer by etching techniques , standard deposition methods and even by cleavage.

In a recent paper [2] it was demonstrated that reintroducing the back — reflected beam dynamically diffracted at $\theta = \Pi/2$ in the storage ring insertion is actually possible and that if a suitable exit port is provided a monochromatic (with harmonics) beam line is available on the opposite side of the beam line(Fig.2). The method outlined in that paper makes use of a channel — cut monochromator that chooses a wavelength tuned so as to be back—reflected into the storage ring by a given crystal. Since the reflectivity of the latter is very high (over 95%) the main loss in intensity will originate in the chan n el— cut monochromator, a normal component in synchrotron radiation beam lines , therefore the monochromatic back—reflected beam intensity will be very high and could be used for any experiment, in particular to study the reflection profile at $\Pi/2$ without the problems normally caused by the incident beam.

The present development results from a combination of both lines of thought, i.e. using the idea of reintroducing a back—reflected beam into the storage ring, and using a thin crystal simultaneously as a monochromator and as the back reflecting crystal. This is possible since as we have shown in references (3,4)and as is quite obviousfrom Fig.1, the reflectivity of the thin crystal at $\Pi/2$ is still very high

Determining the influence of parameters such as thickness, orientation, absorption coefficient and lattice parameters is essential to determine the shape of the reflection and transmission profiles as well as to select the wavelengths in ranges which may be useful for different applications. Finally, we calculate the energy absorbed by thin crystals of graphite to determine whether they will be

able to dissipate the heat and stand the thermal conditions
to which they will be submitted.

THE THIN CRYSTAL MONOCHROMATOR AT Π/2

The main characteristics observed in Fig.1 for a 10 μm
copper crystal are high reflectivity (85%) in an angular
interval of about half a degree, very low transmission

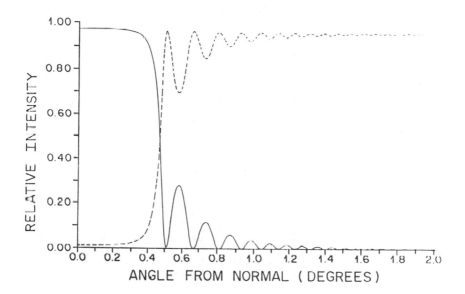

Fig 3.—(004) reflection (solid line) and transmission
(dashed line) for a graphite crystal 5μm thick at near
normal incidence as a function of the angle of
incidence measured as a function from the normal to the
planes.

(between 4' and 10%) within the Bragg diffraction region and
very high outside it. These indicate that within a narrow
spectral window the beam is back-reflected with high
efficiency while the rest of the spectrum traverses the

crystals with small losses of energy. All these
characteristics are enhanced when crystals containing only
light elements, i.e., low absorbing materials, are used.
This is the case for graphite; Fig.3 shows the calculated
values for the (004) reflection of a graphite crystal 5μm
thick reflecting near Π/2 X-ray photons of energy about
3.694 KeV. In this case the maximum reflectivity is about
98% and the angular width of the reflected peak close to

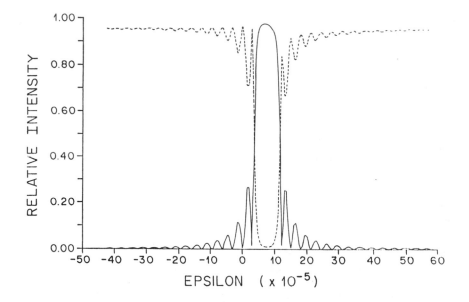

Fig.4. (004) reflection (solid line) and transmission
(dashed line) as a function of energy for a graphite
crystal 5 μm thick. The "detuning" parameter ε
expresses the relative departure of energy as defined
in the text.

one degree. Transmission in the same region goes from a
minimum close to 1% to about 5%, increasing very rapidly
afterwards. The energy width of the peak is about 0.2 eV as
seen in Fig.4 where reflection and transmission

coefficients are plotted against the energy of the photon
for a fixed angle of incidence. The energy of the photon is
conveniently measured as a function of a detuning parameter
ε defined as :

$$\varepsilon = \frac{2 d}{\lambda} - 1 = \frac{\Delta E_B}{E_B} \qquad [1]$$

Typically the range in ε where diffraction occurs is of the
order of χ ($\cong 10^{-5}$) or some tenths of an electron volt,
and less for higher order reflections.
The fact that a thin crystal diffracting at $\Pi/2$ offers a
high reflectivity for wavelengths within a narrow
spectral band while transmitting those outside it with a
very high efficiency can be used with great advantage to
provide a very elegant way of bypassing the problem caused
by the intense radiation power dissipated as heat by usual
monochromators used in conjunction with synchrotron
radiation as well as the subsequent damage of their crystal
lattices. Therefore, two problems that have to be analyzed
are how much of the SR power is absorbed by a thin crystal
$\Pi/2$ monochromator and also how the crystal perfection
influences the performance of the monochromator.
We perform the calculations for a typical synchrotron
radiation incident beam such as that produced by SPEAR Bend
Magnet operating at 2 GeV and a thin graphite crystal
operating as a $\Pi/2$ monochromator.
The spectral distribution function of SR expressed as the
number of photons/(sec.mrad.mA.10%bandwidth) has been
given, for instance, by Winick[7]. The total incident
power calculated from this curve is 0.3
Watt/(mA.horiz.mRad), or 30 Watt/horiz.mRad for a nominal
current of 100 mA.
The necessary data for graphite are given in Table I. The
linear absorption coefficients μ were calculated by using

TABLE I
GRAPHITE DATA

Melting point : 3527 $^\circ$C , C Kα = 44 Å
Density : 2.26 g/cm^3 , K$_{abs, edge}$ = 43.65 Å or 0.28 KeV

Planes	d(Å)	λ(Å)	$\hbar\omega$(KeV)	μ(cm^{-1})	Λ_e(μm)
002	3.36	6.71	1.846	770.	13
004	1.678	3.36	3.692	101.	99
006	1.120	2.24	5.538	30.5	328
008	0.841	1.68	7.384	13.2	757

TABLE II

POWER ABSORBED BY A THIN GRAPHITE CRYSTAL MONOCHROMATOR

	1st Crystal		2nd Crystal		P$_a$ for I=100 mA	
P$_i$	t$_1$	P$_a$	t$_2$	P$_a$	1st Crys.	2nd Crys
0.3	5	0.022	5	0.007	2.2	0.7
0.3	10	0.029	5	0.005	2.9	0.5
0.3	5	0.022	10	0.012	2.2	1.2
0.3	10	0.029	10	0.008	2.9	0.8

the empirical Victoreen equation [8]. The lengths $\Lambda_e(\lambda)$ in μm are the mean path of a photon of energy $\hbar\omega$ in graphite. In Table II we give the values P_a of the power absorbed by a crystal of thickness t_1 (5 or 10 μm) standing in front of the incident beam of power $P_i = 0.3$ Watt/(mA.mRad), (1st crystal) and for a second graphite crystal (thickness t_2, 2nd crystal) when there is an interposed graphite sheet (t_1). For a nominal current of 100 mA in the storage ring, $P_i = 30$ Watt/mRad, the P_a values for both crystals appear in the last two columns. It is perhaps worth pointing out that P_a is the power absorbed by one square centimeter of the crystal at a distance of 10 meters.

In Fig.5 we have represented the spectral distribution of the power incident on the crystal (curve A) adapted from ref.7, and the spectral distribution of the power absorbed by a graphite crystal 5 μm thick (curve B). Notice that photons of energy less than about 1 KeV are almost totally absorbed while for higher energies the crystal is practically transparent. Curve C shows the spectral distribution of the additional power absorbed by a second crystal 5 μm thick placed behind the first. The sum of curves B plus C is, of course, the power absorbed by a 10 μm thick crystal. Since most of the power is absorbed by the first crystal (or the equivalent amount of the same amorphous material) the second crystal will be protected against undue heating and would certainly have a much longer useful life as a reflector.

In Table II we show the values of the calculated total absorbed power. These values are low enough that they can be easily dissipated by the thin graphite crystals. This finds an experimental confirmation in the fact that pyrolitic graphite absorbers of 5 to 10 μm installed before the beryllium windows are routinely used to protect them from the long wavelength radiation[7].

254

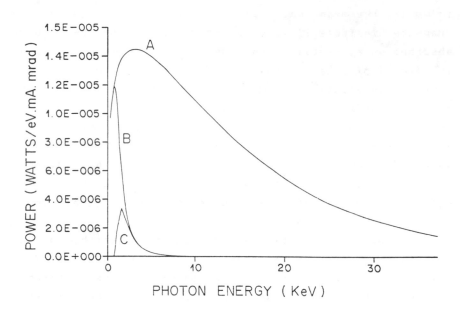

Fig 5 Curve **A** represents the spectral distribution of energy of the power incident on the crystal (adapted from **Ref.7**). Curve **B** is the spectral distribution of the power absorbed by a **5** μm thick graphite crystal. Curve **C** shows the spectral distribution of power absorbed by a second **5** μm crystal placed behind the first.

As for the influence of crystal perfection, we recall that in the diffraction regime we are dealing with here, the angular width of reflection calculated by using the Dynamical theory of X-ray scattering, is about three orders of magnitude larger than those for Bragg angle far from $\Pi/2$,[9] (some tenths of minutes rather than seconds of arc). Therefore, the change of reflectivity due to a change of Bragg angle will be entirely different in the two cases[2] For a nearly perfect crystal diffracting at an angle far from $\Pi/2$, a small change of a fraction of a second may produce a large change in reflectivity, a well known fact which is responsible for the high stability and mechanical precision needed to perform such experiments. For Bragg angles near $\Pi/2$, that we use here, the angular width for graphite is about one degree (Fig. 3), so that the incident beam direction is not so critical. A relatively large angular deviation from its mean position will produce a small change in reflectivity. Conversely, for crystals which are not perfect or have been damaged, possessing a mosaic spread of several minutes, the different mosaic blocks are still within the limits of the reflectivity peak, they reflect with practically the same intensity, and there will be little fall-off in reflectivity. For this reason the experiment can be done with imperfect or moderately damaged crystals, which is very convenient for the life expectancy of the thin crystal $\Pi/2$ monochromator, particularly those with a high melting point. That is why a HOPG (highly oriented pyrolitic graphite) crystal, in spite of its imperfections, would be quite suitable as a $\Pi/2$ monochromator using the basal reflections (00l).

CONCLUSIONS

1) Our previous suggestion [3,4] of using thin crystals at Bragg angles near $\Pi/2$ as SR monochromators has been combined with the idea of reintroducing the back-reflected beam into the storage ring [1,2].

2) This new arrangement simplifies considerably the proposal recently made in ref. (2), since the thin crystal $\Pi/2$ monochromator would substitute both the channel- cut monochromator and the crystal reflecting at $\Pi/2$. The geometry and most constructive details thus become considerably simplified.

3) Heating problems due to the X-ray absorption in thick crystals, such as in the channel-cut monochromator are eliminated. The heat absorbed by thin crystals (Table II) can be easily dissipated as is well known from daily experience in synchrotron radiation.

4) A HOPG thin crystal of thickness of about 5 to 10 μm may perhaps be oriented within the vacuum chamber in the same position where it is normally used to protect the beryllium window to produce the desired back-reflected monochromatic beam. Since the angular orientation is not so critical, there is a non-negligible chance that in some beam lines presently operating the HOPG is already back reflecting a monochromatic beam, although without a back exit port it cannot be observed.

5) Should the implementation of the orientation device for the internal HOPG crystal turn out to be impractical in existing beam lines a second crystal may be placed outside the storage ring close to the beryllium window. The calculations which appear in Table II under the heading 2nd crystal are then applicable.

6) The present proposal would allow one to obtain two beam lines out of a single one:

(a) A monochromatic (with harmonics) back-reflected beam of high intensity. Since the reflectivity of the thin crystal is higher than that of the channel-cut monochromator, the proposed back-reflected beam should have a correspondingly higher intensity.

(b) A polychromatic transmitted beam line which should be practically unaffected by the HOPG crystal except for the removal of a few spectrally thin slices of energy width about 0.2 eV or less at the specific energies given in Table II. Thus practically the whole continuum spectrum will continue to be available and usable in the same way as before.

7) The additional back-reflected monochromatic beam can

be created at a remarkably low cost.

8) As in the proposal of ref. (2) the wavelength of the back- reflected beam can be changed by appropriately selecting different thin crystals.

Acknowledgments

The authors acknowledge financial support from FINEP, FAPESP and FAP and a useful discussion with Dr. J. Arthur.

References

1.-Caticha-Ellis,S.,Anais do Encontro"Técnicas e Aplicações da Radiação Sincrotron" (In Portuguese),CBPF,Rio de Janeiro, 240-257 (1983).

2.-Caticha-Ellis,S. Boyce,R. and Winick,H. .Paper presented to the 6th. National Conference on Synchrotron Radiation Instrumentation, Berkeley,Ca. USA Aug.1989.Accepted for publication in the Proceedings to appear in Nucl.Instr.& Meth.

3.-Caticha,A. and Caticha-Ellis,S.. To appear in Phys. St.Sol.(b).

4.-Caticha-Ellis, S. and Caticha, A., Proceedings of the Hefei International Conference on Synchrotron Radiation Applications (Hefei, People's Republic of China, May 1989).

5.-Dix, W.-R., et al, Nucl. Instr. and Meth. A246, 702 (1986).

6.-Renninger, M., Acta Cryst. A31, 42 (1975).

7.-Winick,H.,in "Synchrotron Radiation Research",Winick,H. and Doniach,S.,(eds.), Plenum Press, New York and London (1980).

8.- International Tables for X-ray Crystallography, Vol. III, The Kynoch Press, Birmingham, England (1989).

9.-Caticha, A. and Caticha-Ellis, S.,Phys. Rev., B25, 971, (1982).

AN X-RAY BEAMLINE FOR THE LNLS

C. Cusatis & C. Giles

Departamento de Física, Universidade Federal do Paraná

Caixa Postal 19091, 81504 Curitiba, Brazil

Abstract

An x-ray optics and high energy-resolution beamline for the XUV ring at LNLS is described. It consists of a monochromator serving a station for x-ray optics and another for high energy-resolution experiments. The constant offset, vacuum compatible double crystal monochromator is to be mounted in a bending magnet or wiggler port and will be located as near as possible of the ring. One rotation movement of both mechanically linked crystals and one short elastic translation of each crystal covers the energy range of 1 to 10 KeV. For $\theta_B \approx 90$ on the first monochromator crystal the monochromatized beam is sent back through the electron ring and is received on the opposite side of the line at the high energy-resolution station. The main instrument at the x-ray optics station will be a triple axis diffractometer. This station, located as far as possible of the ring and, possibly, outside of main hall, will be used for x-ray interferometry, perfect crystal diffractometry, etc.

1. Introduction

Small and modern low emittance storage rings can be a good source of synchrotron light in the x-ray range (specially from insertion devices) if the optics and the chosen experiments are appropriate.

The LNLS XUV ring (~ 1.15 GeV) is one of such machines. Some interesting experiments with soft (1 to 4 KeV) and normal (4 to 10 KeV) x-rays, that would be difficult or impossible to do with laboratory sources, can be accomplished even with bending magnet light.

Our goal was to design an x-ray beamline for experiments that can benefits from particular properties of the first Brazilian storage ring.

2. Conceptual Design

The XUV ring at LNLS has critical wavelength in the soft x-ray region and a not negligible flux from the bending magnet at 10 KeV energy: 5×10^9 photons/s.mrad 0.1% BW, or 4×10^{11} from a 2 Tesla 12 poles wiggler[1].

The beamline consists of a fixed-exit double crystal monochromator with Bragg angle range of 10 to 80 degrees serving two workstations: an x-ray optics station located in the end of the line, possibly outside of the main hall, to be used for x-ray experiments as perfect crystal diffractometry; and a high energy-resolution station located in the opposite side of the line, served by a backscattered beam from the first crystal of the monochromator diffracting at 90 degrees (see fig.1).

The line will provide monochromatic radiation for experiments in the soft to normal x-ray region (1 to 10 KeV). This spectral range is difficult to be covered because different experimental techniques are employed in the two limiting cases but is the more energetic useful spectral region of this ring.

Soft x-ray experiments are still possible with a light tight 10 μm thick beryllium foil between the source and the monochromator, necessary to decouple the UHV of the storage ring from the monochromator vacuum. At 1 KeV energy, the transmitted intensity is about 33 % of the incident beam or 3.3×10^{12} of flux. The attenuation for such energy at the normal vacuum (10^{-2} torr), from the monochromator till the experiment at the end of the line, if the residual air is not changed by helium, is only 8 % of the incident beam.

A removable (for soft x-ray experiments) beryllium window of 250 microns before the x-ray optics station attenuates less than 4 % an 8 KeV beam and allows x-ray experiments to be performed at atmospheric pressure. The moderate energy of the storage ring reduces drastically the problem of harmonics at the normal x-ray region.

The monochromator, placed the nearest possible of the source ($\sim$ 5 meters) allows small crystals, 60 mm in length for an acceptance angle of 10 mrad, to be used. The calculated power incident on the first crystal is approximately 6.4 W /100mA; so, beam heating shall not be a serious problem.

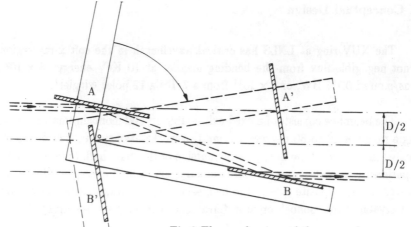

Fig.2 The mechanism of the monochromator. Crystals positions (A and B) and (A' and B') corresponds to Bragg angles of 10 and 80 degrees, respectively. Point O denotes the center of rotation and D is the constant offset in the beam height.

Fig.1 Schematic view of the x-ray beam line for the LNLS XUV ring.

3. Monochromator

Several fixed-exit double crystal monochromators has been proposed and constructed for synchrotron radiation[2-5]. Basically, the conceptual design differ in the number of translational and rotational degrees of freedom of each crystal. Two classical designs can be distinguished: two rotational and one translational degrees of freedom[2] and one rotational and two translational degrees of freedom[3-5].

The monochromator proposed here follows one of these classical designs: is a two independent but angularly coupled crystals with linear movements in perpendicular directions in order to keep a constant output beam position as the energy is scanned. The system, with two possible settings, is shown in fig.2.

The main feature of this monochromator is its mechanical simplicity, with one rotational movement and one short elastic translation of each crystal. It differs from Golovchenko's monochromator[3] by the fact that the center of rotation is not placed directly on the first crystal but at the point of intersection defined by the surface of the second crystal and the normal to the surface of the first crystal, halfway between the incident and the outgoing beams.

The first crystal not just rotates, as in the Golovchenko's monochromator, but it moves back and forth on the input direction. This could be a drawback since the acceptance angle varies for different energies, but for the Bragg angle range of 10 to 80 degrees with a small constant offset, the first crystal translation produces very small variations in the acceptance angle.

Elastic translation systems were chosen for the good angular stability during translation, that can be better than 1 arcsecond of wobbling for 12 mm displacement and better than 1 arcsecond per hour for long time stability[6]. A possible model for the elastic translator is shown in fig. 3.

This type of system becomes awkward for long displacements. Translations of about 50 mm, as proposed for this monochromator, are easily achieved with good angular stability.

From geometrical considerations of the principle upon which the monochromator works it can be shown that the maximum translation range, T_{max}, and the constant offset, D, are related by the following expression (for the first crystal):

Crystal holder

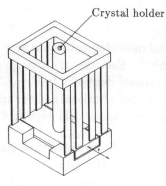

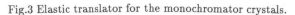

Fig.3 Elastic translator for the monochromator crystals.

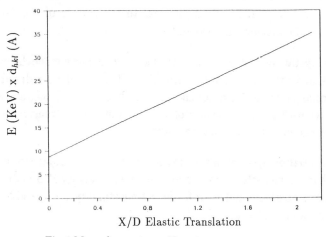

Fig.4 Monochromator calibration curve.

$$T_{max} = \frac{D}{2} \frac{(\cos\theta_i - \cos\theta_f)}{(\cos\theta_i \cos\theta_f)} \qquad (1)$$

where θ_i and θ_f are the initial and final Bragg angles. So, a short maximum translation can be obtained choosing a small constant offset. For the chosen Bragg angle range and maximum translation a constant offset value of 21.1 mm is obtained.

The calibration curve for this type of monochromator is shown in fig. 4, allowing conversion of the linear positions of the second crystal to x-ray energies (in KeV). It was calculated using

$$E \times d_{hkl} = 24.8\frac{\chi}{D} + \frac{12.4}{\sin\theta_i} \qquad (2)$$

where E is the beam energy in keV, d_{hkl} is the Miller plane spacing in Angstroms, θ_i is an arbitrary origin angle, D is the offset beam height and χ is the linear position of the second crystal.

The rotational movement of the monochromator is provided by a standard heavy weight goniometer, placed outside of the vacuum system and with motion transmitted using a feed-through . Schematic designs of the monochromator are shown in figures 5 and 6.

Since the energy range can not be covered by a unique pair of crystals, a carousel system allows the interchangeability of crystals without breaking the vacuum of the monochromator. Table 1 shows the energy ranges of four crystals that can be mounted in one of the carousels.

Table 1. Energy ranges with different crystals for Bragg angles between 10 and 80 degrees.

Crystals	Bragg Planes	2d ($\overset{\circ}{A}$)	E_{min} (KeV)	E_{max} (KeV)
Beryl	(10$\bar{1}$0)	15.95	0.8	4.5
InSb	(111)	7.48	1.7	9.6
Si	(111)	6.27	2.0	11.4
Ge	(220)	4.00	3.2	17.9

Several other optional features for the crystals monochromator are possible like sagittal focusing, elastic θ_B detuning, and thermal stabilization. An ultra thin

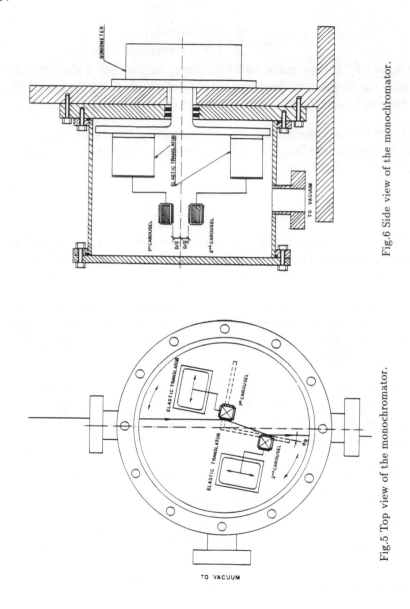

Fig.6 Side view of the monochromator.

Fig.5 Top view of the monochromator.

crystal[7] can be used, if necessary, as the first monochromator crystal, to avoid beam heating problems.

4. Workstations

The x-ray optics station is to be used as general purpose port for different techniques like perfect crystals diffractometry (interferometry, double crystal rocking curves, topography, standing waves) and for different experiments like measurements of the real and imaginary part of scattering factors ($f_0 + f'$ and f'' or n_R and n_I), structural characterization of semiconductors, energy-dispersive fluorescence spectrometry and instrumentation.

A triple-axis diffractometer and a solid-state detector are the basic instruments for such station, besides electronics and computer. High vacuum is not necessary for 1 KeV experiments and 10^{-2} torr feed-throughs are not difficult to implement.

In backscattering, as the energy resolution is proportional to the structure factor[8], the forbidden reflection Si(222), with 4 KeV photons (not far from the XUV ring critical energy) should give ΔE better than 10 meV[9]. Beams such this, backscattered from the first crystal of the monochromator, can be used at the high energy- resolution station, located on the opposite side of the line, for experiments like measurements of diffraction curves at $\theta_B \approx \frac{\pi}{2}$, high energy- resolution EXAFS, x-ray scattering, etc. The scanning is made by careful variation of the monochromator temperature (energy scan). The space available between the poles of the bending magnet (or wiggler) and around the front-end for this station may allow some room for theta scanning on the horizontal plane, but not much. Different crystals and reflections may be used to obtain the required energies.

5. Acknowledgments

We would like to thank the LNLS staff for their support, specially to L.R.Baracho for help with drawings and M.C.Correia for useful comments and suggestions. Financial support from FINEP is gratefully acknowledged.

6. References

1. A.Craievich, in this Proceedings.

2. J.Cerino, J.Stohr, N.Hower, R.Z.Bachrach, *Nucl. Instr. and Meth.* **172** (1980) 227.

3. J.A.Golovchenko, R.A.Levesque, P.L.Cowan, *Rev. Sci. Instrum.* **52** (1981) 51.

4. D.M.Mills, M.T.King, *Nucl. Instr. and Meth.* **208** (1983) 341.

5. T.Murata et al, *Journal de Physique* **47** (1986) c8-135.

6. V.H.Etgens, C.Cusatis, X Reunião da Soc. Bras. de Crist., Campinas (1988).

7. C.Cusatis, X Encontro de Física da Mat. Cond., Poços de Caldas (1987).

8. B.Dorner, H.Peisl,*Nucl. Instr. and Meth.*, **208** (1983) 587.

9. I.R.Entin, I.A.Smirnova, *Acta Cryst.* **A45** (1989) 577.

BENDING-MAGNET VACUUM CHAMBERS FOR VUV RING AT LNLS

A. Rubens B. de Castro [*]
A. Ricardo D. Rodrigues
Paulo A. Paes Gomes
Carlos A.R.P. Baptista

Laboratório Nacional de Luz Síncrotron/CNPq
13085 - Campinas, SP - Brasil
[*] also at IFGW/UNICAMP
13081 - Campinas, SP - Brasil

ABSTRACT

We discuss design criteria dictated by optical, thermal, electrical impedance and structural considerations. The proposed chambers will provide 3 conventional light ports. A fourth port will allow extraction of back scattered soft X-rays. Cooled absorbers will collect the unused radiation while confining the photo-stimulated desorption to a vacuum antechamber away from the electron beam path. We describe the thermal considerations relating to the cooled sapphire filters needed in the visible light ports and the cooling requirements for the copper radiation absorbers.

1. INTRODUCTION

The bending-magnet vacuum chamber is a rather demanding piece of equipment for the following reasons:

a) It must provide light ports for the radiation produced in the bending magnet itself and by any insertion device installed in the upstream straight section.

b) It must provide a smooth channel of large aperture for the electron beam.

c) The top and bottom walls close to the electron beam must be thin in order to make it possible to ramp the field after low energy beam injection, keeping eddy current effects small.

d) Structural supports designed to prevent the chamber from collapsing due to atmospheric pressure may create RF disturbances which cause bunch instabilities. If irradiated with photons, such supports may present hot spots: thermal and photo-induced degassing at undesirable locations in the chamber may raise the pressure at the electron beam channel and reduce stored beam lifetime.

e) Only a fraction of the radiated power leaves the chamber through the light ports. The rest is dissipated in the walls, which must be cooled.

f) Due to its flat geometry, the chamber is liable to warp during welding, on pump-down and on bake-out.

In the following we discuss mechanical, thermal and optical aspects of our design, which is shown on figure 1. The vacuum pumping requirements have been discussed elsewhere [1].

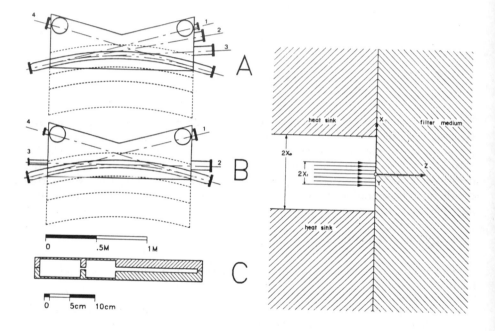

Figure 1:
(A) Top view of chamber 'A';
(B) Top view of chamber 'B';
(C) Cross-section at the center.

Figure 2:
Model geometry for the visible light filter heat transfer analysis.

2. GEOMETRICAL AND THERMAL CONSIDERATIONS

All chambers have the same shape and dimensions. There are, however, two sets of positions for the light ports. Table I lists the positions and intended usage of the various ports.

Chamber	Port no.	Position of Port (degrees)	Usage of Port	Hor Ang Acceptance (mrad)
'A'	1	0	Alignment	
			Visible light photons	7
	2	4	Bending-magnet photons	40
	3	12	Bending-magnet photons	40
	4	30-180	Alignment	
			Free-electron laser (with port B1)	
'B'	1	0	Alignment	
			Insertion-device photons	40
			Free-electron laser (with port A4)	
	2	15	Bending-magnet photons	40
	3	15-180	Backscattering experiments (with port B2)	
	4	30-180	Aligment	

Table I: Light ports in the bending-magnet vacuum chambers.

The internal geometry is that of a central curved channel with rectangular cross-section of 36 x 60 mm^2, connecting to lateral vacuum pumping antechambers. Most radiation not exiting to beam lines will be collected by a single water cooled copper absorber located very close to a high pumping speed pump port.

Care was taken in the project to reduce the RF coupling between the electron beam and geometrical discontinuities in the chamber. These are "seen" by the electron beam only through a gap that is narrow in the vertical and wide in the horizontal direction.

The absorber will dissipate 1kW (worst case, at beam current 400 mA, energy 1.15 GeV). The area in contact with flowing water will be close to 270 cm^2, hence we are well bellow the limit of 1 MW/m^2 for water boiling at the copper surface [2]. For a 2 deg C water temperature difference between inlet and outlet, the flux should be .12 l/sec. Water velocity would be 3.3 m/sec, half the estimated threshold for cavitation [2], yet well in the optimum turbulent regime [3].

3. STRUCTURAL CONSIDERATIONS

Two main aspects are considered: stiffness of the chamber walls and warping due to the welding process. The structural material is AISI 304 stainless steel, a chromium-nickel steel alloy referred to as the austenitic type, manufactured also in Brasil.

The chamber walls are treated as panels, designed to withstand uniform load due to atmospheric pressure. Stresses resulting from bending moment and vertical shear must not exceed 550 MPa, which is the tensile strength of steel. Maximum deflection is to be kept bellow .5 mm.

Welding may cause distorsion and residual stresses in the vacuum chamber. The hot weld tends to shrink as it cools, and this may cause the plates to flex. Thus, joint design and welding steps must be carefully determined to minimize stresses and deflection of the chamber walls.

4. VISIBLE LIGHT PORTS

Port number 4 in chamber 'A' is intended for preliminary alignment, for beam position monitoring and for extraction of near UV light (energy < 11 eV).

The visible light apertures would be sealed with fused silica viewports. Viewport thermal failure is of concern here; at SuperACO, for instance, cooled filters are used to reduce the heat load at windows [4].

We intend to install a filter on the cooled copper absorber inside the bending-magnet vacuum chamber. Figure 2 shows the geometry assumed in our thermal analysis of this filter. Our assumptions are as follows:

i) A sheet of light parallel to the yz plane propagates in the z direction.

ii) The light intensity distribution is a step function of width $2x_1$.

iii) The filter fills the half-space $z > 0$. It is in thermal contact with a heat sink kept at $T = 0$. The heat sink has a narrow slit along z, of width $2x_0$, $x_0 > x_1$, to let the radiation pass through.

iv) All of the incident radiation is absorbed at the surface of the filter.

A Green's function for the problem can then be obtained via conformal mapping and is written

$$G(x, z, x') = -(1/2\pi) \ln \left\{ \frac{[(u - u')^2 + (v - \pi)^2]}{[(u - u')^2 + (v + \pi)^2]} \right\}$$

$$u = (1/2) \ln \left\{ \frac{[(x - x_0)^2 + z^2]}{[(x + x_0)^2 + z^2]} \right\}$$

$$u' = (1/2) \ln \left\{ \frac{(x - x_0)^2}{(x + x_0)^2} \right\}$$

$$v = \arctan[z/(x - x_0)] - \arctan[z/(x + x_0)]$$

At the center $(0,0)$ of the filter surface, in the limit $x_0 \gg x_1$, this leads to the following result for the temperature:

$$T(0,0) = (j/k)(2\pi) \left[1 + \ln \left(\frac{\pi x_0}{x_1} \right) \right]$$

where j is the power input per unit length and k is the thermal conductivity of the filter medium.

Table II lists parameters for two cases: a fused silica and a sapphire filter. We find a temperature of 4500 deg C for silica and of 155 deg C for sapphire.

Storage ring parameters (worst case)	
Electron Energy	1.15 GeV
Current	400 mA
Radiated Power	3.6 W/h. mrad
Distance from source to absorber	1400 mm
Heat load	25.7 W/cm
Thermal conductivities	
Fused Silica	0.0142 W/cm.deg C
Sapphire	0.41 W/cm deg C
Model dimensions	
x_0	2.00 mm
x_1	0.35 mm

Table II: Parameters used for the filter temperature calculations.

The results of this model are compatible - once the various quantities are appropriately scaled to Aladdin values - with the maximum temperatures calculated by Brodsky with a finite element analysis, for glass viewports exposed to synchrotron radiation at SRC [5].

For sapphire, most of the heat loss will be by conduction to the cooled absorber. Blackbody radiation heat losses will be negligible in this case. For silica, the opposite would be true, however. This is seen by the following upper bound estimate. The power loss per unit area due to blackbody radiation is

$$P = (c/2)\sigma T^4$$

where c is the speed of light, T the absolute temperature and σ the Stefan-Boltzmann constant. We have assumed unit emissivity. For an area equal to 1 cm^2 at a temperature of 500 deg C (sapphire case) the heat loss is 0.7 Watt, while the power input is 26 Watts. The heat loss due to blackbody radiation would equal this power input at a temperature T = 1040 deg C, and it will hence be dominant in the case of fused silica.

Sapphire is therefore a most suitable material for the filter. It can also be obtained at a reasonable cost. Thermal contact to the heat sink could be made inserting a soft gold foil between the sapphire and the filter seat in the copper absorber.

5. CONCLUSION

The geometry of the bending-magnet vacuum chamber for the LNLS VUVIII ring has been described, with emphasis on the light ports which will be available to users. Structural and thermal aspects were discussed. The thermal performance of the absorber and of a sapphire filter for the visible light lines have been assessed.

ACKNOWLEDGEMENTS

One of the authors (A.R.B.C.) acknowledges very helpful discussions on viewport heat load with F. Cerrina and E. Brodsky. Expert Latex file processing by Ms. E. Tarchiani is gratefully acknowledged.

REFERENCES

[1] Gomes, P. A. P.; de Castro, A. R. B.; Rodrigues, A. R. D.; "Vaccum system of the VUV source of the Brazilian Synchrotron Light Laboratory", Proc. of 11th Intl. Vacuum Congress, 25 - 29 Sept 1989, Koln, FRG.

[2] Youngman, B.; private communication.

[3] Swain, T.; "Thermal absorber design for ALS beam lines", LBL Engineering Note AL2000 - M6803 (26 Jan 1989).

[4] Depautex, C.; private communication.

[5] Brodsky, E.; "Heating of glass viewport from synchrotron radiation", SRC Technical note SRC-17, Univ of Wisconsin (11 Oct 1984).

PRIMARY SHUTTER AND GAMMA RAY TRAP

A. Rubens B. de Castro
Paulo de Tarso Fonseca

Laboratório Nacional de Luz Síncrotron/CNPq
Rua Lauro Vanucci, 1020
13085 - Campinas, SP - Brasil
and
IFGW/UNICAMP
13081 - Campinas, SP - Brasil

ABSTRACT

The main radiation shutter and gamma ray trap, which will be used at LNLS front-ends, has been designed. The components external to the UHV chamber have been assembled and are undergoing tests. Vacuum requirements for the chamber have been estimated

1. INTRODUCTION

The LNLS project involves the construction of a storage ring, a linac and beam lines, among other things. There are many components and devices in the beam lines. One of these is the primary shutter and gamma ray trap. Its purpose is to provide radiological protection for the personnel close to the light beam lines in case one loses control of the electron beam during injection, and to shut the photon beam when it is not needed.

The standard front-ends for the VUV-III ring have been designed to employ the same components as the front-ends for the x-ray ring[1], and are shown in figure 1. The angular acceptance will be 40 hor mrad x 3 vert mrad. The main components are:

1) Bellows (ID 91.3mm);

2) Manual vacuum valve (all metal, VAT 48 ID 100 mm), intended for tests of the front-end while there is no stored electron beam. Not intended to intercept any radiation;

3) Main radiation shutter and gamma ray trap;

4) Pneumatic vacuum valve (all metal, VAT 48 ID 100 mm);

5) Fast-closing shutter (VG FAS 20, ID 100 mm);

6) Bellows (ID 117.2mm);

7) Acoustic delay line;

8) Fast pressure sensor (mini ion pump VG 92 F);

9) Cooled mask or mirror box, followed by secondary radiation shutters and vacuum valves of smaller ID.

Only two of the parts listed above will be built at LNLS: parts (3) and (7). Part (3), the main radiation shutter and gamma ray trap, is discussed below.

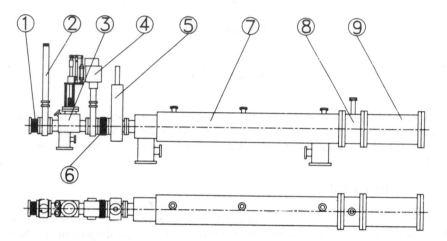

Figure 1: LNLS standard front-end. The components are listed in the text.

2. SHUTTER MECHANICAL ASSEMBLY

Figure 2 shows the shutter assembly. The shutter itself is a pneumatically driven copper plate 50 x 80 mm^2 10 mm thick. It will be water-cooled in order to dissipate 144 Watts. This plate is mounted in front of a stainless steel clad lead brick 50 x 80 x 150 mm^2. The lead brick length of 150 mm is required in order to provide radiological protection. We assumed a maximum electron energy of 1.5 GeV at 100 mA and 14 injections/week.

A bellows-sealed hollow shaft acts as a linear motion feedthru to move the shutter and gamma ray trap up and down, over a course of 30mm. The hollow houses OFHC copper tubing for the photon absorber water cooling.

The UHV components were made out of 304 stainless steel. All others were made out of carbon steel. The shaft centralizer wadding was made out of phosphor bronze.

The shutter chamber is also shown in Figure 2. There are four CF100 flanges. The top one is for the shutter mechanism and the bottom one for a vacuum pump. The front and rear flanges are for connecting with the front-end. The top CF35

275

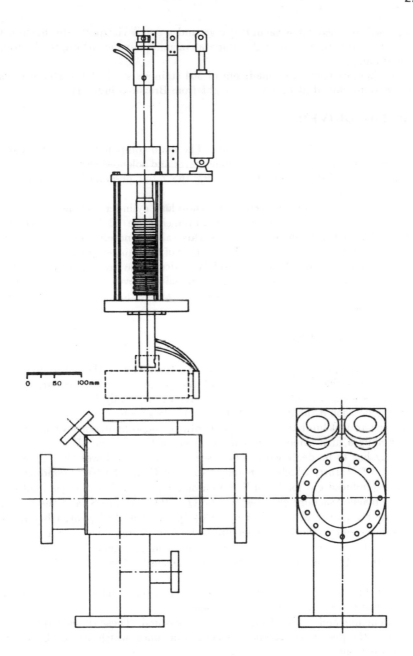

0   50   100mm

Figure 2: Primary shutter and gama ray trap mechanical assembly, and its chamber.

flanges will be used for a vacuum gauge and a small viewport; the bottom CF35 flange is fitted with a right angle all-metal vacuum valve attaching to the roughing vacuum pump.

The chamber parts were made out of 304 stainless steel. All mechanical components were machined at LNLS, or bought from Brazilian industry.

3. THE DRIVER

The shutter is driven pneumatically. The main components are: cylinder, pressure regulator, cylinder lubricator, manometer and solenoid valve.

The cylinder force is about 45 kgf for the 7 bar pneumatic pressure. This is enough for our purpose.

The lubricator is very important to insure long cylinder lifetime.

The solenoid valve eletric power requirements are 12 V DC at 380 mA. An eletronic board has been built to drive this valve remotely. Limit switches have been provided to allow for remote monitoring of the shutter status.

Notice that there will be suitable safety devices. One example is a pneumatically driven device, which generates an eletronic signal whenever the drive system pressure falls below a safe level. In this case, the gravitational force will move the absorber and shut down the beam path.

4. THE VACUUM SYSTEM

The vacuum pumping requirements were estimated with the parameters given in Table I. Notice that the initial photo-induced gas load is 620 times larger than the thermal gas load. Since, however, the shutter will normally be open, it is not clear whether one should incur the added cost of a large ion pump. It might be more convenient to just limit the pressure rise into the bending magnet vacuum chamber by installing a high impedance baffle in front of the shutter. If only the thermal degassing has to be dealt with, a 60 l/sec ion pump will lower the pressure down to 8.5×10^{-10} Torr, which is enough. Now, let C_b be the baffle conductance, Q_p the photo-induced gas load and S the pumping speed. Then the gas load into the bending magnet vacuum chamber will be $Q = (Q_p C_b)/(C_b + S)$ and the pressure in the shutter chamber will be $P = Q_p/(C_b + S)$. The specified photon beam angular acceptance requires the baffle aperture to be 4×72 mm^2, yielding a conductance $C_b = 33.4$ l/sec. Then the gas load into the bending magnet chamber is $Q = 1.1 \times 10^{-5}$ Torr. liter/sec and the pressure in the shutter chamber is $P = 3.3 \times 10^{-7}$ Torr.

In conclusion, a primary shutter was designed, constructed and is being tested. Some adjustments have already been made.

The opening and closing times were not measured. These times will probably be limited by the pneumatic component actuation times, which are much longer than the eletronic ones.

Total internal area:	5000 cm^2
Degassing rate:	1 X 10^{-11} Torr.liter/sec. cm^2
Thermal gas load:	5 X 10^{-8} Torr. liter/sec
Photon exposure:	6.8 X 10^{18} photons/sec (40 mrad)
Electron generation:	2.2 X 10^{17} electrons/sec
Desorption efficiency:	5 X 10^{-3} (initial rate) 5 X 10^{-6} (ultimate rate)
Photo-induced gas load:	3.1 X 10^{-5} Torr. liter/sec (initial rate) 3.1 X 10^{-8} Torr. liter/sec (ultimate rate)

Table 1: Parameter values for estimating the required vacuum pumping speed.

ACKNOWLEDGEMENTS

Our mechanical design was based on the primary shutters used in the X-ray ring at NSLS, Brookhaven. Help from D. P. Siddons (NSLS, Brookhaven) is gratefully acknowledged. Expert Latex file processing by Ms. E. Tarchiani is gratefully acknowledged.

REFERENCE

[1] Craievich, A. ; and de Castro, A.R.B.; "Scientific Instrumentation at LNLS", in "Synchrotron Light: Applications and Related Instrumentation", Proc. of I Workshop, pg. 279-291, Campinas SP Brazil 25-28 Jul 1988, ed. Craievich A; World Scientific, Singapore (1989).

ELECTRONICS FOR 2-DIM POSITION-SENSITIVE PHOTON COUNTING

J. Eduardo de A. Verdugo
Fernando Ferreira
A. Rubens B. de Castro [*]

Laboratório Nacional de Luz Síncrotron/CNPq
R. Lauro Vanucci, 1020
13085 Campinas SP Brasil
[*] also at
IFGW/UNICAMP
13081 Campinas SP Brasil

ABSTRACT

We describe the LNLS design of the electronics for readout of a resistive anode detector system and report on the performance of our charge pre-amplifiers and peak- hold amplifiers.

1. INTRODUCTION

Position-sensitive electron, ion and photon counters are of prime interest in a VUV storage ring facility.

These detectors consist of Micro Channel Plate Electron Multiplier stacks followed by a resistive anode[1,2]. A diagram is shown in figure 1. The principle of operation is as follows: a particle or photon of suitable energy strikes the inside of a pore and generates secondary electrons. These are accelerated to generate further secondary charge. Several multipliers are cascaded to insure large gain and a narrow pulse height distribution of the charge reaching the anode. The charge packet deposited on the anode divides among four connections. By comparing the amount of charge flowing from each connection, the position of the packet centroid can be obtained from

$$x = \frac{(x_2 - x_1)}{(x_1 + x_2 + y_1 + y_2)}$$

$$y = \frac{(y_2 - y_1)}{(x_1 + x_2 + y_1 + y_2)}$$

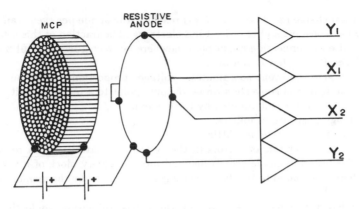

Figure 1: Micro-channel plate electron multiplier and resistive anode detector system.

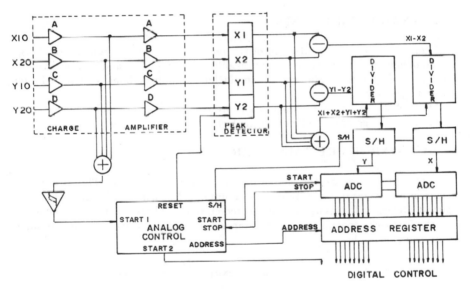

Figure 2: Block diagram of the analog electronics.

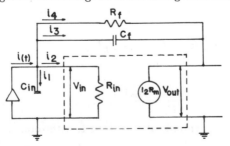

Figure 3: Simplified equivalent circuit of a transresistance amplifier.

The total charge $(x_1 + x_2 + y_1 + y_2)$ reaching the anode per event can be made to be almost constant and of order 10E8 electrons. The fraction of this total charge collected at each connection might be somewhere between 10E5 and 10E8 electrons (a few dozen fC to a few dozen pC).

x and y give the event coordinates. Voltages proportional to x and y are fed to 8-bit analog digital converters whose outputs point to a memory position that is incremented at each event counted by the system.

Our design goals are as follows:

- Maximum count rate of 1 MHz.

- Noise and other random errors in the system compatible with a resolution of 256. In this way, the anode area is mapped into a memory block of n x 256 x 256 bytes, where n is related to the dynamic range. It is limited by the memory available for the video buffer.

If the detector diameter were 25 mm, the spatial resolution would then be 100 micra.

2. ANALOG PROCESSING

Figure 2 shows a block diagram of the read-out circuitry. It consists of charge pre-amplifiers, peak-hold amplifiers, sum- difference amplifiers and analog dividers. For pipelined operation at full speed, sample/hold amplifiers should be inserted after the analog dividers.

Many of the necessary building blocks are commercially available, but we chose to build the charge pre-amplifier and the fast peak-hold amplifier.

2.1. CHARGE PRE-AMPLIFIER

It converts to voltage the charge flowing into each collector. This is done by means of a transresistance amplifier [3]; a simplified equivalent circuit is shown in figure 3. Referring to this figure, the injected current $i(t)$ branches through the input and the feedback capacitances and resistances. The output voltage can be obtained easily and is given by

$$V_{out} = \left(\frac{R_m}{T}\right) \int_{-\infty}^{t} dt' i(t') \exp\{\frac{-a(t - t')}{T}\} \qquad eq.1$$

where

$$T = C_{in} R_{in} + C_f R_{in} - C_f R_m \qquad eq.2$$

$$a = \frac{(R_f + R_{in} - R_m)}{R_f} \qquad eq.3$$

For a fast current pulse centered at time $t_o < t$, with total charge

$$q = \int_{-\infty}^{\infty} dt' i(t') \qquad\qquad eq.4$$

and for typical values of the capacitances and resistances, our result reduces to

$$V_{out} = \frac{q}{C_f} exp\left\{\frac{-(t-t_o)}{R_f C_f}\right\} \qquad t > t_o \qquad eq.5$$
$$= zero \qquad\qquad t < t_o$$

Thus, we have a linear relationship between input charge and peak output voltage.

The circuit we built is based on the design of Lo et al[4], which was, however, modified to allow for +-12 Volts supply. The slew rate of the last stages of the charge pre-amplifier was reduced also, in order not to exceed that of the peak-hold amplifier. This is necessary for good linearity.

The fall time should be given, according to the above model, by $R_f C_f$ in the slowest stage of the charge preamplifier. This is the third stage, with $R_f C_f = 140$ nsec. The measured fall time is 350 nsec, and the pulse has, of course, a more complicated shape than that predicted by eq. 5. This is due to the fact that (i) the input current in the third stage is not a pulse much shorter than $R_f C_f$, and hence the complete eq .1 should be used, not eq. 5; (ii) the analysis based on the equivalent circuit of figure 3 did not take into account the parasitic capacitances in the transistors used to build the charge preamplifier. These are, however, properly taken into account in the computer simulations which we carried out, and which agree with actual measured performance closely.

The output pulses of the pre-amplifier first stage are also used, after analog addition of all channels, to trigger the TTL logic that controls the analog processing.

2.2. PEAK-HOLD AMPLIFIER

The voltage pulses that come from the charge pre-amplifier are too fast to be processed by the analog divider. The function of the peak-hold amplifier is to capture the voltage pulse peak and hold its value during a period of time long enough to perform analog division and the subsequent analog digital conversion.

We could not find a sufficiently fast commercial device at a reasonable price, but building blocks are available. The peak-hold amplifier we built is of conventional design[5]. The output is stable 200 nsec after the charge is dumped onto the charge pre-amplifier input. The output range is from zero to 5 Volts.

Both the charge pre-amplifier and the peak-holder amplifier were simulated with PSpice[6]. Figure 4 shows both the simulated and the measured performances. The rise time of the charge pre-amplifier (10% to 90% of full amplitude) is 80 nsec; the fall time is 350 nsec. The overall sensitivity is 0.6 Volts/pC.

Figure 5 shows the measured transfer function of the charge and peak-hold amplifiers.

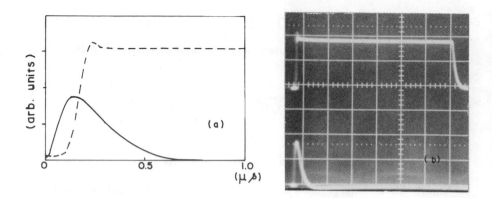

Figure 4: (a) PSpice simulation of the charge preamplifier and peak-hold amplifier. Full line, input; dashed line, output. (b) Measured temporal performance of the board. Horizontal scale is 1000 ns/div.

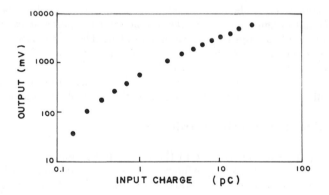

Figure 5: Measured transfer function of the charge preamplifier and peak-hold amplifier.

2.3. ANALOG DIVIDER AND ANALOG-DIGITAL CONVERSION

The analog divider is at present a bottleneck in the system, because of trade-offs between speed and accuracy.

We would like the division to be performed in less than 800 nsec with error less than 1/256, i.e., an accuracy of 0.4 %, since we intend to use 8 bit analog-digital converters. However, the commercially available divider which was selected (AD534L) reaches an accuracy of 0.2 % in 2000 nsec.

In spite of the fact that this divider will not allow us to reach our goals of data throughput, the rest of the system has been designed to reach such goals. We believe that inexpensive dividers with more suitable specifications will be available in the near future.

After the divider, the signals are digitized using high speed 8-bit converters (Datel ADC825MC). The outputs of the two ADC's represent the values of the event coordinates x y.

3. DIGITAL PROCESSING

A block diagram of the digital electronics is shown in figure 6. It includes a memory block for the video buffer, an interface with the host computer, a digital control section and a counter.

Operation is as follows: at each valid event a local clock is started. The digital control section then enables a data read into the counter, from the memory location pointed to by the address held in the address register. The counter is incremented and its contents are written back to the same memory location. This sequence will take 4 local clock cycles and can be done in a time shorter than 1000 nsec.

The control logic was designed to reject a signal if, during the analog processing, another event happens. This feature is needed in order to avoid erroneous position computing due to pulse pile-up.

After a preset number of events is accumulated, or if a memory position overflows, an interrupted is generated and the video buffer becomes available for transfer of its contents to the host computer.

Considering the time (200 nsec) for capture of the input pulse, the time (from 1000 to 2000 nsec) needed for analog division and the time (1000 nsec) needed for digital conversion, the total time needed for analog processing of one event is from 2.2 to 3.2 microsec, yielding a data acquisition rate somewhere between 0.31 and 0.45 MHz. The dead time can be shortened by 1000 nsec if additional sample/hold modules are installed between the analog dividers and the converters, as shown in figure 2. We hope to keep the total acquisition time equal to the time for analog processing by pipelining the analog and digital processings.

284

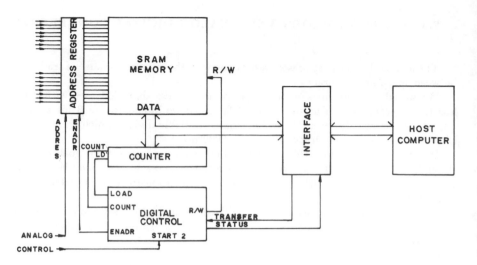

Figure 6: Block diagram of the digital electronics.

4. CONCLUSION

We described the LNLS design of the electronics for readout of a resistive-anode detector system.

A charge pre-amplifier and a peak-hold amplifier were built and tested; the measured performance of the front-end electronics is, within experimental uncertainty, in agreement with the results of PSpice simulations.

One of the authors (A. R. B. de Castro) acknowledges helpfull discussions with K. Veirs (LBL, Berkeley, USA) and with P. von Walter (Physikalisches Institut, Universitat Heidelberg, FRG). Expert Latex file processing by Ms. E. Tarchiani is gratefully acknowledged.

REFERENCES

[1] Lampton, M.; and Carlson, C. W.; Rev. Sci. Instr., 50, 1093 (1979).

[2] Rees, D.; McWhirter, I.; Rounce, P. A.; Barlow, F. E.; and Kellock, S. J.; J. Phys. E: Sci. Instrum., 13, 763 (1980).

[3] Millman, J., and Halkias, C. C.; "Integrated Electronics: Analog and Digital Circuits and Systems", Mc Graw Hill Inc, USA (1972).

[4] Lo, C. C.; Kirsten, F. A.; Nakamura, M.; Jared, R. C.; Goulding, F. S.; Yim, A.; Moss, J.; Freytag, D.; Haller, G.; Larson, R.; Pregernig, L.; IEEE Trans. Nucl. Sci., 35, 142 (1988).

[5] Data Acquisition DataBook 1984, vol. I, 4-127, Analog Devices, Two Technology Way, Norwood MA 02062 USA (1984).

[6] MicroSim Corp., 20 Fairbanks, Irvine CA 92718-9905 USA.

Performance of a position sensitive gas counter for low angle X-ray scattering measurements.

E.L.A.Macchione, K.Koide, O.Dietzsch

Instituto de Física, Universidade de Sao Paulo, Brazil

and

A.Bairrio Nuevo Jr.

Instituto de Física, Universidade Federal do Rio de Janeiro, Rio de Janeiro, Brazil

Abstract: A position sensitive gas counter for X-rays was developed in our laboratory to be used in low angle X-ray scattering experiments. In order to check the detector performance under usual experimental conditions, two samples were analysed: vitreous carbon and sodium dodecil sulfate (SLS). A gyration radius of (22.05±0.01) Angstrons was obtained from the vitreous carbon results and a crystallographic parameter c of (39.1±0.2) Angstrons for SLS, in good agreement with previous studies.

1. Introduction

Position sensitive proportional counters were initially developed for measurements in Nuclear and Particle Physics. Due to their good spatial resolution, efficiency and fast data acquisition capabilities they have also been used in other fields of research (materials science, biology, chemistry,...) as detectors in X-ray scattering measurements[1,2].

With such devices it should be possible to study dynamical phenomena (such as phase transitions) due to the possibility of performing measurements in real time. It should also be possible to investigate many organic and biological materials, which are difficult to analyse with X-rays for long periods of time due to radiation damage.

We report here on the performance of a position sensitive gas counter for X-ray detection which was develoned in our laboratory, making use of integrated delay-lines. Six delay-line chips (50 ns delay each, 35 MHz cut-off frequency) cover a total sensitive length of 150 mm, leading to a delay-risetime ratio that allows for a high-resolution position detection. In previous tests[3] using the 5.9 keV X-ray line from a ^{55}Fe source, an intrinsic resolution of 270 μm, an integral linearity better than 0.1% and a maximum differential linearity of 3% were obtained. Tests with a

8.04 kev Kα X-ray line from a copper X-ray tube resulted in a total position resolution of 330 μm, and the same integral and differential linearity.

In order to check the detector performance under usual experimental conditions two different samples were analysed in the low scattering-angle region. The analysed samples were vitreous carbon and sodium dodecil sulfate (SLS).

2. Theoretical Considerations

The radius of gyration Rg for vitreous carbon can be obtained from the experimental intensity curves for small angle scattering as demonstrated by Guinier[4]. The intensity is given by:

$$I(h) = I_o \exp (h^2.Rg^2 / 3)$$

where $h = (4\pi / \lambda) \sin\theta$ is the scattering vector, λ the X-ray wavelength and 2θ the scattering angle. I_o is the incident beam intensity.

For vitreous carbon the Guinier's region corresponds to the angular range from 0.4° to 1.2°. The angular coefficient (α) of the straight line adjusted to the experimental data in a plot of ln(I) versus h^2 is related to Rg by[4]:

$$\alpha = Rg^2 / 3 \rightarrow Rg = (3 \, \alpha)^{1/2}$$

For the SLS system we used a powder diagram to obtain the crystallographic parameters . Since we measured only the diffraction peaks related to planes 001, 002 and 003, we could only evaluate parameter c of the sample as in ref.5.

3. Experimental Set Up

The measurements were done with a Rigaku X-ray generator using a copper target, that produces 8.04 KeV X-rays. The beam was collimated with a pair of 50 μm slits which produced an image 60 μm wide at the detector. The distance between the sample and the face of the detector was 404 mm resulting in an angular range of ± 12°. The experimental set up is shown schematically in Fig.1.

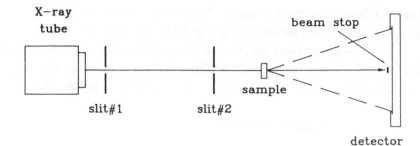

Fig.1 The experimental set up. Slits 1 and 2 are 50μm wide. The distance from the sample to the detector is 404mm.

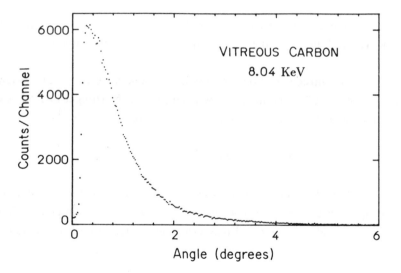

Fig.2 The intensity distribution of scattered X-rays as a function of angle for 8.04 keV X-rays on a vitreous carbon sample. The data were taken with the position sensitive proportional counter for a time interval of 100 seconds.

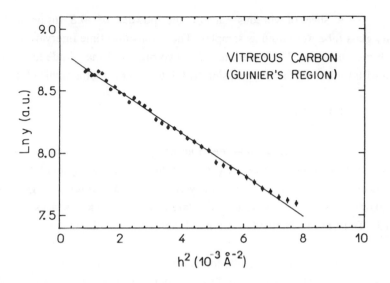

Fig.3 Least-square fit of the Guinier's region for the low angle scattering angular distribution of 8.04 keV X-rays on a vitreous carbon sample. The radius of gyration extracted from the fit (22.05±0.01) Angstrons is in good agreement with that obtained with a rotating NaI detector.

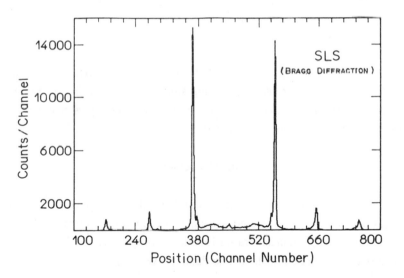

Fig.4 Angular distribution of scattered 8.04 KeV X-rays from a sodium dodecil sulfate sample. The crystallographic parameter c of (39.1±0.2) Angstrons is in good agreement with that obtained with photographic plates using a Laue camera.

A slice of vitreous carbon and powder of SLS inside a 1.5 mm capillary glass tube were used as samples. The acquisition time intervals were 100 s for each measurement. This time interval is two orders of magnitude less than that needed with traditional techniques using NaI detectors or photographic plates.

4. Results

In Fig.2 the angular distribution of the vitreous carbon scattering pattern is presented. Fig.3 shows the corresponding Guinier's region plot along with the adjusted straight line. The analysis shows a radius of gyration of (22.05±0.01) Angstrons. This value is related to the vacant spaces inside the material. The result obtained is in good agreement with analysis of previous works[6].

Fig.4 shows the results for SLS where the peaks corresponding to the planes 001, 002 and 003 can be seen. With the detector calibration it was possible to evaluate the angular position of these peaks and to obtain the crystallographic parameter c. The value found was (39.1±0.2) Angstrons, in good agreement with previous results[5].

5. Conclusion

The results presented here show that this detector can be used to great advantage in measurements involving small angle scattering of X-rays when compared with the more time-consuming traditional techniques making use of a rotating NaI detector or photographic plates.

Acknowledgements

The authors would like to thank R. Itri for her collaboration. This work was supported by Conselho Nacional de Desenvolvimento Científico e Tecnológico (CNPq), Financiadora de Estudos e Projetos (FINEP) and Fundação de Amparo à Pesquisa do Estado de São Paulo (FAPESP).

References

1- Charpak, G.; Petersen, G.; Policarpo, A. and Sauli, F.; Nucl. Instr. and Meth. 148, 471(1978).

2- Boie, R.A.; Fischer, J.; Inagaki, Y.; Merrit, F.C.; Radeka, V.; Rogers, L.C. and Xi, D.M.; Nucl. Instr. and Meth. 201, 93(1982).

3- Macchione, E.L.A.; Koide, K.; Leite, M.A.L.; Sini, S.; Bairrio Nuevo Jr., A. and Dietzsch, O.; "Position Sensitive Gas Counters for X-Ray Detection", in Synchrotron Light: Applications and Related Instrumentation, ed. A.F. Craievich (World Scientific, Singapore,1989)p.72.

4- Guinier, A. and Fournet, G.; "Small Angle Scattering of X-Rays", J. Wiley, New York, 1955.

5- D. da R.S. Bittencourt, Ph.D. thesis, Universidade de Sao Paulo (1986).

6- R. Itri, M.Sc. thesis, Universidade de Sao Paulo (1986).

RECUPERATION OF SEMICONDUCTOR DETECTORS

P. Rizzo and W.M.S.Santos

Instituto de Física, UFRJ, Rio de Janeiro, Brasil

Abstract

Convenient methods to recuperate damaged semiconductor detectors used by various Brazilian atomic and nuclear physics research groups have been applied in our laboratory, and are described in this paper. The recuperated detectors are of Ge(Li), Ge(HP), and Si(Li) types, and in all cases they are mounted in cryostates. Generally these instruments present vacuum leakages in the cryostate, which require the recuperation of vacuum conditions. Subsequently the crystals are warmed up between 10^oC and 30^oC above room temperature, in order to clean the crystal surface. Some clean-up drifting is then performed in the Ge(Li) and Si(Li) detectors, before cooling down the cryostate to liquid nitrogen temperature. When the beryllium window of one of the detectors is damaged, it is replaced by a mylar window. Damaged FET is also replaced. This paper summarizes the results obtained with 3 Ge(Li), 5 Ge(HP), and 4 Si(Li) detectors, from which some general and valuable conclusions have been found.

Introduction

Semiconductor detectors are extensively used in Brazil for nuclear and atomic radiation research involving x and γ rays. The inexistence of technical infrastructure in Brazil for rendering assistance to this type of detectors and the difficulties found to send them abroad for repairs have motivated our group toward the development of this research line.

For investigating γ radiation, mainly Ge detectors are used, seeing that the absorption coefficient of the Ge for γ radiation is high. These detectors are operated at liquid nitrogen temperature in order to decrease the thermal noise, and avoid the migration of Li^+ ions inside the crystal in Ge(Li) detectors. At such low temperatures, the reverse current is very low.

On the other hand, Si(Li) detectors can be stored at room temperature without deterioration of their performance, and they are mainly used for x radiation.

All the crystals must be maintained in high vacuum, lower than 10^{-5} torr, to make sure their surfaces are kept clean, and so the crystals are mounted inside the cryostate. Lack of hermetic conditions in the cryostates, as well as the damages caused to the beryllium window, produces vacuum leakage and, consequently, contamination on the surface of the crystals. This produces an increase in the reverse current, an increase in the noise of the preamplifier output, and the deterioration of detector resolution.

The impurities on the surface of the crystal change the energy band structure, which produces an inversion in the intrinsic region, i.e., in the detection region. This region becomes slightly p-type doped, and the conducting channels on the crystal surface are created between the n^+ and p^+ regions, increasing the reverse conductivity of the detector [1].

Sometimes, in Ge(Li) and Si(Li) detectors doped with lithium, an increase in temperature produces dissociation of the Li^+ Ga^- pairs in the lattice crystal, diffusing towards vacant places inside the lattice where they precipitate [2]. The thickness of the intrinsic region decreases, deteriorating the signal-noise relation and, consequently, the energy resolution.

Initial symptoms of the defective detectors are reported as well as the diagnoses and the applied treatments.

All the detectors repaired at our laboratory recuperated their original characteristics.

Damages Diagnoses

In order to determine the deterioration states of the detectors and their causes we analyze their energy spectra and their reverse current characteristic curves.

When the instrument presents no signal in its energy spectra, the main cause is the high reverse current produced as a result of impurities on the crystal surface. The presence of impurities is caused by an excess of pressure inside the cryostate due to small holes in the beryllium window or in another part of the cryostate. Another possibility for the lack of signal is the damaged FET inside the cryostate.

For detectors which present energy spectra with alterations in their original resolution value and operational voltage, the cause of damage is related to a small vacuum leakage in the system producing impurities on the crystal surface. Therefore, the main problem related to the damaged detectors to be solved is the contamination on the crystal surface. Such a contamination produces a variation in the electrical behaviour of the surface which is fundamental for the determination of the leakage current of the instrument [3].

Depending on the type of contamination, the surface behaves as slightly doped channels (n or p type). Therefore, the channels act as very poor junctions to the bulk and represent the source of poor leakage current characteristics. They can also create a distortion in the bulk electrical field so that the charges generated by the incident radiation are partially collected on the surface. This can cause a loss of efficiency and resolution, observed through the distorted energy spectra. The effect of the surface impurities can also be seen in the form and values of the reverse current curves. For the detectors which operate within their original conditions, the reverse current remains under .5nA, and must also be independent of the applied voltage. When the reverse current is over 10nA, it means that surface contamination has occurred. For Ge(Li) and Si(Li) detectors reverse currents on the order of $1\mu A$ or greater, indicate that there is some contribution of the bulk current produced by spatial thermal charges which are not compensated.

Recuperation Methods

Here we describe the methods used for the recuperation of damaged detectors. The method is generally applied when there is a small hole in any part of the cryostate or in the beryllium window. Under these conditions, there is a high degree of contamination on the surface of the crystal and also in the molecular sieve which is placed inside the cryostate.

In these cases, we start the recuperation process by repairing the hole in the cryostate, or replacing the beryllium window by an aluminized mylar [4]. Then, the system, crystal and cryostate, is heated between $10^\circ C$ and $30^\circ C$ above room temperature, with the reverse voltage applied in the detector and the vacuum remade in the cryostate simultaneously. The molecular sieve is sufficiently clean when the pressure inside the cryostate is lower than 10^{-5} torr. When this order of magnitude for pressure is obtained we can be assured that most of the impurities on the crystal surface have been eliminated. Then we cool the molecular sieve, allowing the crystal to be slightly heated with the applied reverse tension, two or three more times. In this way, the crystal is heated and the residual impurities on the surface are evaporated and adsorbed by the molecular sieve, which remain at a lower temperature. This process permits us to obtain smaller values for the leakage current and make the current independent of the applied voltage. Usually, it is necessary to repeat the warming-up process two or three times in order to obtain the required value for the leakage current [5].

As to the Si(Li) and Ge(Li) detectors, generally the compensation in the intrinsic region is not perfect at the end of the warming process. For this reason, it is necessary to perform the clean-up drifting one or more times. This is done at lower temperatures, i.e., between $-20^\circ C$ and $-50^\circ C$. We use successive clean-up periods at lower temperatures until our objective is achieved [6].

The warm-up and clean-up processes have always been applied without opening the cryostate.

In a Si(Li), a Ge(HP) and a Ge(Li) detector, we noticed that the FET inside the cryostate was damaged. In these three detectors, we replaced the FET in a controlled humidity and temperature environment. For this operation, we had to open the cryostate which produced some contamination of the crystal and in the cryostate. Therefore warm-up and clean-up processes were required after replacing the damaged FET.

In six cases in which the detectors presented deteriorated energy spectra, we remade the vacuum. We also applied the warm-up process for the Ge(HP) detector. For one Si(Li) and two Ge(Li) detectors, after remaking the vacuum and applying the warm-up process, some clean-up was also required.

Final Results

Table 1 shows a list of twelve semiconductor detectors, a summary of their symptoms, the applied treatment as well as the final results, resolution energy and operational high voltage.

Table 1: Recuperated detectors (symptoms, treatment and results).

Detector	Symptoms, inicial parameters	Applied treatment	Final parameters
(1) Si(Li) ORTEC	Damaged Be win-, dow no signal	Replaced by Mylar window, vacuum re-made, warm-up and clean-up.	FWHM = .22 keV E = 5.9 keV ^{55}Fe V = -1500 V
(2) Si(Li) ORTEC	Damaged Be win-, dow no signal	Replaced by Mylar window, vacuum re-made, warm-up and clean-up.	FWHM = .17 keV E = 5.9 keV ^{55}Fe V = -1500 V
(3) Si(Li) ORTEC	No signal and damaged FET	FET replaced, vacuum remade, warm-up and clean-up.	FWHM = .87 keV E = 32 keV ^{241}Am V = -1500 V
(4) Ge(HP) ENERTEC	No signal and damaged FET	FET replaced, vacuum remade and warm-up.	FWHM = 2.2 keV E = 1.33 MeV ^{60}Co V = 4500 V
(5) Ge(Li) ORTEC	No signal and damaged FET	FET replaced, vacuum remade, warm-up and clean-up.	FWHM = 2.8 keV E = 1.33 MeV ^{60}Co V = 2800 V

Detector	Symptoms, inicial parameters	Applied treatment	Final parameters
(6) Ge(HP) ORTEC	No signal, high pressure inside the cryostate	Vacuum remade and warm-up	FWHM = 2.1 keV $E = 1.33$ MeV ^{60}Co V = 3000 V
(7) Ge(HP) SEFORAD	FWHM = 1.3 keV $E = 122$ keV ^{57}Co $V = -1400$ V	Vacuum remade and various warm-ups.	FWHM = .66 keV $E = 122$ keV ^{57}Co V = -1500 V
(8) Ge(HP) ORTEC	FWHM = 6.0 keV $E = 122$ keV ^{57}Co $V = -1200$ V	Vacuum remade and various warm-ups.	FWHM = .5 keV $E = 122$ keV ^{57}Co V = -1500 V
(9) Ge(HP) ORTEC	FWHM = 24 keV $E = 1.33$ MeV ^{60}Co $V = 3000$ V	Vacuum remade and various warm-ups.	FWHM = 2.0 keV $E = 1.33$ MeV ^{60}Co V = 4500 V
(10) Si(Li) ORTEC	Modified spectrum. $V = -800$ V	Vacuum remade, warm-up and clean-up.	FWHM = .21 keV $E = 122$ keV ^{57}Co V = -1500 V
(11) Ge(Li) ORTEC	FWHM = 5 keV $E = 1.33$ MeV ^{60}Co $V = 2000$ V	Vacuum remade, warm-up and clean-up.	FWHM = 3.1 keV $E = 1.33$ MeV ^{60}Co V = 4800 V
(12) Ge(Li) ORTEC	FWHM = 6 keV $E = 1.33$ MeV ^{60}Co $V = -2000$ V	Vacuum remade, warm-up and clean-up.	FWHM = 3.5 keV $E = 1.33$ MeV ^{60}Co V = -3500 V

The final spectra obtained by detectors number 2, 3, 7 and 9 are shown in fig.1.

Conclusions

Fruitful results, related to repairs accomplished on semiconductor detectors, showed us that the reverse current curves and the energy spectra are good sources of information for damage analysis. The values obtained for final parameters

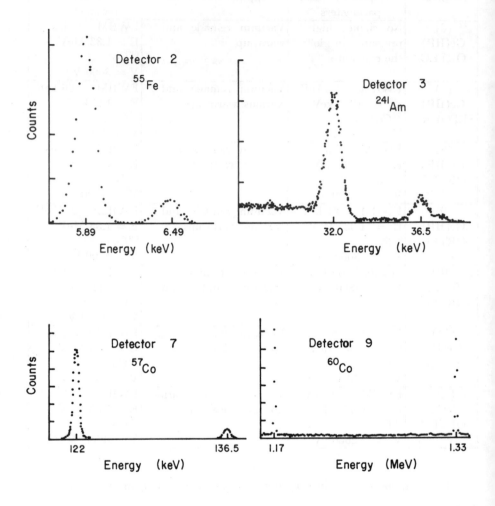

Fig.1 : Spectra obtained from several recuperated detectors.

showed also that the detectors recuperated their original conditions. The applied techniques have improved our knowledge concerning the construction of detectors. Due to this, our laboratory is now developing a project of construction of Si(Li), Si(HP), and Ge(HP) detectors.

References

1) Goulding, F. S., "Semiconductor Detectors for Nuclear Spectrometry,I", NIM 43, 1-54 (1966).

2) Morin, F.J. and Reiss, H.,"Precipitation of Lithium in Germanium", J Phys Chem Solids 3, 196-209 (1957).

3) Goulding, F. S., "Semiconductor Detectors: An Introduction", IEEE Trans on Nuclear Science NS-25, 916-920 (1978).

4) Priyokumar, S., Bhan, C., Chaturvedi, S. N. and Nath, N., "Aluminized Mylar as Si(Li) Detector Window for x Ray Fluorescence Spectrometer", NIM 167, 223-225 (1979).

5) Swer, Y. and Eichinger, P., "A Simplified Procedure for Reactivation of Ge(Li) Detectors", NIM 101, 67-71 (1972).

6) Trammel, R. C., "Semiconductor Detectors Fabrication Techniques", IEEE Trans on Nuclear Science NS-25, 910-915 (1978).